THE NOBEL PRIZE WINNERS

Chemistry

THE NOBEL PRIZE WINNERS

Chemistry

Volume 1
1901 – 1937

Edited by
FRANK N. MAGILL

SALEM PRESS
Pasadena, California   Englewood Cliffs, New Jersey

Copyright © 1990, by FRANK N. MAGILL
All rights in this book are reserved. No part of this work
may be used or reproduced in any manner whatsoever or
transmitted in any form or by any means, electronic or
mechanical, including photocopy, recording, or any information storage and retrieval system, without written
permission from the copyright owner except in the case
of brief quotations embodied in critical articles and reviews. For information address the publisher, Salem
Press, Inc., P. O. Box 50062, Pasadena, California 91105.

∞ The paper used in these volumes conforms to the
American National Standard for Permanence of Paper
for Printed Library Materials, Z39.48-1984.

Library of Congress Cataloging-in-Publication Data
The Nobel Prize winners: chemistry/edited by Frank N.
Magill. p. cm.
Includes bibliographical references.
Contents: v. 1. 1901-1937—v. 2. 1938-1968—v. 3. 1969-
1989.
1. Chemists—Biography. 2. Nobel prizes.
I. Magill, Frank Northen, 1907-
QD21.N64   1990   90-8092
540'.79—dc20   CIP
ISBN 0-89356-561-x (set)
ISBN 0-89356-562-8 (volume 1)

Ry
QD
35
.N64
1990
v.1

PUBLISHER'S NOTE

THE NOBEL PRIZE WINNERS: CHEMISTRY is the third set in a series that will cover the Nobel laureates in all six Nobel Prize categories: Literature, Physics, Chemistry, Physiology or Medicine, Peace, and Economic Sciences. Already completed are the sets covering the literature and physics prizewinners. This series is one of the few reference sources in English to offer comprehensive coverage of the Nobel Prize winners and to be organized according to prize category. As well as describing the laureate's work and career, it covers the speeches and commentary attendant on the Nobel Prize and presents all the information in a manner that is easily accessible to library users.

Volume 1 begins with a substantial "History and Overview" of the Nobel Prize in Chemistry by Dr. Robert Paradowski, a historian of science at Rochester Institute of Technology. Dr. Paradowski first presents a biography of Alfred Nobel, then an examination of the complications that were involved in the interpretation of Nobel's will and the establishment of the Nobel Foundation to administer the awarding of the prizes that came to bear his name. The process of selecting the chemistry prizewinners is reviewed, with insight into some of the issues involved; then a history of the award from its inception in 1901 to 1989 is given.

Following Dr. Paradowski's essay is a time line that lists, in tabular form, essential information about all 113 of the chemistry laureates included: award year, name, birth and death dates, country, and the areas of chemistry with which each is most closely associated.

The articles are arranged chronologically, beginning with Jacobus Henricus van't Hoff, recipient of the first Nobel Prize in Chemistry in 1901, and ending with Sidney Altman and Thomas Cech, cowinners of the 1989 award. Each article is preceded by a display page that provides historical perspective by listing the laureates in other disciplines for the same year; a photograph of each chemistry laureate appears on the left-hand page facing the opening of the essay.

Averaging 3,500 words in length, the articles follow a standard format designed for consistency and quick access to information. Ready-reference listings begin each essay, giving the laureate's name, places and dates of birth and death, nationality, and areas of concentration within chemistry. A brief description of the individual's work and its significance follows, set off in italic type. Rather than duplicating the Nobel Foundation's official citation, it speaks from the perspective of the late twentieth century.

The text of each essay is divided into five sections that provide a wide variety of views—both historical and contemporary—on the accomplishments of the Nobel Prize winner. The first of these, *The Award*, has three subsections: "Presentation," a synopsis of the main points made by the presenter of the award, who is a member of the Royal Swedish Academy of Sciences; "Nobel lecture," an overview of the address in which the laureate describes the prizewinning work; and "Critical reception," a survey of popular and professional responses to the award. A *Biography* sketches major events in the prizewinner's life. *Scientific Career* follows, constituting roughly one-third to one-half of the length of the article. Tracing the laureate's professional life, this section highlights the chemist's most significant experiments, theories, and publications. The *Bibliography* that concludes each essay comprises two sections: The "Primary" bibliography lists the laureate's principal works in chronological order; the "Secondary" bibliography presents works about the laureate and is annotated to provide readers with criteria for selecting appropriate sources for further study.

A comprehensive index at the end of the third volume includes the names of the winners and other principal personages; titles of important works mentioned in the articles; key terms, theories, experiments, and discoveries; and the names of important laboratories and institutions. Laureates are also indexed under their nationalities and under their areas of concentration; the reader can thereby easily locate all the winners from a particular area of chemistry or from a particular country. A complete alphabetical list of the laureates is included in the front matter of each volume.

Acknowledgments

The articles in these volumes are signed essays written by experts in their respective fields. Without the efforts of these many fine academicians in chemistry and the history of science, the compilation of this work would not have been possible. An alphabetical listing of all the contributors and their academic affiliations is included in the front matter of volume 1.

The editors also wish to acknowledge the ongoing cooperation of the Nobel Foundation in providing both historical and current information. Permission to reprint all the photographs of the chemistry laureates reproduced in these three volumes has been kindly granted by the copyright holder, © The Nobel Foundation.

CONTRIBUTORS

Arthur L. Alt
College of Great Falls

Roger W. Armstrong
Russell Sage College

Grace A. Banks
Chestnut Hill College

Patrick G. Barber
Longwood College

G.R. Barker
University of Manchester

George J. Beichl
Saint Joseph's University

Richard B. Bennett
Thiel College

Massimo D. Bezoari
Coker College

Alan Brown
Livingston University

Kenneth H. Brown
Northwestern Oklahoma State University

Helen M. Burke
Chestnut Hill College

Victor W. Chen
Chabot College

Leland J. Chinn
Biola University

Albert B. Costa
Duquesne University

Scott A. Davis
Mansfield University

Trudy A. Dickneider
University of Scranton

Charles Dismukes
Princeton University

Thomas H. Eberlein
Pennsylvania State University

Mary C. Fields
Collin County Community College

K. Thomas Finley
State University of New York at Brockport

Seymour L. Flaxman
City College
City University of New York

Daniel J. Fuller
Kent State University

William J. Hagan, Jr.
Saint Anselm College

C. Alton Hassell
Baylor University

Julius M. Herz
Temple University

David Wason Hollar, Jr.
Roanoke-Chowan Community College

Laura Mays Hoopes
Occidental College

Diane W. Husic
East Stroudsburg University

H. David Husic
Lafayette College

Laylin K. James
Lafayette College

Tonja A. Koeppel
Ocean County College

Jeffrey Kovac
University of Tennessee

Craig B. Lagrone
Birmingham-Southern College

P.R. Lannert
Independent Scholar

Saul Lerner
Purdue University, Calumet

Clarice Lolich
Oklahoma State University

John J. Lucier
University of Dayton

THE NOBEL PRIZE WINNERS

Paul Madden
Hardin-Simmons University

Jane Miller
University of Missouri, St. Louis

Susan J. Mole
Siena Heights College

Robert J. Paradowski
Rochester Institute of Technology

Gordon A. Parker
University of Toledo

John R. Phillips
Purdue University, Calumet

Joseph Rosenblum
University of North Carolina at Greensboro

Nancy Schiller
State University of New York at Buffalo

Joseph Albert Schufle
New Mexico Highlands University

Leslie J. Schwartz
Saint John Fisher College

Richard W. Schwenz
University of Northern Colorado

Larry R. Sherman
University of Scranton

Martha Sherwood-Pike
University of Oregon

R. Baird Shuman
University of Illinois at Urbana-Champaign

B.R. Siebring
United States Military Academy, West Point

Andrew C. Skinner
Ricks College

Clyde J. Smith
Centenary College

Roger Smith
Linfield College

Ernest G. Spittler
John Carroll University

Paris Svoronos
Queensborough College of City University of New York

Eric R. Taylor
University of Southwestern Louisiana

William Van Willis
California State University, Fullerton

William J. Wasserman
Seattle Central Community College

Robert E. Whipple
Fullerton College

Ivan L. Zabilka
Independent Scholar

CONTENTS

ALPHABETICAL LIST OF PRIZE WINNERS

THE NOBEL PRIZE WINNERS

THE NOBEL PRIZE WINNERS

THE NOBEL PRIZE WINNERS

THE NOBEL PRIZE WINNERS
Chemistry

ALFRED NOBEL

THE NOBEL PRIZE IN CHEMISTRY
History and Overview

Alfred Bernhard Nobel was a man of paradoxes. The one most frequently commented on by scholars and most widely known by the public was his dual role as the inventor of dynamite and other explosives that greatly increased the destructiveness of wars and as the benefactor who left a large part of his estate to establish a peace prize. Yet many other enigmas were also part of Alfred Nobel. He often characterized himself as a misanthrope, yet his writings reveal a man with magnanimous feelings toward humanity. His letters document a deep cynicism and a pessimism about the future of the human race, but he also called himself a "super-idealist," and the prizes that he instituted bear witness to his faith that people can improve their understanding of the world and their relationships with one another. Nobel had no appetite for notoriety and looked with irony on those prizes that he himself had received (he once said, "My French Order was conferred on me as the result of a close personal acquaintance with a minister"). Yet he created prizes that were guaranteed to bring notoriety to scientists such as himself.

Nobel believed deeply in the Enlightenment ideals of Reason and Nature, and this faith found its greatest expression in his love for science and especially in his lifelong fascination with chemistry. Although both his own and his biographers' testimony shows that his life was not a happy one, these same witnesses do agree that he was happiest when he was making chemical discoveries. Therefore it is not surprising that when the time came, he left the bulk of his fortune to found a series of prizes, and he would choose to reward scientists who contributed to the "improvement" of chemical knowledge.

The mixture of pragmatism and idealism to be found in Nobel was not unknown in other prominent chemists of the nineteenth century, Dimitry Mendeleyev and Louis Pasteur among them. During this time, chemists were making rapid advances in discovering the general laws governing chemical phenomena. From this new understanding grew flourishing chemical industries. The German dye industry, for example, profited from basic knowledge acquired by university professors as well as from research performed in its own laboratories. Nobel's plants manufacturing dynamite, blasting gelatin, ballastite, and other explosives were very much a part of this development. Having experienced how his own knowledge of chemistry led to discoveries that served as the foundation of factories throughout the world, he became a firm believer in the importance of chemistry for the material progress of civilization. His many patents involving explosives, artificial rubber and silk, and leather substitutes were not merely ways of making money; to him, they were also beautiful applications of scientific principles that would benefit mankind. Nobel considered his inventions minor achievements, not to be compared with the accomplishments of such great chemists as Antoine Lavoisier, Jöns Jakob Berzelius, and Louis Pasteur. Yet he knew that these pioneers would have their counterparts in the years to come, and in his will he entrusted the Royal Swedish Academy of Sciences with the task of rewarding scientists whose discoveries would benefit humanity. In this way he would share to some extent in the discoveries that he so admired.

Alfred Nobel (1833-1896): Chemist and Humanist

Nobel's biographers have described him as the loneliest millionaire, the man nobody knew, and the shy mother's boy who became a bold businessman, at home in the worlds of financial manipulations, patent battles, and power politics. His father, Immanuel Nobel, with modest schooling as an architect and mechanical engineer, had been able to establish himself as an important inventor, builder, and industrialist. Unfortunately, his ventures were overly ambitious, and at the time of Alfred's birth in Stockholm, Immanuel, suffering from a run of bad luck, was spiraling downward into the bankruptcy that would profoundly affect his family. To escape his financial difficulties, he moved in 1837 to Finland, then under Russian rule, and later to St. Petersburg (now Leningrad), where he established himself as a manufacturer of wagon wheels, steam hammers, and other tools. He left his wife and sons in Sweden. Caroline Andriette Nobel eventually had eight children, but only three sons (Robert Hjalmar, Ludvig Emanuel, and Alfred) reached adulthood. After her husband's departure, Caroline managed a small shop that sold dairy products and vegetables, and it provided a sufficient income for the support of her boys.

Since Alfred was a frail and sickly baby, his mother dominated his early years. He once said that his cradle was like a deathbed, and it was only through the solicitous care of his mother that he was able to stumble into childhood. Though his flickering health never burned brightly (illness would dog him in all periods of his life), he did find solace in mental activity. His body may have betrayed him, but his mind could bring salvation. His mother taught him to read, and he read voraciously. At the age of eight, he was well enough to attend a local parish school for a few terms, the only formal education he ever received. By this time, Immanuel's situation had improved as a result of his having interested the Russian government in the construction of naval mines to improve the country's defenses. Caroline Nobel and her younger boys Ludvig, age eleven, and Alfred, age nine, joined Immanuel in St. Petersburg; the oldest son, Robert, would come to Russia later. For the next several years, Alfred and his brothers were privately tutored by Russian and Swedish teachers. More important to their intellectual development, however, was their father's encouragement of their individual inventiveness. Alfred learned much practical chemistry by observing and listening to his father, and by the time he reached sixteen he was a competent chemist.

All three of Immanuel Nobel's sons became participants in the booming business of turning out tools, torpedoes, and mines. In the course of these activities, the family became aware of Alfred's extraordinary talents. To capitalize on these, Immanuel sent Alfred abroad to study in America and Europe, to represent the family business by buying raw materials, tools, and machinery, and to supply his family with up-to-date technical and financial information. Alfred also traveled through Europe, consulting with chemists and industrialists in France, Germany, and Italy. He probably studied in Paris with Théophile Pelouze, a French chemist who was interested in explosives. Throughout these *Wanderjahre*, the years in which this journeyman scientist traveled to gain experience, Nobel not only improved his knowledge of chemistry but also added to his mastery of Swedish and Russian a facility in English, French, German, and Italian.

Upon his return to St. Petersburg in July, 1852, Alfred found his family involved in great projects, such as the successful testing of his father's naval mines. Czar Nicholas I, however, who was making preparations for a major war, ordered an end to these tests and asked the Nobel family to concentrate their efforts on meeting Russia's immediate military needs. During the Crimean War (1853-1856), Alfred Nobel worked in his father's factory, where he deepened his understanding of chemical explosives by assisting in the manufacture of large quantities of war matériel. After the war, a new government assumed power and disregarded the commitments the former administration had made with Immanuel Nobel's enterprises. As a result, Nobel's workshop went bankrupt, and in 1859 he returned to Stockholm with his wife and their youngest son Oscar Emil, nearly as poor as when he had left more than two decades before. Ludvig and Alfred remained in Russia to liquidate their father's business. Ludvig also began a business of his own, manufacturing drilling and boring instruments. Alfred, who had already applied for a few patents, helped his brother in this new business, despite his desire to be on his own. Their older brother Robert had tired of the frustrations of life in Russia, and he moved with his wife to Finland, where he started a lamp business.

During the Crimean War, the great Russian chemist Nikolai Nikolayevich Zinin had shown Alfred and his father some nitroglycerin experiments. The Nobels considered this oily, colorless liquid a potentially more powerful explosive than the gunpowder that they were using in their mines. An Italian doctor and chemist, Ascanio Sobrero, had discovered nitroglycerin in 1847, but its great instability and extreme sensitivity to shock had dissuaded him from extensive experimentation. In 1862, Immanuel Nobel became the first person to demonstrate a simple way of producing nitroglycerin on a factory scale, and he soon began commercial manufacture of the substance in Sweden. Although nitroglycerin was to become inextricably linked with Alfred Nobel, it was his father who, with the initiation of its commercial manufacture, was most intensively involved with the explosive. One of the reasons for Alfred Nobel's return to Sweden was to help his father in this dangerous enterprise.

In 1863, Alfred Nobel developed his own important invention, a percussion detonator, later called the "Nobel lighter." This simple device—a small wooden cylinder containing a sealed charge of gunpowder with an attached fuse—revolutionized the way chemicals were exploded. Some scholars consider this invention the greatest of its kind after gunpowder. Mining companies, road builders, and railway developers made extensive use of percussion detonators in their blasting of rock.

By 1865, the Nobel family had established a company in an isolated area outside Stockholm to produce Nobel lighters and nitroglycerin. Alfred Nobel became deeply involved in this company, acting not only as managing director but also as chemist, engineer, advertiser, salesman, and treasurer. His experience with Nitroglycerin Limited would set the pattern for the rest of his life as he developed new products and founded factories throughout the world.

An appalling accident that occurred at the plant on September 3, 1864, had a profound effect both on the Nobel family and on the direction of Alfred's research. A violent explosion caused the deaths of Alfred's youngest brother, Oscar Emil, and four other persons. This disaster crushed Immanuel's spirit, and he suffered a stroke shortly after it occurred. Although he eventually made a partial recovery, he never regained his physical or mental powers (he died in 1872). News of other devastating explosions in factories making nitroglycerin in America, Australia, and other countries in Europe convinced Alfred Nobel that he needed to find some way to make nitroglycerin less dangerous. Unlike his father, who had been crippled by grief, Nobel was a man of action who believed that the best way to handle this tragedy was to solve its root problem. He began by mixing nitroglycerin with sawdust, then powdered cement, then charcoal, and then a series of other substances. Finally, in 1867, he found a way of incorporating nitroglycerin into kieselguhr, an absorbent siliceous material containing the shells of diatoms, which made the explosive comparatively safe to use. He named the material "dynamite" and patented it in the year of its discovery. Nobel had transformed nitroglycerin, which threatened to become a dreadful danger to humanity, into a tame explosive, one that made possible such great accomplishments as transcontinental railways and tunnels through the Alps.

During the late 1860's and early 1870's, Alfred Nobel and his collaborators constructed many factories for making dynamite and other explosives in Sweden, Norway, Finland, France, Spain, Portugal, Germany, Switzerland, Austria-Hungary, Italy, England, and the United States. In most of these countries, Nobel's factories were extremely successful, and he accumulated a colossal fortune. He also began to lead the peripatetic life for which he became famous. Since the manufacture of dynamite was an easy process to copy, Nobel was often forced to travel from country to country to protect his patent rights. Through his lawsuits against offenders, he acquired concrete experience of the ways unscrupulous businessmen had tried to take advantage of him. These lawsuits contributed to a deepening of his pessimism about humanity.

Nobel found refuge from the dispiriting lawsuits in his chemical laboratory, where he continued his research on explosives. He made another important discovery, blasting gelatin, in 1875. This material, sometimes called rubber dynamite, is a colloidal solution of nitrocellulose (gun cotton) mixed with nitroglycerin. Nobel found that this viscous, jellylike substance had a greater blasting power than dynamite, was less sensitive to shock, and was totally consumed on ignition. He put blasting gelatin into production in most of his factories, and its success added still more to his already great wealth. In the 1880's, he did extensive research on smokeless powders. For example, in 1888 he developed ballistite, sometimes called Nobel gunpowder, by increasing the proportion of nitrocellulose mixed with nitroglycerin from 7 to 50 percent and kneading the mixture between heated rollers. A precursor of cordite, this smoothly burning powder was extremely important in the manufacture of ammunition for firearms and ordnance pieces.

During the 1870's and 1880's, Nobel's research interests were not confined to explosives. He also did work in electrochemistry, biochemistry, and optics. He obtained patents on methods for making synthetic rubber, artificial silk, and semiprecious stones. Although these patents did not then result in commercial exploitation, Nobel's preliminary studies aided later inventors in making these synthetic products industrial realities. These researches of Nobel represent only a small proportion of his creative output. A better indication of the phenomenal fertility of his inventiveness is to be found in the list of his more than 350 patents.

Nobel moved to Paris around 1870, to be at the business center of Europe. Here he set up a home, business, and laboratory that served as a haven in the midst of his many travels. During the 1870's, one of his destinations was southern Russia, where Robert Nobel, who had become an oil trader, was exploiting the petroleum that poured from the ground in the neighborhood of Baku. In 1877, the Russian state abolished its monopoly on oil, and Robert and Ludvig Nobel bought a large section of the Baku oil fields for their newly formed company; Alfred Nobel became a significant shareholder of this company in 1878. Within a short time, the Nobel brothers created a powerful world industry. Alfred, still bothered by his father's experience with the broken promises of a previous Russian government, never devoted much time to this enterprise, though its great success would eventually add substantially to the Nobel fortune.

On a trip to Austria in 1876, Alfred Nobel (a lifelong bachelor) met Sofie Hess, a pretty young girl working in a florist's shop at a resort near Vienna. This accidental meeting marked the start of a serious love affair that lasted eighteen years. The affair remained unknown to the public until the 1950's, when the Nobel Foundation revealed the 216 letters that Nobel had written to Sofie Hess. At roughly the same time that Nobel met Sofie Hess, he began corresponding with Bertha Kinsky, a thirty-three-year-old governess for the daughters of Baroness von Suttner. She was personable, idealistic, well educated, and highly cultured; she also had a title and important connections with the aristocracy in several European countries. Nobel was fascinated by her, but she had fallen in love with Arthur von Suttner, the noble son of her previous employer. After serving as Nobel's secretary and participating in some of his social and business activities for a short time, she received a telegram from Arthur and left Nobel's employ abruptly while he was on a business trip to Sweden. Without the knowledge of their families, Bertha and Arthur married in a small church outside Vienna. Nobel did not meet Bertha von Suttner again until many years later, when, during the last decade of his life, she became a strong influence on his interest in the peace movement. She had by then become well known as a leader in the disarmament movement in Europe. She also served as the inspiration for some of the guiding principles behind Nobel's will and even for some of its specific provisions. She was awarded the Nobel Peace Prize in 1905.

During the late 1880's, Nobel suffered from angina pectoris. He found it an ironic twist of fate that doctors prescribed nitroglycerin for his ailment. Sometimes his pain became so severe that nitroglycerin did not mitigate it, and he went to bed for weeks. His angina was not the only reminder of his approaching death, which terrified him; other reminders occurred with the death of his brother Ludvig in 1888 and of his mother in 1889. Ludvig's death in particular caused important changes in Nobel's attitudes and actions, because a newspaper named Alfred rather than Ludvig in its obituary notice. In reading this brief appraisal of his life, he was shocked to learn that the world thought of him primarily as a merchant of death. He had attached no importance to pacifism early in his career, for he believed that his explosives would end war long before peace congresses would: He thought that if his explosives made war horrible enough, then civilized nations would abandon war. In his later career, however, he saw wars grow progressively more ruinous and horrendous without nations losing their taste for them, and he came to realize that more sophisticated and powerful explosives would not prevent wars. During this time he came to recognize his business life as a necessary evil and retreated to his laboratory, where he found some comfort in his chemical experiments and inventions.

Important changes in his life occurred in 1891. In the spring, Sofie Hess surprised him with the news that she was expecting a child fathered by a Hungarian cavalry officer. After the birth of her daughter, the captain married her, but as soon as the ceremony was over, he abandoned Sofie and his daughter forever (he later committed suicide). Nobel continued the liaison with Sofie for three more years, although it was sporadic and more formal, but it was obvious to most who knew of the relationship that Alfred would never marry her. During the time that he learned of Sofie's child, he also discovered that one of his managers had been involved in dishonest deals concerning glycerin supplies. Though he corrected the situation, the French government nevertheless forced him to close his laboratory. Full of resentment, Nobel left his French home, business, and laboratory and moved to Italy. At San Remo, on the Italian Riviera near the French border, he purchased a pleasant villa in a scenic setting, where he built a laboratory and where he hoped the mild Mediterranean climate would alleviate his several illnesses. Despite the time that he had to spend overseeing his business interests around the world, he always considered himself basically a chemist and looked forward to the time spent in his laboratory.

By 1893, when he reached the age of sixty, his health, which had always been frail, began to deteriorate rapidly. Rheumatism complicated his heart troubles, and although he sought the care of physicians, he regarded their opinions as idiotic. Despite his failing health and his doctors' advice that he curtail his activities, he could not refrain from continuing to expand his business interests. He did make a concession in hiring Ragnar Sohlman, a young Swedish chemical engineer, as his personal assistant, and they became close friends. In 1894, Nobel bought an iron-works and weapons foundry in Sweden. This was later complemented with his purchase of a steel mill, with its blast furnances and rolling mills. Despite his developing pacifism, Nobel continued to augment his fortune by producing explosives, firearms, artillery, and other military materials.

During the last years of his life, he did not allow his serious illnesses to interfere with his business activities, which by this time had become deeply ingrained habits. He regularly visited his factory and laboratory in Sweden, and he often stopped in Paris before returning to San Remo. He may have written a will in 1889, but if so, it was destroyed. In his will of 1893, which was later canceled, he assigned part of his estate to reward pioneers of science and the most effective worker for peace each year. These peace awards were to be distributed for thirty years, because, according to Nobel, if in thirty years the nations of the world "have not succeeded in reforming the present system, they will infallibly relapse into barbarism." In 1895, while on a trip to Paris to consult with doctors, he wrote a new will before four witnesses in the Swedish Club of Paris, in which he left most of his estate for the benefit of humanity through prizes. He then returned to San Remo, and, despite the advice of his doctors that he take great care of himself, he resumed work at his desk and in his laboratory. His brother Robert died of a heart attack in August, 1896, and so even more of the family fortune passed into Alfred Nobel's hands. On December 7, 1896, he experienced a cerebral hemorrhage. His French servants found him collapsed in his chair. They summoned an Italian doctor, but the stroke had paralyzed parts of Nobel's brain so that he was unable to speak in any language but Swedish. Alfred Nobel died on December 10, 1896, in precisely those circumstances he had so greatly feared—among strangers, unable to communicate, with "no kind hand of a friend or relative to close my eyes and whisper in my ear a gentle and sincere word of comfort."

Alfred Nobel's Will

The pastor of the Swedish church in Paris, who was a longtime friend, accompanied Nobel's body back to Sweden. Nobel had a lifelong fear of being buried alive, so, as requested in his will, his body was drained of blood; only when qualified physicians certainly confirmed his death were his remains cremated. Nobel's will had been deposited in the Enskilda Bank in Stockholm, where it had been read soon after news of his death was received. The contents of the will came as an unpleasant surprise to his relatives, in particular to his two nephews, who learned that the bequests made to them and other family members constituted only 3 percent of the assets. When the total wealth of the Nobel estate was finally calculated, it reached 33.2 million Swedish crowns (*kronor*), and after debts were settled, the net amount remaining was 31.6 million crowns, or roughly $9 million. Also contained in the will was the news that no member of the family was to be an executor of the estate. Instead, Nobel had appointed as executors Ragnar Sohlman, his personal assistant, and Rudolph Lilliquist, a Swedish industrialist. Both executors were, like Nobel, chemical engineers. When Sohlman first learned that he had been named an executor, he found the news very upsetting. He was only twenty-six years old, he had no legal experience, and he had never even met Lilliquist. He eventually came to the conclusion that Nobel had chosen him because he knew that he could trust his personal aide to carry out his intentions meticulously. Sohlman learned that the Russian sense of the term "executor" was "spokesman for the soul," and he resolved to be as faithful as possible to Nobel's spirit.

Sohlman expected Nobel's relatives to contest the will—a legal battle for which he was ill-prepared. The principal legatee of Nobel's will was a foundation that did not yet exist; indeed, Sohlman was uncertain how such a foundation could be established. Emanuel Nobel, one of Alfred Nobel's nephews, came to San Remo to discuss the will; he was particularly interested in the Nobel Brothers Naphtha Company of Baku, in which Alfred Nobel had owned a substantial interest. Sohlman was pleased when Emanuel decided not to oppose his uncle's will. The nephew and the executor became friends, and Emanuel was Sohlman's chief supporter among Nobel family members. Returning to Stockholm, Sohlman and Emanuel Nobel met Lilliquist. They turned for legal assistance to Carl Lindhagen, a Stockholm judge; he became, in effect, an associate executor.

Sohlman, Lilliquist, and Lindhagen soon learned of the series of legal problems confronting them. They expected lawsuits contesting the will's validity from some of Nobel's relatives. They learned via an Austrian lawyer that Sofie Hess contended that she had been Alfred Nobel's common-law wife, and she threatened to make the more than two hundred letters that Nobel had written to her public unless she were properly recompensed. Also, Nobel had left Sweden as a child, and he had never taken the time to become a legal resident of his native country, a situation that presented thorny legal questions. Nobel's business affairs were extraordinarily complex, and the liquidation of his many interests and the reinvestment of the money in safe securities would be complicated. Furthermore, the executors anticipated problems with the Swedish government and Swedish scientific institutions. One of the executors' first successes occurred when Nobel was declared a legal resident of Sweden, thus giving the Swedish courts jurisdiction over the estate and defeating the threat that the will would be pronounced invalid by a French court. Tackling this problem first was also an adroit political move, for the decision and the attendant publicity made the will's provisions a matter of Swedish national concern.

The basic idea of Nobel's will was clear: The major portion of his estate should be set aside for a fund whose interest income should be distributed annually as prizes in five different fields. The will's legal form, however, was unsatisfactory. Alfred Nobel had an intense hatred for lawyers, the result of years of debilitating patent battles. Therefore, he did not consult an attorney when he composed his will, and he left many essential details unexpressed and many necessary directions inexplicit. The executors found themselves forced to carry out his intentions without his being there to answer questions and clarify ambiguities.

It was obvious from both wills Nobel had composed that he wanted to dispose of his fortune in a way that would benefit society and not his heirs. The witnesses to the will in Paris heard him say that he was a social democrat who believed that inherited fortunes were actually misfortunes, serving to retard rather than promote the progress of humanity. To provide his heirs with a massive fortune would mean encouraging their indolence, thus depriving the world of the products that the healthy development of their individual abilities would generate. Nobel's intentions may have been clear to himself, to the will's witnesses, and to the executors, but they were not clear to some members of Nobel's family. They were prepared to argue that Nobel, weakened by illness, had been unduly influenced by "peace fanatics and particularly by women" in making out his 1895 will. Without Emanuel Nobel's cooperation with the executors, the threatened court actions against the will by the disappointed relatives might very well have succeeded, resulting in the destruction of Nobel's prizes even before they had begun.

The executors' position was bolstered in May, 1897, when the Swedish government decided to protect its own interests as they related to the will. On the other hand, the institutions that were to be the deciders of the prizes were not so helpful. In fact, from the executors' point of view, these institutions, which were looking out for their own interests, actually complicated the legal battles over the will. For example, on June 9, 1897, the Royal Swedish Academy of Sciences, which was to award the prizes for physics and chemistry, stated that it would be unable to select representatives for preliminary discussions with the executors until it became clear that the will would be legally recognized. This refusal effectively blocked probate of the will, and the impasse forced the executors to explore compromises with Nobel's relatives.

Early in 1898, as part of the strategy to put pressure on the Nobel relatives to settle, Emanuel Nobel publicly announced his desire to respect his late uncle's wishes as expressed in the 1895 will and his intention not to dispute its provisions. This public declaration pressured the members of the Swedish branch of the Nobel family into negotiations, since his agreement meant that a large portion of the estate, especially that tied up in the family's Russian holdings, could now be used for the purposes intended by Alfred Nobel. The executors consequently found the Swedish branch of the family more amenable to negotiating a financial settlement that would end their opposition to the will. The executors also were negotiating with the lawyer representing Sofie Hess. After delaying as long as they could, they eventually agreed to continue the annuity that Nobel had provided for Sofie during his lifetime and to pay for her legal expenses.

The executors began discussions with the Swedish institutions appointed in Nobel's will to select the winners of the prizes. The idea of linking the awarding of the prizes to relevant institutions had come from the French Academy of Sciences, with whose history and activities Nobel became familiar during his many years in Paris. When Nobel composed his 1895 will in Paris, he emphasized to the witnesses that he wanted his prizes to reward scientists whose work had shown promise; therefore, the prize money would serve as a lifelong grant that would give these scientists the financial independence necessary to carry on their work. The Royal Swedish Academy of Sciences, Sweden's oldest corporation of scientists, was modeled on the French Academy of Sciences, and it, too, recognized scientific achievement by electing distinguished scientists as members and by publishing research, awarding grants, and presenting prizes. In the negotiations between the executors and the Academy of Sciences, however, officials of the academy made it clear that they wanted to use a portion of the Nobel fund to endow research institutes and to meet their own expenses connected with the awarding of the prizes. After long negotiations, the Academy of Sciences and the Karolinska Institute got their research institutes and their annual allotments in exchange for agreeing to play the parts created for them in Nobel's will.

The executors were now in a position to resolve the difficulties connected with the liquidation of Nobel's many holdings, which they tried to accomplish in a way that would be consistent with Nobel's wishes. In the course of making these arrangements, the executors reached a compromise agreement with the Nobel relatives in late May and early June, 1898, during which time the relatives agreed to accept payments of about 1.5 million crowns (which was to be added to the legacies already made to them in Nobel's will). The executors were finally ready to bring the will before Swedish officials; the government would play a role in determining the administration and organization of the prize-awarding system. With these preliminary matters settled, the legacies could be paid to the relatives, which left the Nobel fortune at more than 31 million crowns. This became the initial capital of the Nobel Foundation.

The Nobel Foundation

In his will, Nobel stipulated neither that a foundation be established nor that it be named for him. He simply stated that, after his holdings had been liquidated, the capital was to be invested in reliable securities, the interest from which was to be distributed each year in prizes. These five prizes were to be awarded by four institutions: two academies (the Royal Swedish Academy of Sciences and the Swedish Academy [of literature]), a medical institution (the Karolinska Institute), and a parliamentary body (the Norwegian Storting). After the legal challenges to the will were settled, the Large Nobel Committee, composed of members from the four institutions, was formed to create the Nobel Foundation, since these institutions had to be bound by common regulations. These statutes were to be derived from the few explicit provisions of the will as well as from its implicit underlying principles. After extensive discussions of the Foundation's purpose, the fund's management, and the method by which the prizes were to be awarded, the committee members reached their first major agreement: There would be a strict separation of powers between the board of the Nobel Foundation and the committees of the prize-giving institutions. Therefore, the foundation and the institutions would each have a detailed set of regulations. In the case of the institutions, each prize was to have a separate Nobel Committee. The Academy of Sciences, for example, was to appoint two committees, one for chemistry and one for physics. These committees would play a pivotal role in the selection process. Each committee would have five members, but these members could request help from specialists. The prize-awarding institutions would elect their own committee members, whose main job was to give their informed opinions on the nominations. The nominators were to be drawn largely from the personnel of Swedish and foreign faculties of science.

In his will, Nobel mentioned the prize for chemistry as follows: "one part to be given to the person who has made the most important chemical discovery or improvement." This statement contained a minimal amount of information, and in the draft statutes, Carl Lindhagen, with the help of Svante August Arrhenius, a Swedish physical chemist, tried to clarify Nobel's intentions for the chemistry and physics prizes by elaborating on them. Arrhenius would have great influence on the founding procedures and early history of the Nobel Prizes in physics and chemistry. Lindhagen and Arrhenius drafted a statement, a central element of which was that "chemical discovery" should be understood to mean not only practical but also theoretical chemistry. This interpretation reflected Arrhenius' interests in promoting his own interdisciplinary field of physical chemistry and also his attempt to prevent Nobel's word "improvement" from being interpreted as a justification for prizes to be given for advances in chemical engineering.

The Large Nobel Committee failed to reach agreement on a specific mechanism for determining lists of candidates, so the machinery for nominations and for prize selection was left mostly to the prize-awarding institutions, which took advantage of this freedom to draw up their own principles of decision making. In the process of drafting its own regulations, the Academy of Sciences discovered deep differences of opinion over the nominating system. Some committee members wanted only Swedish and foreign members of their own Academy to be nominators, whereas another group wanted members of Swedish and foreign universities also included. The Nobel Committee for Chemistry took the broad view with regard to the nominators, and its views on the selection of prizewinners had great influence on the other committees.

The Nobel Prizes for chemistry and physics gave a new dimension to the activities of the Royal Swedish Academy of Sciences. Although it continued its traditional tasks, it become best known to the scientific world for its selection of Nobel Prize winners in physics and chemistry. The Academy therefore became responsible for a growing number of administrative responsibilities. At the turn of the century, the Academy had about a hundred members divided into nine sections, the largest of which were the ones in the biological and medical sciences. By contrast, the physics section had only six members, and chemistry (which was combined with mineralogy) had only twelve. The pressures of selecting Nobel Prize winners in physics and chemistry made Academy members aware of the need to strengthen the sections having primary responsibility for the prizes. In line with this need, the physics section was expanded in 1904 to ten members, as was the chemistry section, which was also dissociated from mineralogy.

On April 27, 1899, when the Large Nobel Committee approved the final version of the statutes, which were mainly concerned with the administration of the fund, this group ceased to exist. Early in 1900, the Swedish government invited the prize-awarding institutions to submit their special regulations for approval, and on June 29, 1900, King Oscar II, meeting with his cabinet, approved the statutes of the Nobel Foundation and the special regulations of the prize-giving institutions. With this royal seal of approval, the Nobel Foundation became a reality. The Foundation's main objective was to ensure, through the wise management of the Nobel inheritance, that winners would receive substantial prizes. A large and secure amount of capital would also give the Foundation and its allied scientific institutions freedom from outside influence.

The Nobel Foundation was located in Stockholm and had a five-member board, all Swedes. Four of these members came from the prize-awarding bodies, and the fifth, who was to be Chairman of the Board, was nominated by the king. Ragnar Sohlman was a member of this board from its inception until 1946, and he served as its managing director for the last seventeen years. His influence in establishing the Foundation and shaping it during its formative years was considerable. The first Chairman of the Board was Gustaf Boström, a former prime minister. This appointment exemplified the powerful political influence that characterized the choice of the chairman in the early years of the Foundation. The prize-giving institutions as well as the Nobel family felt strongly that the authority and prestige these figures carried would help to strengthen the fledgling institution.

The Swedish government's promulgation of the statutes in 1900 concluded the work, begun in 1897, of laying the foundation of the Nobel institutions. Sohlman and his associates had transformed Nobel's vague ideas into a functioning structure. They had solved the legal problems involving the Nobel family and overcome the initial resistance and skepticism of the academies as well as their later vacillations. Although the executors had to compromise the will somewhat in awarding settlements to family members, the major financial sacrifice was caused by the institutes and annual allotments that were granted to the awarding institutions. The Academy of Sciences, for example, had an initial grant of six million crowns for the establishment of its Nobel Institute. Despite the compromises, or perhaps because of them, Sohlman and his colleagues were able to transform the idealistic vision expressed in Nobel's will into a reality.

The Selection of a Nobel Prize Winner in Chemistry

The specific procedures for selecting Nobel Prize winners in chemistry evolved from a series of decisions about practical problems that had been ignored or inadequately dealt with in the will, statutes, and special regulations. The Nobel institutions certainly had statutes governing the selection of the winners, but these had to be interpreted, adapted, and modified to meet the special conditions within each of the prize-awarding institutions. Elected committees in these institutions had the primary responsibility for inviting nominations, investigating candidates, and selecting the winners. Regulations require that committee members serve for renewable terms of three to five years. The physics and chemistry committee members, who are elected by their fellow scientists in the Academy of Sciences, always include the heads of the physics and chemistry sections of the Nobel Institute. Since the committee members determine the nominators of the candidates, and since they control the evaluation process, they possess great power to select and reject potential prizewinners.

The work of the Nobel Committee for Chemistry is based on three requirements set down in the will and statutes: (1) the works rewarded should constitute discoveries, inventions, or improvements; (2) these achievements must be recent, and older discoveries can be considered only when their importance has been recently demonstrated; and (3) these discoveries should, in some way, confer great benefit on mankind. During the early years of the chemistry committee, members were careful, in the light of the first and third requirements, to include references to the utilitarian value of the discoveries they chose to honor. For example, Emil Fischer's work on sugars provided useful information for the food industry, and Adolf von Baeyer's work on indigo benefited the dyestuffs industry. Later, however, a discovery's immediate utilitarian aspect became less and less important.

In his will, Nobel required that the prizes be awarded for work done during the preceding year, but in the statutes of the Nobel Foundation this provision was broadly interpreted to mean that past achievements could also be rewarded, since properly assessing a discovery's importance often necessitated tracing its influence over a long period. The Academy of Sciences in particular wanted to reward discoveries that would stand the test of time, and this led to a cautious conservatism that, initially at least, helped to enhance the prestige of the prizes by honoring only those achievements that had undergone extensive scrutiny. Early committee members realized that a Nobel Prize, unlike previous awards, was not given for a lifetime's work but for a specific discovery; in practice, however, this requirement has been very loosely interpreted, for scientists with no outstanding specific discovery but with a body of substantial accomplishment have often received the chemistry prize. For example, Linus Pauling in 1954 was given the prize essentially for a lifetime of work on the nature of the chemical bond.

The committees in chemistry and physics had the greatest difficulty in translating Nobel's prescription that scientific discoveries should confer "the greatest benefit on mankind" into workable criteria for decisions. For the most part, this provision was not a determining standard in choosing which candidates would receive a prize; rather, it served to remind committee members not to stray too far from the basic plan that Nobel had set down in his will. In some cases, "mankind's benefit" was interpreted in the light of the first requirement; that is, committee members preferred to reward discoveries that had utilitarian value. Nobel's phrase, "the greatest benefit on mankind," was frequently interpreted quite vaguely—to mean, for example, that the discovery fostered scientific progress (and what great scientific discovery does not?).

Although Alfred Nobel had great admiration for the theoretical achievements of such chemists as Antoine Lavoisier, Jöns Jakob Berzelius, and Dimitry Mendeleyev, the language of his will suggests that he, as an accomplished inventor, had experimental rather than theoretical discoveries in mind when he asked that "the most important chemical discovery or improvement" be rewarded. He had made important discoveries in chemical technology, and so he had concrete experience of such achievements. Chemical theories were certainly very useful to him in his work, but he knew that theories often changed. Unlike the constant changes in scientific ideas, however, he believed that what remained unchanged was experimental fact, such as kieselguhr's ability to mitigate the dangers of nitroglycerin. According to some interpreters, these are the types of discoveries that Nobel wished to reward. If this was indeed Nobel's intention, it was largely ignored, for committee members often chose to honor theoreticians for their revolutionary ideas, regardless of whether they resulted in specific "improvements."

The system that the committee members established was put into practice in the fall of 1900, when the Royal Swedish Academy of Sciences met to elect the members of its Nobel Committee for Chemistry: two professors of chemistry from Uppsala and three professors from Stockholm. One of the first steps of the committee was to send out invitations for nominations of prospective candidates for the chemistry prize. The nominations that the members received provided the committee with a sense of the support that each candidate enjoyed in Swedish and international scientific communities. This process also helped to narrow the number of candidates to a short list of serious contenders. In setting up this system of nominations, each committee developed its own procedures independent of the Academy. Members also found that the rules established by the Nobel Foundation often had to be broadly interpreted to facilitate their decision making. For example, many nominators proposed scientists on the basis of their general superiority rather than for a specific discovery, and these nominations were accepted. In these early years, large numbers of nominations came from chairholders in chemistry at prominent universities, both in Sweden and throughout the world. On the other hand, though nominations from members of the Nobel Committee were numerically small, they carried great weight, since these nominators could implement their preferences through recommendations to the Academy.

If the Academy were to be more than simply a ratifier of a committee's choice, it had to be provided with information that would enable its members to form an independent judgment about alternatives to the individual recommended by the committee. The initial request of the Academy, put forward at the time of the first prize decisions, was a modest one: It simply wanted to know the names of all the nominated candidates and those who had proposed them. In 1902 the Academy became more ambitious and requested that the committees supply it with an overview of all candidates, comparing their discoveries and stating why the scientists proposed for the prizes should be preferred over the other candidates. Committee members interpreted this request as a threat to their independence, since detailed analyses about alternatives to the committee's recommendation could be readily challenged by the Academy. Seeking to preserve their prerogatives, the science committees balked, and a compromise was reached: Comparisons would be confined to the prospective winner and the remaining candidates as a group. This proposal, put into effect in 1903, led to the system of special reports—detailed analyses of the scientist's work written by experts. At the beginning, these reports concerned only candidates recommended for the prize, but with an increase in the number of eminent contenders and a lack of convergence in nominators' choices, the special reports also increased.

The pattern of nominations established in the early years has continued. Every September, the prize-awarding institutions send invitations to nominators. In the case of the Nobel Committee for Chemistry, these invitations, during the early years, were sent to the Swedish and foreign members of the Academy, to professors of chemistry at Scandinavian universities, and to prominent chemists at ten institutions of higher learning outside Scandinavia. As years went by, the letters soliciting nominations for the chemistry prize increased from 300 to 650 (in the 1980's, the Academy distributed more than a thousand invitations to nominate, resulting in roughly 250 annual nominations). Invitations were sent to chemists and physicists at colleges and universities in countries representing the chief language regions of the world. They were also sent to distinguished scientists in various foreign academies and research institutions. Finally, as time went by, a new and valuable group of nominators formed, namely, past winners of the Nobel Prize for physics and chemistry. Suggestions from these nominators carried much influence with committee members. Nominators, whoever they are, may propose several candidates, but since many nominators propose the same chemists, the number of candidates is smaller than the number of nominations. After all the nominations have been received, the selection officials undertake the daunting task of isolating, then investigating the worthiest nominees.

During the early years of the chemistry awards, certain countries—most notably Germany—had a greater influence in the nominating system than others. Since the Nobel Foundation has opened its secret files on the early awards, it has become clear that the nominators of some countries were nationalistic in their proposals. On some occasions, Swedish nominators favored their own chemists, for example, but Swedes were not as prejudiced as the French, who were notorious for proposing mostly French chemists for the Nobel Prize. Scholars have constructed a chauvinism index for these early prizes, in which a score of one hundred means that all the nominations for the candidates of a certain country were from that country's nominators, whereas a zero means that a given country's nominators selected only foreign scientists. During the early years of the Nobel Prize in Chemistry, France was the most chauvinistic at 71, followed by the United States at 53, Great Britain at 39, and Germany at 33. Also in the data released by the Nobel Foundation were pairs of countries that tended to nominate each other's scientists, such as Sweden and Germany. Indeed, Sweden nominated more German chemists than it did chemists from all other countries combined. German nominators reciprocated by proposing many Swedish candidates, though there was no balance, the proportion being vastly in Germany's favor. Germany also had the largest percentage of nominations from several other countries. This extraordinary position of Germany in the early history of the Nobel Prizes in Chemistry is not surprising when one realizes that German universities were magnets that attracted chemists from all over the world to their superior doctoral programs.

According to the regulations of the science committees, nominations must be received by the end of the first month of the award year. At that time, the work of the committees begins, and from February until September, members and their consultants evaluate the nominated candidates, first through calculating nomination statistics, then through studying the material that many nominators send to support their choices. Since the members of the chemistry committee do not have the expertise to make informed judgments in all the fields of the candidates, they often call in specialists to aid their assessments. During the spring and summer months, the chemistry committee meets several times to assign research tasks to various members as well as to outside experts, all of whom try to determine the originality and significance of the nominees' accomplishments. After completing this preparatory work, the committee members examine the accumulated evidence and make their recommendations (all written reports as well as the committee's deliberations are secret). During the early years of the prize, all candidates were new, so the committee's investigative work was considerable. As years went by, members found that some candidates kept being nominated again and again, and this made the committee's work easier, since these repeat candidates did not have to be examined as comprehensively as the new ones.

Because of the large amount of information that the Nobel Foundation has made available about the deliberations of the science committees in the first decade and a half of the Nobel Prizes, scholars have been able to analyze how early decisions about winners were made. Surprisingly, rational weighing of the merits of each candidate did not always take place in the private considerations of the committee, although the decision, when it was publicly announced, was so buttressed with justifications that the chosen candidate seemed to be the logical consequence of the state of chemistry at the time. In effect, committee members tried to make their decision appear inevitable, even though they recognized that their decision was, more often than not, a largely arbitrary selection of one scientist's work from a large number of similarly attractive alternatives. Despite the arbitrary elements in many of their choices, members habitually strove for consensus, both because it helped to create solidarity in the group and in its choices and because this consensus safeguarded the committee's independence from the Academy of Sciences.

The process by which the list of candidates was reduced to a small number of names, and finally to a few, sometimes took place quickly and easily, and in these instances committee members could make their recommendations as early as May. When complications developed, however, the final decision on a candidate could be delayed until the end of September, the statutory deadline for the committee's submission of its selection to the Academy. The chemistry committee experienced more difficulties in reaching consensus about its candidates than the physics committee did, and it was unusual for the chemistry committee to recommend a candidate in the spring (which the physics committee often did). One reason for the chemistry committee's dilatoriness in making decisions was the large number of special reports it commissioned. This proliferation of reports, in turn, resulted from the divergence of opinion that often characterized the committee; members would ask for reports in arguing for the superiority of the candidates they favored. Other reasons for the chemists' difficulties were the committee's lack of strong leadership and the disciplinary chauvinism that characterized many members. The traditional antagonism between physical and organic chemists was not absent from the committee. A final reason for the hard-fought battles among chemistry committee members was their penchant not to divide their prize into two or three parts, as the physicists often did, but to award it to an individual chemist.

By late September or the start of October, the chemistry committee submits its recommendation to the Academy of Sciences, which usually, though not always, accepts its choice. In the early years, winners were announced by the middle of November, but since then, selections have usually been made public by the middle of October. Winners are generally notified of their selection by telegram and by telephone before their names are announced at a press conference in Stockholm. Committee members and Nobel officials have not always been scrupulous about keeping the names of prizewinners secret before the public announcement, and some scientists—for example, Linus Pauling and Alexander Todd—first learned of their award from the press. (Richard Feynman, a Nobel laureate in physics, was concerned about the inroads that fame makes into a scientist's work; he felt strongly that prizewinners should be first given the opportunity of refusing the award in private, thus avoiding the controversy that would attend a public turndown.)

In the course of their deliberations, the chemistry committee has often rejected, for various reasons, extremely strong candidates, among them Dmitry Mendeleyev, Stanislao Cannizzaro, and Gilbert Newton Lewis. By 1901, when the Nobel Prizes began to be awarded, chemistry had become so intimately connected with several other sciences that it was often difficult for committee members to match a candidate's work precisely with a prize area, since discoveries frequently involved interdisciplinary fields between chemistry and physics, or chemistry and biology, or chemistry and medicine. Therefore, over the years, physicists and medical researchers have occasionally won this greatest of chemistry awards. Although members of the chemistry committee have not always strictly followed the standards set down in Nobel's will, and even though they have not been able to meet scholars' requirements of excellence, representativeness, and historical significance in all their choices, the members have been able to pick discoverers and discoveries of sufficient standing in the scientific community that the Nobel Prize has become the symbol par excellence of scientific achievement.

The Awarding of the Nobel Prize in Chemistry

Nobel Prizes are traditionally awarded on December 10, the anniversary of their founder's death in San Remo, Italy, in 1896. The prize ceremony takes place in the Concert Hall in Stockholm and, in recent years, has generally been attended by more than a thousand persons. During the cold and dark days of winter, Stockholm becomes the focus of a glittering social event. In the presence of the royal family, of members of the Swedish government and international diplomatic corps, as well as of distinguished academics and clerics, the King of Sweden, following brief analyses of the winners' achievements presented by representatives of the prize-awarding institutions, gives the laureates their awards. Around this pivotal ceremony revolve the awards banquet, the Nobel lectures, and a formal dinner at the Royal Palace hosted by the king.

Each award in chemistry consists of a gold medal, a diploma bearing a citation, and a sum of money, the amount of which depends on the annual interest income of the Nobel Foundation and the number of prizewinners (although the prize money may be divided, the prize itself is not—there are no fractional Nobel awards). The profile of Alfred Nobel on the front of the gold medal is common to all the Nobel Prizes in various areas; the chemistry prize has, on the back, an allegorical representation of knowledge, in the form of a scientist, unveiling Nature, in the form of a woman. Prominent Swedish artists design and do the calligraphy for the personal diploma, which consists of a symbolic painting and a statement describing why the Royal Swedish Academy of Sciences has awarded the scientist its Nobel Prize.

The monetary value of the Nobel Prize has varied considerably over the years. In 1901 the prize was worth 150,800 Swedish crowns, an amount approximately equivalent to what a university professor would then earn in twenty-five years. Because of the conservative management of the Nobel Foundation, the cash value of the Nobel Prize has generally increased. The purchase value, however, has varied more than the cash value; for example, the Nobel Prize's purchase value plummeted after both World War I and World War II. Since 1960, both the cash value and the purchase power of the Nobel Prize in Chemistry have increased. Nevertheless, during the 1980's, when the cash value of the prize rose from about $300,000 to $400,000, the purchase value, adjusted for inflation, still lagged far behind the purchase power of the very first Nobel Prizes given in 1901. In real material terms, therefore, the Nobel Prize, though substantial, no longer provides the liberating lifetime endowment that Alfred Nobel originally intended.

History of the Chemistry Prizes

During the first eighty-seven years of the chemistry prizes, three countries have accounted for three-quarters of the Nobel awards: Americans have won thirty-three, Germans twenty-seven, and the British twenty-three. German chemists dominated the prize prior to World War II, whereas American chemists have won the majority of the chemistry prizes since the war. Three countries have accounted for more than half of the remaining awards: France has seven chemistry laureates, while Sweden and Switzerland have four each. Canadian and Dutch chemists have each won two chemistry prizes, while the following countries each have one Nobel Prize winner in chemistry: Argentina, Austria, Belgium, Czechoslovakia, Finland, Hungary, Italy, Japan, and the Soviet Union.

Of the three science prizes, the chemistry prize stands alone in having been given most often to individuals rather than to groups of two or three scientists. Between 1901 and 1989, the Nobel Committee for Chemistry of the Royal Swedish Academy of Sciences selected 114 individuals to receive Nobel Prizes in Chemistry. Most of these were men from the industrialized countries of the West. Only three women have won the chemistry prize: Marie Curie, in 1911, the first woman so honored; her daughter Irène Joliot-Curie, who shared the 1935 prize with her husband; and Dorothy Crowfoot Hodgkin, who won the prize in 1964. Marie Curie had earlier (1903) won the Nobel Prize in Physics, which she shared with her husband Pierre and with Antoine-Henri Becquerel for her work in radiation (her chemistry prize was for discovering polonium and radium). She was the first person to be honored twice. More than four decades later, Linus Pauling received the 1954 Nobel Prize in Chemistry, and in 1963 he received the 1962 Nobel Peace Prize, the only person ever to have won two unshared Nobel Prizes and the only person ever to have won both the chemistry and peace awards.

As with other Nobel Prizes, the award in chemistry has sometimes been reserved. The 1914 chemistry prize, for example, was not given that year because of the outbreak of World War I, but in 1915 the prizes for 1914 and 1915 were awarded together. Sometimes, as allowed by the statutes, prizes have been omitted for more than one year, and in these cases the prize money reverts to either the main fund or a special fund to support work in specific areas. For example, the prize was reserved in 1916, and in 1917 the prize money for 1916 was allocated to the special fund for the chemistry section. World War I obviously disturbed the nomination process and the work of the committees, but war has not been the only factor to cause the omission of awards. Occasionally, committee members could not agree on a candidate, or they decided that the pool of candidates was not sufficiently accomplished to produce a winner of the excellence demanded by the Nobel Prize. Several reservations of these types occurred in the 1920's and 1930's. As might be expected, World War II also caused prize omissions. The chemistry prizes for 1940 through 1942 were not given, and the prize money was allocated as follows: one-third to the main fund and two-thirds to the special fund. Since World War II, the Nobel Prizes in Chemistry have been awarded without interruptions.

The Early History of the Nobel Prize in Chemistry (1901-1914)

During their formative years, the Nobel Prizes did not have the great prestige they later acquired. At first, the general public was more interested in the science prizes than scientists themselves were. The early prizes received extensive treatment in the popular press, whereas notices appearing in leading scientific journals were either scanty or nonexistent. For example, during the early history of the Nobel awards,

Science, the journal of the American Association for the Advancement of Science, totally ignored the prize announcements made annually by the Royal Swedish Academy of Sciences. Instead, this journal ran articles criticizing the prize awarders for contravening Alfred Nobel's will by diverting foundation funds to Swedish science in creating the Nobel Institute for Physical Chemistry.

The small number of responses that came from foreign scientists invited to nominate candidates for the chemistry prize exemplified the low esteem in which the Nobel Prizes were held during their early years. In 1900, when the first nominations were solicited, those supervising the chemistry prize sent out roughly three hundred invitations. From the replies they received, committee members learned that the nominators had been puzzled by the requirement that the discovery to be honored should be of recent date. The largest group of nominators contained members of the Royal Swedish Academy of Sciences as well as chairholders in chemistry at distinguished foreign universities, who naturally interpreted the Nobel Prize in the light of the traditional science prizes with which they were familiar. These eighteenth and nineteenth century awards most often honored great chemists for a lifetime of significant work. Besides dealing with misinterpretations of the prize, committee members had to contend with a backlog of eminent chemists whose work had received widespread recognition in the late nineteenth century (and whose selection, they realized, would confer enhanced prestige upon their newly established prizes). Though choosing these distinguished chemists went against the intentions that Nobel had expressed in his will and to the will's witnesses, committee members saw it as their duty, through the first decade of the awards, to recognize the achievements of those who, according to common consensus, had done great work, and not to encourage young talent. Svante August Arrhenius, a pragmatist, realized that this practice was probably necessary during the developmental period of the awards, but he hoped that, after the prestige of the Nobel Prize in Chemistry had been established, what Nobel had wanted should be fulfilled: Young chemists who had done excellent work should receive the prize even if some "old fogeys" were against it.

In these early years, then, the Nobel Committee for Chemistry tended to err on the side of conservatism. Taking a broad understanding of Nobel's stipulation for recency, the committee considered discoveries made within the previous two decades for its prize. In doing this, the chemistry committee was more likely than the physics committee to choose older candidates. Indeed, some chemistry candidates, most notably Adolf von Baeyer, were in their seventies. Despite this long backward search for prizewinners, the chemistry committee did not crown all nineteenth century chemical giants with a Nobel Prize. They actually turned down some candidates—most prominently, Dmitry Mendeleyev and Stanislao Cannizzaro—because their achievements belonged to a prior era. Although Mendeleyev was nominated in 1906, and although his candidacy received considerable support, he eventually was refused the prize because the discovery and establishment of his periodic law of the elements dated from the 1860's and 1870's. Some committee members argued that the discovery of the inert gases (helium, argon, and so on) in the 1890's brought about a deeper understanding of the periodic table, namely, a new group with zero valency. Since Mendeleyev had neither predicted these elements nor made a place for them in his table, however, he was narrowly defeated for the prize, which went to Henri Moissan for his investigations of fluorine.

The usual practice, during the early years of the prize for chemistry, was for committee members to make recommendations based on the clustering of nominators' opinions around certain candidates. As the prizes became better known and better understood, the number of nominations received by the committee increased, usually to between four hundred and five hundred (multiple nominations by a single individual were permitted). In this and later periods, however, the nominating system did not function on the basis of majority votes, since the average number of nominations received by prizewinners in chemistry was 6.6. This number was not very much different from the average number of nominations received by all candidates, 5.7. Clearly, the nominating system did not act as a voting system: The chemist nominated most often was the prizewinner in only seven of the first fifteen years. Although in some years, the winner received ten nominations or more (indicating that the committee's decision was influenced by the opinion of the nominators), in other years, the winner received a very small number of nominations. For example, Marie Curie had a total of only three nominations for the two years that she won her prizes in physics and chemistry.

From the documents that have been made available about the early prize decisions, scholars have detected a sense of inferiority on the part of the Swedish awarders. The awarders realized that they were, for the most part, unknown internationally. They were acquainted with the traditional reward system in science—the prizes, medals, and diplomas dispensed by their own and other national scientific societies. They were also aware of how difficult it was to reward scientific achievement without being unduly influenced by political, institutional, or peer-group pressures. The way the Swedish awarders got around their provincial impasse was to choose for their Nobel Prizes scientists who had previously received major awards. For example, in this early period, all the French scientists who received the Nobel Prize in Chemistry had already been awarded prizes or medals by the French Academy of Sciences. By rewarding scientists who had already garnered significant national and international honors, the Swedish prize givers hoped to lift their new prize to the level of these other prizes. Their tactic proved to be an excellent one, and the Nobel Prizes soon took on the symbolic significance in the international scientific community that they have maintained ever since.

The Nobel Prizes in science filled a void. Since other prizes were basically national awards, the Nobel Prizes could become a supranational arbiter of scientific achievement. Alfred Nobel, through his fortune, had given a small group of Swedish scientists the opportunity to judge which scientific discoveries made throughout the world were truly outstanding. In the internationalizing of the chemistry prize, a principal figure was Svante Arrhenius. Although formally a member of the Nobel

Committee for Physics, Arrhenius became the most influential scientist with regard to prize selections in chemistry. He was a buoyantly optimistic person with the ability to make, hold, and influence friends. Early in his career, he had received little support in Sweden for his theory of ionization (while working for his doctorate at Uppsala, he proposed that salt molecules, when they dissolve in water, split apart, or dissociate, into oppositely charged particles that he called "ions"). Seeking support elsewhere, Arrhenius wrote to many of the prominent chemists of Europe. His ideas were eventually championed by Wilhelm Ostwald and Jacobus Henricus van't Hoff, scientists who were helping to construct the new field of physical chemistry. By the time the Nobel Prizes were instituted, Arrhenius' theory of solutions had become widely respected, and he wanted to use the prizes to reward chemists such as Ostwald and van't Hoff who had supported him.

The members of the Nobel Committee for Chemistry were in a unique position during the first few years of the award. The number of chemists obviously deserving the award was larger then than it has ever been since. During the last two decades of the nineteenth century, several fields of chemistry had experienced accelerated development, creating a group of many distinguished discoveries to be rewarded. Furthermore, as previously mentioned, fewer candidates were nominated during the first six years of the award than in any later time. This situation bred special conditions and needs with regard to the early prizes. In a way, the committee's work was facilitated by the assuredly deserving older candidates, since committee members simply had to decide the order in which these candidates would receive their awards. Members found it difficult to hierarchize the achievements of these chemists, however, since they worked in such diverse fields. Consequently, members used the number of nominations submitted to the Academy of Sciences as a guide. For example, more than 50 percent of the nominators proposed van't Hoff for the 1901 chemistry prize. In 1874 he had used the asymmetric arrangements of atoms within molecules to explain why these molecules had the ability to rotate the plane of polarized light, but this important discovery was, by 1901, more than a quarter of a century old and, by a strict interpretation of Nobel's will, ineligible for a prize. Fortunately, van't Hoff, influenced by Arrhenius' ideas, had more recently formulated an influential theory explaining the effect of temperature on increases in the speeds of chemical reactions. He had also been able, by studying the passage of materials through membranes, to make important discoveries in the field of osmotic pressure. Therefore, under the influence of Arrhenius, the chemistry committee was able to give their first Nobel Prize to van't Hoff in recognition of his discoveries in chemical dynamics and osmotic pressure.

In 1902 van't Hoff, in his capacity as a Nobel Prize winner, nominated Arrhenius for the physics prize, since he saw ionization as a physical process. This nomination represented a situation that would recur often in the history of the Nobel Prizes for science. Chemists often did research in areas that overlapped with the work of physicists, and vice versa. The situation became more complex in the 1920's and 1930's, as chemists became interested in such biological materials as proteins, carbohydrates, and nucleic acids. After World War II, certain fields of chemistry and medical research began to converge. Thus, van't Hoff's nomination of Arrhenius symbolized the start of a concern that would engage the prize awarders, off and on, throughout most of the twentieth century. In 1902, however, the chemistry committee had another concern. Since they had honored a physical chemist with their first prize, they decided to give their second prize to an organic chemist. This practice of alternating prizes among fields would become common in the later history of the chemistry prize. In 1902 Arrhenius, a physical chemist, received votes along with Marcelin Berthelot and Emil Fischer, both organic chemists. Berthelot, who was seventy-five years old, had helped to found modern organic chemistry by being among the first to synthesize organic substances that do not occur in nature. His best work had been done decades earlier, however, so the Academy of Sciences honored Fischer, whose outstanding work on the structure and synthesis of sugars was more recent.

Because he had used physical methods, principally thermodynamics, to justify his theory of chemical activity in solutions, Arrhenius wanted to be awarded the physics prize, but the members of the physics committee, by late 1902, were adamant in opposing an undivided prize for Arrhenius. His supporters therefore changed their strategy and proposed that he receive a share of the prize in both physics and chemistry. Van't Hoff renewed his proposal that Arrhenius receive the 1903 prize in physics, but he also nominated Arrhenius for the chemistry prize. Others acted similarly, for Arrhenius received seven nominations in physics and twelve in chemistry, both representing significant proportions of the nominations. After lengthy discussions between members of the physics and chemistry committees, it became clear that the physicists would not recommend Arrhenius for any part of their award. Furthermore, a substantial group in the chemistry committee did not want to give the chemistry award to Arrhenius; instead, they wanted to reward William Ramsay for his discovery of the inert gases. The chemists, though divided among themselves, tried to hammer out a compromise with the physicists, but they failed. Further complicating matters was the physics committee's decision to recommend Henri Becquerel and the husband-and-wife team of Pierre and Marie Curie for its prize. This upset the chemists, who argued that Marie Curie's discovery of radium was of greater importance to chemistry than to physics. The discovery of new elements had traditionally been the domain of chemists, and radium was the most significant new chemical element found in the past century. For example, radium had changed the long-held idea that elements are invariable. Despite all these arguments, the physics committee gave its prize to Becquerel and the Curies, though they left open the possibility that the chemists might, in the future, reward Marie Curie for her discovery of polonium and radium. Meanwhile, after much wrangling and compromising, the chemistry committee decided to award the 1903 prize in chemistry to Arrhenius.

The award to Arrhenius did not end the Royal Swedish Academy of Sciences' problems with this chemist, for in 1904 he threatened to take a prestigious post in

Berlin unless the Academy made him director of the Nobel Institute for Physical Chemistry. The Academy complied, even though this institute did little investigating of the work of candidates who were proposed for a Nobel Prize. In the negotiations between the executors and the members of the prize-awarding institutions, one of the arguments that the scientists used for the institutes was that they would have to conduct experimental investigations of the discoveries of candidates, in order to ensure their worthiness of a prize. The committees discovered early, however, that they could dispense with these experimental verifications, since they had been done, often many times, by other scientists. After the establishment of Arrhenius' Nobel Institute, committees called on it only three times to examine works proposed for prizes. Important discoveries spawned so many replications that further confirmatory experiments were unnecessary. Furthermore, chemists and physicists around the world were generating such a variety of results with such an assortment of new methods that verification of many of these were beyond the capabilities of Arrhenius' institute.

The award to Ramsay in 1904 escaped the sorts of disagreements between the physicists and chemists that the prize to Arrhenius had caused. More than two-thirds of the nominators had proposed Ramsay, whose discovery of argon and other inert gases ideally fit the definition of a discovery in Nobel's will. Indeed, several early Nobel Prizes in Chemistry were connected with the discovery of new elements, and almost all of their discoverers were rewarded with Nobel Prizes before World War I: Ramsay for isolating and investigating the properties of argon, helium, krypton, neon, and xenon; Moissan for fluorine; Marie Curie for polonium and radium; and Rutherford for various radioactive isotopes. In finding these elements, these chemists and physicists used either conventional chemical methods or new techniques, such as bombarding known elements with high-speed subatomic particles to bring about transmutations into new elements.

Dmitry Mendeleyev's name was inextricably linked with the periodic table of the elements, and the discovery of these new elements renewed interest in his candidacy for a Nobel Prize. This movement, however, occurred at the same time that the organic chemists wanted to recognize Adolf von Baeyer, their great master, for his achievements, even though his best work had been done decades earlier. Although his sponsors were careful to cite such specific accomplishments as his work on organic dyes and ring compounds, it was clear that his 1905 award was based on a lifetime of contributions to organic and industrial chemistry. Similarly, in 1906, the inorganic chemists wanted to honor their master, Mendeleyev. His narrow defeat to Moissan, compared with Baeyer's victory, illustrates how arbitrary the application of the statutes of the Nobel Foundation could be.

Another example of the Nobel systems' arbitrariness is the case of Josiah Willard Gibbs. This American physicist had, in the 1870's, applied thermodynamic methods to chemical substances and their reactions, thereby providing a firm theoretical foundation for much of physical chemistry. Gibbs's work is now widely acknowledged as richly deserving of a Nobel Prize in either chemistry or physics. At the time his research was done, however, American science was denigrated by European scientists. Moreover, Gibbs published his work in an obscure American journal. His highly mathematical approach also kept readership of his papers small, and the importance of his ideas was slow to spread. Even as late as the start of the twentieth century, his work was not fully appreciated, though scientists and industrialists were finding increasing applications for his phase rule (an equation relating the phases, components, and degrees of freedom of a chemical system). Unfortunately, Gibbs was never nominated for a Nobel Prize in either chemistry or physics, and he died in 1903, at sixty-four, before the full significance of his work to chemistry had been recognized.

Like Mendeleyev and Gibbs, another nineteenth century scientist who could, and perhaps should, have been honored with a Nobel Prize in Chemistry was Stanislao Cannizzaro. Since he lived until 1910, the committee had sufficient opportunity to celebrate his great work in establishing an accurate system of atomic weights. Inexplicably, his name was not proposed until 1907. The committee then agreed that his work on atomic and molecular theories was of fundamental importance for modern chemistry, but so much time had elapsed since the publication of his results that most committee members believed that the regulations of the Foundation made it impossible to give the prize to him.

After 1907, the Nobel Prize in Chemistry entered a new period. Most of the great chemists from the end of the nineteenth century had been honored, and nominations for the chemistry award increasingly became less helpful in guiding the committee in choosing prizewinners. A great many chemists in a wide variety of fields were now being proposed, and there was little clustering of the nominators' opinions. The candidates nominated most often were those who had received fewer than ten votes. Moreover, the chemistry committee's problems with the physics committee over interdisciplinary work continued. Lacking a common definition of what constituted significant chemical or physical discoveries, committee members experienced difficulties in arriving at any consensus. Furthermore, the chemists in the committee came from a range of fields, and without a strong chairman, their members often were as divided among themselves as they were estranged from the physicists. One example of the types of problems that cropped up was the competition between the chemistry and physics committees over Ernest Rutherford's Nobel Prize. This physicist was given the 1908 Nobel Prize in Chemistry, and his citation reads that he was being honored for "his investigations into the disintegration of the elements, and the chemistry of radioactive substances." The citation reveals the dichotomy between the physics and chemistry committees, because his disintegration theory was predominantly physics, whereas his work on the radioactive elements was predominantly chemistry. On the other hand, he regarded himself as a physicist, and the award in chemistry surprised not only him but also many later scientists and historians of science.

As in previous cases, the decision to give the chemistry prize to Rutherford was actually the result of a compromise. Arrhenius was an ardent supporter of the atomic hypothesis, and by the early twentieth century, it was clear to him that atoms could no longer be regarded as the indivisible particles that John Dalton had proposed early in the nineteenth century. Rutherford's great discovery—that the atoms of an element could spontaneously decay into the atoms of a different element—proved this. His discovery was fraught with physical and chemical consequences. In their earlier disputes with the physicists over the Curies, the chemists had made it clear that in the future they would assert their right to make awards in the field of radioactivity. The deliberations of the chemistry committee in the spring of 1908 show that members moved quickly to guarantee that Rutherford should receive their prize. Arrhenius enthusiastically backed the chemistry prize for Rutherford, and he was able to convince influential members of the physics committee to choose another candidate for their prize (they chose Gabriel Lippmann, whose work turned out to be much less significant than Rutherford's). Although the chemistry committee succeeded in claiming Rutherford for its award, its success left a bad taste in the mouths of the physicists, who came to believe that they had been manipulated into relinquishing their best candidate to the chemists.

The disputes between chemical disciplines within the chemistry committee itself were often as heated as the interdisciplinary battles between the physicists and chemists. Some members of the chemistry committee were great admirers of German physical chemistry, and they saw the Nobel Prizes as a useful way to promote the advancement of their field. Similarly, the organic chemists had their own heroes and sought to advance their discipline. In 1909, Arrhenius, who was a strong advocate of physical chemistry, wanted Wilhelm Ostwald to be given the award in chemistry. According to some chemists, Ostwald was the founder of the field, since, in 1887, he had started the *Zeitschrift für physikalische Chemie* (journal for physical chemistry). As many historians of chemistry have pointed out, however, physical chemistry's development was well under way by the time Ostwald began his journal. Nevertheless, his important work on chemical equilibrium and on the rates of chemical reactions assured his place as one of the principal founders of the field. He had earlier been considered as a potential candidate for the prize, but a special report pointed out difficulties, since no particular achievement among his many discoveries could be isolated as truly great. His candidacy was therefore put in abeyance until 1909, when the committee reversed its position; Arrhenius was decisive in bringing this about. In 1909, the chemistry committee was in disarray over the candidate it should propose to the Academy. Arrhenius nominated Ostwald and wrote a report on his work, emphasizing Ostwald's research on how certain ions speeded up chemical reactions without reacting themselves (a phenomenon known as catalysis). Arrhenius also showed how the rapidly developing new field of enzyme research could be related to this older work on catalysis, thus making Ostwald's prize a logical successor to Eduard Buchner's 1907 prize, awarded for his biochemical researches on the role of enzymes in cell-free alcoholic fermentation. Although the arguments offered were sufficiently persuasive to convince committee members to choose Ostwald for the 1909 prize, historians of chemistry have since found these arguments weak, because Ostwald had no strong theory of catalysis and his work actually left many basic questions about catalytic reactions unanswered. Chemists on the committee had similar misgivings, but Arrhenius' influence was strong enough to push through the candidacy of Ostwald. (He was also able to block the candidacy of Walther Nernst, who did not receive his 1920 Nobel Prize until 1921.)

By 1910, Nobel Prizes in Chemistry had been awarded in the fields of physical, organic, inorganic, and biological chemistry. Ensuring a good representation of both traditional and important new fields became a criterion in the committee's choices. Indeed, a principle of rotation developed that continued through later periods of the prize's history. The principle was useful in directing the committee's attention to areas that had so far gone unrewarded. By 1910, too, the committees of physics and chemistry had agreed to discuss together candidates who had been nominated in both disciplines. Members of both committees recognized that such things as elements were subjects of investigation for both physicists and chemists, and they wanted to forestall controversies by deciding on formal boundaries between their two sciences. For example, such agreement made it possible for the chemistry committee to reward Marie Curie in 1911 with a chemistry prize (to add to her earlier physics prize) for her discovery of the new elements polonium and radium.

These interscience agreements did not prevent interfield disagreements from continuing to arise within the chemistry committee. For example, in 1910, several members wanted to honor Victor Grignard for his discovery of a reagent that had proved to be of great utility in organic synthesis, but a controversy had developed over the priority of this discovery between Grignard and his former teacher at the University of Lyons, François-Antoine-Philippe Barbier. Because of the basic conservatism of the chemistry committee, members steered away from candidates involved in priority controversies, and Grignard had to wait until 1912 for his prize, which he shared with Paul Sabatier (this was the first time that the chemistry prize was divided). The 1910 award was given to a "safe" candidate, Otto Wallach, basically for his past services to organic chemistry.

In 1911 the Nobel Prizes were ten years old. A Swedish newspaper marked this anniversary by conducting a study of the prizes. Reporters questioned all the previous science laureates about a variety of issues. They found that most winners had used the prize money to hire assistants and purchase equipment so that they could expand their research. In this sense, the laureates saw their awards as another example of the traditional reward system in science, whereby prizes, medals, and other honors were dispensed by national scientific societies to make the good work of excellent scientists even better. By 1911, however, the Nobel prizes in science had acquired a constituency of interested scientists outside Sweden. Though the Nobel Prizes were still not firmly established in the scientific culture of the time, they were well on their way to becoming the first truly international scientific prizes.

The prize in 1913 was the last undisturbed selection before the chaos brought by World War I. Largely because of the support of Arrhenius and several inorganic chemists, who hoped to rally their comrades to a new field within inorganic chemistry, Alfred Werner, a Swiss chemist, was given the 1913 chemistry prize. His work on the two principal ways atoms link in complex inorganic compounds made sense of a series of complex stereochemical reactions. In the year that Werner won his prize, Henry Gwyn-Jeffreys Moseley, a young British scientist, used various metals as targets in an X-ray apparatus, and by studying the wavelengths of the chief radiations produced, he discovered that the order of the elements in the periodic table is not attributable to chance but to a basic principle of atomic structure (later called the atomic number). Arrhenius quickly recognized the importance of Moseley's discovery and suggested him for a Nobel Prize in Chemistry. Although some chemistry committee members admired Moseley's work, they also felt that, because it was so new, his award could wait. World War I had already begun, causing the 1914 chemistry prize to be reserved. Several months later, in August, 1915, Moseley was killed during the Battle of Gallipoli.

From World War I Through World War II (1914-1945)

World War I brought with it an intensification of international scientific competition that was diametrically opposed to the cooperative spirit that Nobel had tried to encourage with his awards. The war impelled both scientists and the public to view the awards from nationalistic perspectives. German journalists inaugurated statistical comparisons of the prizes won by each country, pointing out, for example, that German scientists had won the great majority of the chemistry prizes. Wilhelm Ostwald used the statistics of the science prizes to trumpet Germany's superiority in the sciences. When Arrhenius recommended to the Academy of Sciences in 1915 that the prizes be suspended until the war's end, he cited Ostwald's statements as evidence that the belligerent parties were unable to treat the Nobel Prizes in the spirit of their founder. Alfred Nobel had hoped that his prizes would contribute to the lessening of international tensions, but countries involved in the conflict began using them as a means of taking stock of their scientific and technical accomplishments and as a basis for jingoistic propaganda.

When World War I broke out, the Nobel committees for physics and chemistry were about to submit their recommendations for the 1914 prizes. At first, the committee members did not believe that the war would interfere with the process of prize selection. The committees made their choices—Max von Laue for the physics prize and Theodore William Richards for the chemistry prize—but these recommendations never reached the Academy's plenary meeting, because the Nobel Foundation, acting independently of the various prize-awarding bodies, petitioned the Swedish government for permission to defer the prize decisions until 1915. The government granted the request.

By 1915, it was obvious that the war was not going to end quickly. Indeed, the conflict had expanded, with many scientists of the warring nations becoming deeply involved. Several Swedish scientists agreed with Arrhenius that, in this hostile environment, no science prizes should be awarded, but the Academy decided against interrupting the awards until the war ended and went ahead with the prize decisions for both 1914 and 1915. The Nobel Prizes had become an important part of Swedish life, and awarding them would assure a war-weary world that Alfred Nobel's ideal of internationalism lived on. Despite this brave façade, the war seriously interfered with the Nobel Prizes in Chemistry. The only prizes actually given during the war were the two awarded in 1915: the 1914 prize to Richards, an inorganic chemist, and the 1915 prize to Richard Willstätter, an organic chemist (a capsule illustration of the principle of rotation at work). Richards, the first American to win a Nobel Prize in Chemistry, was honored for his accurate determinations of the atomic weights of many chemical elements. Willstätter, the "Einstein of chemistry," won for his studies of chlorophyll and other plant pigments.

Some historians have called World War I the "chemists' war," because chemists on both sides played vital roles in providing essential materials for the conflict, from explosives and poisonous gases to optical glass and fine chemicals. The war also contributed to changing the organizational structure of science. Because of generous government funding, universities were able to expand their scientific research (and most Nobel laureates did their prizewinning work in universities). Industry, too, increased its support for research both in its own laboratories and in university laboratories. In 1901, when the Nobel Prizes were founded, scientific research was largely an avocation pursued by professors between classes. After World War I, it became an integral part of university life, financed by universities, foundations, industries, and government agencies.

The first postwar chemistry prizes were awarded to Germans. In what seemed a very strange choice to chemists in the Allied countries, Fritz Haber won the 1918 chemistry prize, awarded in 1919, for the synthesis of ammonia from hydrogen and atmospheric nitrogen. This process had permitted Germany to produce tons of nitrates for its explosives during the war. Haber had also helped to develop the poisonous gases that Germany used against the Allies, and he even directed the first use of chlorine gas on the battlefield. The Haber process for synthesizing ammonia could also be used to produce nitrogen fertilizers, however, and members of the chemistry committee emphasized the importance of the Haber process for agricultural rather than military purposes.

Walther Nernst, a German physical chemist, received the 1920 Nobel Prize in 1921 for his work in thermochemistry. His significant work had been done in the 1880's and 1890's, and Arrhenius had met him in Würzburg in the late 1880's. Both men had huge egos, and both vigorously attacked each other's experimental and theoretical work, leading to a complete rupture of their relationship at the turn of the century. During the first two decades of the twentieth century, Nernst had been regularly proposed for the chemistry prize, but Arrhenius' opposition inevitably led to a negative recommendation. By 1921, the ardor of Arrhenius' resistance had cooled, and Nernst was finally able to receive his award.

During the 1920's and 1930's, radioactivity continued to be the domain of the chemists. In 1922, the 1921 Nobel Prize for chemistry was given to Frederick Soddy and the 1922 prize to Francis Aston—to Soddy for his investigations into the origin and nature of isotopes, and to Aston for his discovery, through his mass spectrograph, of isotopes of nonradioactive elements. More than a decade later, Irène Joliot-Curie and her husband Frédéric Joliot won the chemistry prize for their 1934 work on the synthesis of new radioactive elements. In one of their classic experiments, they bombarded aluminum with alpha particles, transmuting it into a radioactive isotope of phosophorus, which then decayed into silicon: They had produced artificial radioactivity.

During the interwar period, new fields of chemistry were created at a much more rapid rate than they had been before World War I, and committee members began to use the prizes to recognize these new fields. For example, Fritz Pregl, an Austrian physiological chemist, devised techniques for working with a few milligrams of various substances; in doing so, he helped to create the new field of microanalysis, for which he received the 1923 Nobel Prize. Similarly, Richard A. Zsigmondy, an Austrian-born chemist who did his work in Germany, helped develop the field of colloid chemistry by skillful use of the ultramicroscope, an instrument that enabled scientists to determine the sizes of tiny particles and to show that colloidal systems are intermediate between the molecular and the microscopically visible (Zsigmondy's 1925 Nobel Prize for this work was awarded in 1926). The desire of the committee to reward new fields continued into the 1930's. For example, Carl Bosch and Friedrich Bergius won the 1931 prize for their invention and development of high-pressure methods whereby coal could be combined with varying amounts of hydrogen to produce fuels and lubricating oils. In 1932, Irving Langmuir, an American physicist and chemist, won the chemistry prize for his discoveries in surface chemistry, a field ignored by the committee up to then.

In addition to recognizing new fields, the chemistry committee continued to honor discoveries in traditional disciplines. As in the prewar years, committee members carried on the policy instigated by Arrhenius by rewarding significant research in physical chemistry. For example, Harold Urey, an American physical chemist, won a Nobel award in 1934 for his discovery of deuterium, an isotope of hydrogen (also called heavy hydrogen), and in 1936 Peter Debye won for his contributions to molecular structure achieved through the powder method of X-ray diffraction that he had developed. It is unfortunate that one of the greatest physical chemists of this period, Gilbert Newton Lewis, never received the Nobel Prize. Lewis not only made fundamental contributions to the theory of the chemical bond (his idea of the shared-electron-pair bond had great influence) but also was the first to produce pure heavy water (deuterium oxide). At the University of California at Berkeley, where he spent most of his career, he also conducted a series of elegant investigations to verify the third law of thermodynamics (his pupil, William Francis Giauque, continued this work and won the 1949 Nobel Prize in Chemistry). Indeed, by the mid-1960's, the University of California at Berkeley had ten Nobel Prize winners on its faculty, and scholars have traced every one of them back to Lewis, their great master.

The discipline with the most recipients in the interwar period was organic chemistry, which continued to be dominated by Germans. Heinrich Otto Wieland, for example, received the 1927 chemistry award in 1928 for his research on the constitution of the bile acids, and Adolf Windaus won the 1928 prize for his research into the structures of various sterols, including cholesterol, and their relationship with the vitamins. Investigations on chlorophyll were rewarded in 1930, when Hans Fischer of Munich received the prize for his work on the structures of hemin and chlorophyll; Fischer's award marked one of the rare instances when the committee was actually able to reward important work done during the preceding year. Vitamins attracted the interest of chemists during the 1930's, and in 1937 the Englishman Walter Haworth and the Swiss Paul Karrer shared the chemistry prize, Haworth for his work on the constitution of the carbohydrates and vitamin C and Karrer for his work on the constitution of vitamins A and B_2.

For the most part, the chemistry committee spread the prizes among various fields judiciously, leading to a great growth in the prestige of their awards. This, in turn, led to a steady rise in the number of nominations. Unfortunately, political problems developed for the Nobel Prizes during the late 1930's. The difficulties began when the Nobel Foundation awarded its 1935 Peace Prize in 1936 to Carl von Ossietzky, a prominent German pacifist who was deeply involved in the German Peace Society and who was a vociferous critic of secret German rearmament. Adolf Hitler was outraged at the Nobel Foundation's action, and he forbade any German to accept a Nobel Prize. In his 1937 decree, he also prohibited Germans from sending in nominations, which helped bring about a sharp decline in nominations after 1938. The Academy tried to make up for the decline by increasing the invitations sent to scientists in other parts of the world, especially in the United States, where so many of the scientists fleeing Nazi Germany had gone.

Hitler's decree had a specific effect on the chemistry prize when the 1939 award was divided between Leopold Ružička, a Croatian-born organic chemist who did his work in Switzerland, and Adolf Butenandt, a German biochemist. Butenandt, who won for his work on sex hormones, notified the Academy that, in accordance with the policy established by Hitler, he would not accept the Nobel Prize. Richard Kuhn, who was notified of his 1938 chemistry prize at the same time as Butenandt, also informed the Academy that he could not accept the award. When Butenandt and Kuhn did not claim their prize money, it reverted to the general fund. (In 1948, after the Third Reich had been defeated, Butenandt and Kuhn wrote to the Academy, stating that they had refused the prize under threat of violence; the Academy replied that it could do nothing about the forfeited prize money, but, by special decree, it awarded the two Germans their diplomas and gold medals in July, 1949.)

As in World War I, so in World War II, hostilities made it impossible for the Nobel Foundation and the academies to function normally. The Academy of Sciences was unable to award the chemistry prizes for the first three years of the war. Scientists whose energies were devoted to the war effort had no time for international prizes, and letters inviting nominations remained largely unanswered. Furthermore, access to the scientific literature during wartime was limited, so that scientists on one side of the conflict could not form an accurate assessment about scientific research on the other side. Many scientists even questioned the suitability of awarding Nobel Prizes during such a violent international struggle. Despite these misgivings, prizes were awarded in 1944 and 1945, and it is interesting that the 1944 chemistry prize was given to Otto Hahn in 1945 for his discovery of the fission of atomic nuclei; committee members made their decision during the summer that atom bombs were dropped on Hiroshima and Nagasaki.

The Postwar Period (1946-1989)

The Nobel Prizes did not quickly recover their former glory with the cessation of hostilities. Nominations continued to be low in the years immediately following the war, and it was not until 1948 that the high level of the early 1930's was again attained. With the countries of Europe devastated and with its own infrastructure relatively unscathed, the United States of America, having accumulated a vast supply of human scientific capital because of the illustrious immigrants from Europe, emerged as a giant of science. The large number of Nobel Prizes in science won by Americans during the postwar period attests the great change that had occurred. In the forty years before World War II, Americans had won a total of fourteen prizes; in the forty years after World War II, they won more than seven times as many. By 1976, American scientists had accumulated more Nobel Prizes than the scientists of any other country.

Chemistry was very much a part of this development. Before World War II, Americans had won only three chemistry prizes; in the period from 1946 to 1989, they won thirty-two. Postwar American chemistry drew its strength from increasing government support through agencies such as the National Science Foundation. The "big science" developed during the war continued, and the United States government generously funded scientific research in universities, institutes, industries, and private as well as state agencies. When three Americans won the Nobel Prize in Chemistry for 1946, many interpreted this as a symbol of a new era. James B. Sumner won for his discovery that enzymes could be crystallized; John Northrop and Wendell Stanley won for their preparation of pure virus proteins. The prize to Northrop and Stanley illustrates another aspect of postwar chemistry—the importance of teams, even large groups, in scientific research. This trend, which would increasingly characterize European research as well, presented a problem for the science committees, since Nobel intended his prizes for individuals, not large groups.

With the economies of so many countries in chaos because of the war, it is easy to see why the United States initially had so many prizewinners. Yet why did American chemistry's superiority continue, even after such countries as Germany, which had earlier dominated the chemistry prizes, completed their renewal? Certainly the wealth of the United States played a role. Since the war, the federal government far outstripped even the wealthiest foundations in supporting scientific research. Many scholars have pointed to such salient characteristics of American institutions as decentralization, antiauthoritarianism, and pluralism in explaining this scientific success. Unlike many countries, the United States has no national university system; instead, public and private academic institutions compete side-by-side. In the postwar period, various granting agencies also assumed a multiplicity of roles. This diversity of approaches, and the competition and ingenuity that it fostered, encouraged a multipronged strategy to solve the problems of scientific research.

In the decades after the war, scientists also achieved great prestige in American life. This can be seen in the discovery of the elements beyond uranium in the periodic table (the transuranium elements). Before the war, they had all been discovered by Europeans, but after the war, all the transuranium elements were discovered by Americans. In 1951, Edwin McMillan and Glenn Seaborg were given Nobel Prizes in Chemistry for their discoveries in the chemistry of the transuranium elements. McMillan had discovered neptunium and made a start on the discovery of plutonium, then was called away to do war work. Seaborg completed the plutonium work and went on, with many collaborators, to discover several other transuranium elements. President John F. Kennedy's appointment of Seaborg as chairman of the Atomic Energy Commission is an indication of the prestige that American chemists had achieved in their country.

One outstanding representative of American chemistry in the twentieth century is Linus Pauling, who won two unshared Nobel prizes—in 1954 for chemistry and in 1962 for peace (awarded in 1963, when the Partial Nuclear Test Ban Treaty went into effect). Pauling's significant work on the nature of the chemical bond was done in the 1930's; many chemists assumed that he would win the Nobel Prize then, but as the years went by with no invitation to Stockholm, he came to believe that his style of research, which involved the methodical study of molecular structures through such techniques as X-ray and electron diffraction, did not generate the dramatic discoveries that the Nobel Foundation rewarded. By the 1950's, however, the value of Pauling's approach, which gave him insight into the structures not only of complex inorganic substances such as the silicate minerals but also of such complex organic substances as antibodies and proteins, had become clear to members of the chemistry committee, and he was awarded his Nobel Prize—not for any specific discovery, but for his overall work on the nature of the chemical bond. Similarly, Robert Mulliken was honored in 1966 for his lifelong work on the molecular-orbital theory of the chemical bond, which had paralleled Pauling's work in the early phases of its development and then became more popular than Pauling's valence-bond theory in its later development.

In the period since the war, the country closest to the United States in the number of its chemistry Nobel Prizes has been Great Britain. British chemists did outstanding work in determining the structures and properties of molecules of biological importance. Robert Robinson, for example, won the 1947 chemistry prize for his investigations into such vegetable products as the alkaloids, complex nitrogen-containing compounds that have had important medical uses. His student, Alexander Todd, won the 1957 prize for his work on nucleotides, another class of nitrogen-containing compounds, which form an essential part of the deoxyribonucleic acid (DNA) molecule. Frederick Sanger of the University of Cambridge received the 1958 award for working out the structure of insulin, which turned out to have two chains held together by sulfur bridges. Also at Cambridge, John Kendrew and Max Perutz performed their work on the structure of globular proteins that led to a 1962 Nobel Prize. Cambridge was not the only British university producing Nobel Prize-winning chemists. At the University of Oxford, Dorothy Crowfoot Hodgkin, with an excellent group of collaborators, determined the structures of penicillin and vitamin B_{12}, accomplishments for which she received the 1964 Nobel Prize.

Though severely maimed by the war, German chemistry eventually revived, leading to a number of postwar prizes. Initially, some of the discoveries that the Nobel Committee for Chemistry rewarded had actually been made before the war. For example, in the 1920's and 1930's, Otto Diels and Kurt Alder, who won the 1950 prize, had worked out a procedure for making complex organic compounds that had extremely wide applicability (similar to Grignard's method, which had been honored earlier). Another example of prewar work rewarded after the war is Hermann Staudinger's 1953 prize for his discoveries in the field of macromolecular chemistry. In the 1920's, Staudinger had suggested that gigantic molecules, called polymers, are formed when certain substances react. Many chemists initially resisted this idea of monumentally large molecules, but Staudinger's idea turned out to be a valid and influential one. By the 1960's, however, German chemists were winning their Nobel Prizes for work done after the war. Manfred Eigen of the Max Planck Institute for Physical Chemistry in Göttingen won the 1967 prize (shared with Ronald Norrish and George Porter) for his studies of extremely fast chemical reactions.

Like the chemistry committees before the war, the postwar committees appeared to use a principle of rotation in determining the fields of chemistry to honor. On the other hand, work in organic chemistry, physical chemistry, and biochemistry was much more likely to be recognized than, say, work in inorganic chemistry. Indeed, a significant proportion of chemistry prizes in the postwar period—some would say too large a proportion—has been for discoveries in organic and biological chemistry. For example, Robert Burns Woodward won the 1965 award for developing techniques for synthesizing such complex organic compounds as chlorophyll and the steroids. Luis Leloir, an Argentine biochemist and one of the few Third World scientists to have won a Nobel Prize, was honored in 1970 for his discovery of the sugar nucleotides, coenzymes that determine how well living things can store chemical energy. Leloir's award was one among many that resulted from the chemistry committee's interest in nucleic-acid studies in the 1960's and 1970's. In 1972, Christian Anfinsen won for his work on ribonuclease, an enzyme that decomposes ribonuleic acid (RNA), a prize that he shared with Stanford Moore and William Stein, whose work also involved ribonuclease. Paul Berg and Walter Gilbert won the 1980 prize for their studies of how DNA functions.

Another characteristic of the postwar chemistry prizes has been the greater willingness of committee members to honor theoretical achievements. Even when theorists were honored in the prewar period, the relationship of their theories to experimental discoveries was stressed. Since World War II, chemists who are primarily theoreticians have been honored principally for their theories. Pauling's and Mulliken's theories of the chemical bond have already been mentioned; another example is Ilya Prigogine, who won the 1977 chemistry prize for his contributions to nonequilibrium thermodynamics. His theory of dissipative structures explains how molecules in a state of utter chaos are able to evolve into a state of order.

From their studies of previous centuries, historians of science have become familiar with shifts in scientific accomplishment from country to country. In antiquity, for example, Greece was the country where many of the greatest scientific discoveries were made. By the time of the scientific revolution of the sixteenth and seventeenth centuries, the most important discoveries were being made by European scientists. By the middle of the twentieth century, a shift had obviously taken place from Europe to the United States. Since then, many American scientists have expressed concern that the United States might be losing its position of eminence to Japan. They point to such evidence as fewer students taking science courses in American high schools and colleges; they also mention the low scores of American students on tests of scientific understanding (as compared to the high scores of Japanese and European students). These facts may indeed constitute the prelude to a coming shift in scientific superiority to the Far East, but, if the number of Nobel Prizes is any indication, such a shift is not yet under way, for American scientists continued to dominate the prizes during the 1980's. American scientists may perhaps be living off the intellectual capital accumulated during and after World War II, but they also seem to have invested this capital sufficiently wisely—in governmental, industrial, and, especially, university institutions—that it will contribute to American scientific achievement well into the future.

Conclusions

The Nobel Prizes in Chemistry by themselves provide neither a balanced nor a complete record of the development of this science in the twentieth century. For one thing, the evolution of chemistry is much more than a drama enacted by the great chemists. It is, rather, a rich mix of people and institutions of varying degrees of ability and achievement, and the Nobel Prize winners make up only a very small part of this complex socio-scientific network. Nobel chemists undoubtedly wrote many of the important scenes of the story of twentieth century chemistry, but, in singling out their accomplishments, one must remain aware of their own often-expressed conviction that their work could not have been done without the discoveries and cooperation of many others. Most historians of science agree that the Nobel Prizes actually distort the histories of the various scientific disciplines. On the other hand, members of the Nobel Committee for Chemistry might respond that their prizes were not intended to give a well-balanced picture of twentieth century chemistry or physics. If understood in proper perspective, the Nobel Prizes in Chemistry do give an idea of what chemical achievements attained the greatest international recognition in their time.

Initially, the Nobel Prizes in science had little prestige, and some scholars believe that the prize would never have attained the impressive stature it has today if Alfred Nobel's intentions had been strictly followed. Many errors and inequities would have been committed, for example, if the stipulation that the prize be awarded for a discovery of the previous year had been religiously adhered to. The Swedes who drew up the statutes of the Nobel Foundation wisely realized that truth is the daughter of time, and they therefore allowed the committees the freedom to reward scientists who were well past their prime and discoveries that were many years old. Particularly during the first few decades of the prize, committee members selected a distinguished series of venerable chemists in order to add their fame and glory to their new award. Committee members were also dispensing huge sums of money, and this made them judicious, as did the selection mechanism established by the Nobel Foundation. All these factors, together with the conscientious work of the nominators and science committees, helped to make the prizes reliable symbols of significant work in chemistry or physics.

The prizes were also created at the right time and in the right place. The scientific world was ready for an international prize. Although foreigners had occasionally been beneficiaries of medals and awards from the French Academy of Sciences or the Royal Society of London, these tokens of esteem never shed their provincial character, and these national societies never made grants of large sums of money to scientists of other countries. With a growing appreciation of the international character of their vocation, scientists had been prepared for a set of prizes to reward those who were preeminently successful in discovering the truths of the natural world. Sweden was the right place for this to take place, since it was outside the spheres of influence of the Great Powers. Nobel's homeland was therefore in an ideal position to be a neutral and objective guarantor of the awards.

Today, the Nobel Prize in Chemistry is widely recognized as the pinnacle of achievement for a chemist. It is one of the few science prizes generally known by name to nonscientists, and among chemists themselves it is generally accepted that no other professional award carries the prestige of a Nobel Prize. When scientists have been surveyed, they consistently rank the Nobel Prize ahead of such older prizes as the Copley medal of the Royal Society of London and such richer prizes as the Robert A. Welch award in chemistry. The scientific excellence of early Nobel Prize winners set in motion a process of reciprocal transfer of prestige between recipients and prizes that has continued.

The Nobel Prizes have also served a social function, providing an occasion to celebrate science. They have bestowed public recognition on scientists, scientific achievements, and scientific professions, and, in doing so, have helped to educate the public about scientific activities. Although the prizes in literature and peace have held the greatest interest for the general public, the extensive reporting surrounding the science prizes has often steered budding scientists into new fields and helped scientists in one field appreciate the important developments in another. Originally, the names of the prizewinners were kept secret from the public and press until the formal ceremonies, but journalists were quick to rise to the challenge of discovering the awardees before the ceremonies. This often caused problems for the laureates, who were sworn to secrecy, and the procedure was changed in 1910, when the prize-awarding institutions began to announce their decisions soon after they had been made, a practice that has continued to the present.

Although the Nobel Prizes in science have not been criticized as often as the prizes in literature and peace, they have not been without controversy. Initially, the science committees were attacked for their hubris in believing that Sweden's small scientific community, perched on the periphery of Europe and far from the great centers of science, could make astute judgments about scientific excellence. Once an extensive list of Nobel laureates in chemistry had been established, other criticisms surfaced. The prize in chemistry has been won mostly by Western Europeans and American men, and feminist critics have often commented on the small number of women in the ranks of the Nobel laureates. This is especially true in chemistry, where, between 1901 and 1989, only three of the 114 winners have been women. Other critics have noticed the lack of prizewinners from Australia, Africa, and the Arab countries. Despite the great accomplishments of Russian chemists, only one of them has ever won the Nobel Prize, leading some to accuse the chemistry committee of an anti-Russian bias. During the 1920's and 1930's, American critics complained of an anti-American and pro-German bias on the part of the Swedish prize givers (only two Americans won Nobel Prizes in this period, whereas nine Germans did). Others complained of a pro-Swedish prejudice when Hans von Euler-Chelpin won his Nobel Prize, since they felt that his work on enzymes was not as significant as the work of many chemists who were passed over.

Some chemists have been critical of what they see as a disciplinary bias in the chemistry committee's decisions. The statistics of the award do indeed reveal that the great majority of Nobel Prizes have been awarded to either organic or physical chemists and only a very small number to inorganic and analytic chemists. Furthermore, chemists who, like Alfred Nobel, did their major work in chemical technology have received only two awards. In the early history of the prizes, the evidence is clear that some chemists lobbied to enhance the reputation of their disciplines by proposing colleagues, students, or disciples for the prize. Svante Arrhenius certainly wanted to enhance the new field of physical chemistry by awarding prizes to van't Hoff, Ostwald, and himself. As the prestige of the prizes grew, they also began to assume a role in legitimating particular specialities and research areas. In response to these criticisms, some historians of science have justified the committee's actions by explaining that the prizes simply reflected the special conditions of twentieth century chemistry. During this period, for example, inorganic chemistry's development was glacially slow: Compared with organic chemistry, it lacked a powerful system, and compared with physical chemistry, it lacked rigorous logic. Even when a field was generously rewarded by Nobel Prizes, as was organic chemistry, criticism was not wanting; some pointed out how many prizes were given for work on natural products (did the committee have a biochemical bias?).

Although many of these criticisms have bite, it is also true that the Nobel committees and the Royal Swedish Academy of Sciences were confronted with an impossible task, since there have generally been many more worthy candidates than prizes. Arne Tiselius, the 1948 Nobel laureate in chemistry, once said that the Nobel Prize simply cannot be given to the "person who is best," since "you cannot define who is best." One is therefore "left with the only alternative: to try to find a particularly worthy candidate." In determining these worthy candidates, politics often played a role, but on the whole the prize awarders acquitted themselves honorably in their difficult task.

The future of the Nobel Prize in Chemistry is impossible to predict. Some foresee an increasing number of prizes to Far Eastern scientists, following the great scientific, technical, and economic development in these countries. As Third World countries advance, they too may win an increasing share of the future prizes. With the growth in the number of worthy scientists and discoveries all over the world, some see an acceleration in the trend for Nobel Prizes to be shared among three winners (the individual winner may even vanish). Contrary to the intentions of Alfred Nobel, his prizes have often served as a barometer of scientific prestige and competitiveness among countries. Even within countries, the awards have been used by universities, research institutions, and granting agencies as a measure of their productivity and worth. For example, the Rockefeller Foundation has proudly claimed that it funded the work of nearly a hundred laureates, almost always before they won the Nobel Prize.

Seen in historical perspective, the Nobel Prize is only one indicator among many of the importance of scientific work. In itself, it does not guarantee the significance or immortality of a scientist's discoveries. The durability of any scientific achievement derives from its depth of understanding of the natural world—that is, how insightfully it reflects the fundamental laws of the universe. These insights sometimes are and sometimes are not recognized by prizes. In the twentieth century, people have become ever more aware of the ability of chemists to transform their world, not only with dyes, plastics, and other synthetic materials but also with mind-altering drugs, epidemic pollution, and terrifying weapons. In this way the paradoxes that dogged Nobel's own life and work live on in his prizes; some of the scientific discoveries that have been rewarded have the power to destroy as well as to help humanity. Like Alfred Nobel, many of the chemists who won his prize devoted their lives to satisfying their intellectual curiosity about matter and its reactions. Like Nobel, they wanted to help advance the material welfare of mankind. Like Nobel, they were forced by historical circumstances to see that their discoveries could cause irreparable damage to human beings and their planet. Finally, like Nobel, they were led into a deeper realization of the social consequences of their activities. Since the founding of the Nobel Prizes, the world's chemists have achieved much in their understanding of the natural world, and they have grown in status, power, and prestige. Yet they, like Nobel, exist in an uneasy tension between the paradoxes of their profession, since they now know that their esoteric knowledge has profound potentialities for great evil as well as for great good.

Selected Readings

Bergengren, Erik. *Alfred Nobel: The Man and His Work*. Translated by Alan Blair. Nashville: Thomas Nelson, 1962. This is the official biography of Alfred Nobel, written with the cooperation of the Nobel Foundation. Bergengren emphasizes Caroline Andriette Nobel's strong infuence on her son. He weaves anecdotes and analyses into a mostly reliable account of the development of Nobel as a chemical inventor and industrial entrepreneur. He also deals sensitively with Nobel's relationship with Bertha von Suttner. This 1962 edition contains Bergengren's collection of Alfred Nobel's aphorisms as well as N. K. Ståhle's supplement on the Nobel institutions and Nobel Prizes.

Crawford, Elisabeth T. *The Beginnings of the Nobel Institution: The Science Prizes, 1901-1915*. New York: Cambridge University Press, 1984. Crawford, who had access to the early papers of the Royal Swedish Academy of Sciences and its Nobel Committees for Physics and Chemistry, makes good use of the information she gathered to give an inside look at how Academy members actually selected prizewinners during the first decade and a half of the Nobel Prizes in Physics and Chemistry. She also shows how the Nobel institution and its prizes evolved from historical and contemporary international scientific institutions. She frankly discusses how Swedish academic politics and the relationship of Academy members to international scientists and scientific societies influenced the selection process. Contains a helpful set of appendices and an excellent bibliography.

Evlanoff, Michael, and Marjorie Fluor. *Alfred Nobel: The Loneliest Millionaire*. Los Angeles: Ward Ritchie, 1969. Michael Evlanoff lived for some time with the Nobel family in Paris and often traveled on business for Nobel's nephew. He published an earlier book, *Alfred Nobel: Prize Donor*, in which he began his revelations about Alfred Nobel and his family. This 1969 edition updates and completes his revelations. He does not present a balanced account of Nobel as an inventor, engineer, and entrepreneur, but he does give an interesting account of Nobel's personal and family relationships, especially his relationship with two women, Countess Bertha von Suttner and Sofie Hess. The book, illustrated with photographs, contains a list of Nobel laureates and an appendix by Arnold Beckman on the Nobel Prizes.

Farber, Eduard. *Nobel Prize Winners in Chemistry, 1901-1961*. Rev. ed. New York: Abelard-Schuman, 1963. Farber, a historian of chemistry who has written and edited anthologies of biographies of chemists, presents in this book short biographies of the Nobel Prize winners in chemistry together with discussions of their work. The first edition of this book, published a decade earlier, covered the laureates from 1901 through 1950, and this second edition updates the previous work with sketches of recipients between 1951 and 1960. He sees the Nobel laureates as an eminent group of chemists whose lives and discoveries can be used to illustrate the evolution of twentieth century chemistry.

Gillispie, Charles Coulston, ed. *Dictionary of Scientific Biography*. New York: Charles Scribner's Sons, 1970-1978. This fifteen-volume work, with two supplementary volumes, is the major reference source on the lives, careers, and achievements of the greatest scientists in history. The biographical essays, written by knowledgeable scholars, average two to three pages in length, with more extensive coverage for the most important scientists. Annotated bibliographies of primary and secondary sources conclude each article. Since scientists were not eligible for inclusion in this work until several years after they died, many recent Nobel Prize winners are not included, but Supplement II, published in 1989 and edited by Frederick L. Holmes, adds biographical essays on scientists who have died since 1970, the original cutoff date for inclusion in the initial set of volumes. The *DSB*, as it is familiarly known, is comparable in authority and scope to such traditional reference works as the *Dictionary of National Biography* and the *Dictionary of American Biography*.

Halasz, Nicholas. *Nobel: A Biography of Alfred Nobel*. New York: Orion, 1959. The author, a Hungarian-born journalist, did research for this book at the Nobel Institute in Stockholm as well as in Paris, where he found some of Alfred Nobel's papers (many documents were lost or destroyed during the Nazi occupation in World War II). Intended for a popular audience, Halasz's book is anecdotal rather than analytic, but since he draws on hitherto secret papers and letters, he has been able to construct an interesting narrative of the private and public life of Nobel. The book has neither footnotes nor a bibliography, but there is an index.

Jorpes, J. Erik. "Alfred Nobel." *Journal of Chemical Education* 37 (July, 1960): 328-334. This article was written by a member of the Karolinska Institute on the occasion of the 150th anniversary of its founding. Jorpes' emphasis is on Nobel as a chemist, industrialist, and entrepreneur, but his article also contains sections on Nobel's personality, his relationship to peace movements in the second half of the nineteenth century, and an analysis of Nobel's will. The article concludes with references to studies of the Nobel Prizes in Chemistry that have been published in several countries.

Nobelstiftelsen. *Nobel Lectures: Chemistry*. 4 vols. New York: Elsevier, 1964-1972. The lectures delivered by the Nobel laureates in chemistry make their initial appearance in an annual publication, *Les Prix Nobel*, within a short time of the ceremonies. The above series collects these lectures and adds the presentation speeches and biographies of the laureates. Nobel Prize winners have taken a variety of approaches in their lectures: Some are popular and require little understanding of chemistry to follow them, whereas others are intended for a highly trained scientific audience.

Opfell, Olga S. *The Lady Laureates: Women Who Have Won the Nobel Prize*.

Metuchen, N.J.: Scarecrow Press, 1978. Feminists have often commented on the small number of women who have been awarded Nobel Prizes in peace, literature, and science. Nevertheless, several women have won prizes in all these areas, and Opfell examines the lives and accomplishments of the seventeen women who won Nobel Prizes to the date of the book. The three chemists—Marie Curie, Irène Joliot-Curie, and Dorothy Crowfoot Hodgkin—who have won prizes are included. The book contains full-page portraits of the laureates, chapters on Nobel and the Nobel Prizes, and a chapter analyzing why so few women have been honored. Though the vignettes are uncritical, they may be suitable for general readers.

Wasson, Tyler, ed. *Nobel Prize Winners*. New York: H. W. Wilson, 1987. Intended for students and the general reader, this biographical dictionary contains fifteen-hundred-word profiles of all 566 men, women, and institutions that received the Nobel Prize in all areas between 1901 and 1986. Wasson enlisted the aid of experts in the fields of physics, chemistry, physiology and medicine, economics, literature, and peace for these narrative overviews of the prizewinners (Erwin H. Hiebert, a historian of science at Harvard University, oversaw the profiles in chemistry). Selective bibliographies of original and secondary sources available in English are included at the end of each sketch. There are prefatory essays on Alfred Nobel and on the Nobel Prizes and Nobel institutions. Each biographical article has a small photograph of the prizewinner.

Westgren, Arne. "The Chemistry Prize." In *Nobel: The Man and His Prizes*, edited by Nobelstiftelsen. 3d ed. New York: Elsevier, 1972. This book, first published in 1950, had a second edition in 1962 and this third, revised and enlarged edition appearing in 1972. It was written with the cooperation of the Nobel Foundation (Nobelstiftelsen) to commemorate the first fifty years of the prizes, and its succeeding editions have served as the institution's official history. Although Westgren's account of the chemistry prizes from 1901 to 1970 exaggerates the importance of the Nobel Prize winners in the history of chemistry, his essay contains interesting information about the scientific work of the laureates as well as some indication of the reasoning that led to their selection. The book also contains a biographical sketch of Alfred Nobel by H. Schück and an essay on Nobel and the Nobel Foundation by Ragnar Sohlman.

Wilhelm, Peter. *The Nobel Prize*. London: Springwood Books, 1983. Wilhelm, a Swedish engineer, visited and interviewed Nobel Prize winners in several countries for this book. Capitalizing on his experiences with the organizations and institutions behind the Nobel Prizes, he presents incisive accounts of Alfred Nobel's life and work, the history of the Nobel Foundation, and an analysis of the nomination procedures and selection process. He also traces the personal odyssey of one of the recent Nobel Prize winners, from the announcement of his award through his reception of the Nobel Prize in Stockholm. The book, which is beautifully illustrated with many color and black-and-white photographs, concludes with an analysis of the effect of the prize on the lives of the laureates.

Zuckerman, Harriet. *Scientific Elite: Nobel Laureates in the United States*. New York: Free Press, 1977. This book evolved from a doctoral dissertation that Zuckerman wrote in 1963. She focuses on the ninety-two Nobel laureates who did their prizewinning work in the United States between 1901 and 1972. Her book is based on primary and secondary sources as well as on interviews with many of the American prizewinners. She emphasizes how this elite of American science was educated, recruited, and funded. Though neither her research nor her analyses are always reliable, she does convey how American science has become stratified and how scientists advance in this hierarchized structure. The book contains an excellent bibliography and a helpful set of appendices.

_____. "The Sociology of the Nobel Prize." *Scientific American* 217 (November, 1967): 25-33. Zuckerman, a sociologist of science, analyzes in this article the Nobel Prize winners from America, with special emphasis on their origins and the impact that the prizes had on their lives, careers, and countries. One of her major conclusions is that the science prizes have achieved such prestige that they now affect institutions and nations as well as the reputations of the laureates. Illustrated with helpful charts and photographs.

Robert J. Paradowski

TIME LINE

YEAR	RECIPIENT	COUNTRY	AREA
1901	Jacobus Henricus van't Hoff (1852-1911)	The Netherlands	chemical dynamics/ stereochemistry
1902	Emil Fischer (1852-1919)	Germany	carbohydrate and purine chemistry
1903	Svante August Arrhenius (1859-1927)	Sweden	physical chemistry
1904	Sir William Ramsay (1852-1916)	Scotland	physical chemistry
1905	Adolf von Baeyer (1835-1917)	Germany	organic dyes/structural analysis
1906	Henri Moissan (1852-1907)	France	high-temperature reactions/fluorine chemistry
1907	Eduard Buchner (1860-1917)	Germany	enzyme chemistry/ fermentation
1908	Ernest Rutherford (1871-1937)	New Zealand	nuclear physics/ radioactivity
1909	Wilhelm Ostwald (1853-1932)	Latvia/Germany	reaction kinetics/ catalysis
1910	Otto Wallach (1847-1931)	Germany	alicyclic and terpene chemistry
1911	Marie Curie (1867-1934)	Poland/France	radioactivity
1912	Victor Grignard (1871-1935)	France	organomagnesium reagents
	Paul Sabatier (1854-1941)	France	catalysis/applied chemistry
1913	Alfred Werner (1866-1919)	France/ Switzerland	coordination chemistry/ chemical bonding
1914	Theodore William Richards (1868-1928)	United States	atomic weights
1915	Richard Willstätter (1872-1942)	Germany	plant pigments/ enzymes
1918	Fritz Haber (1868-1934)	Germany	electrochemistry/ nitrogen fixation
1920	Walther Hermann Nernst (1864-1941)	Germany	thermodynamics/ electrochemistry
1921	Frederick Soddy (1877-1956)	Great Britain	nuclear chemistry/ nuclear structure
1922	Francis William Aston (1877-1945)	Great Britain	atomic chemistry and physics
1923	Fritz Pregl (1869-1930)	Austria	microanalysis
1925	Richard Zsigmondy (1865-1929)	Germany	colloid chemistry

YEAR	RECIPIENT	COUNTRY	AREA
1926	Theodor Svedberg (1884-1971)	Sweden	colloid chemistry
1927	Heinrich Otto Wieland (1877-1957)	Germany	structure of bile acids
1928	Adolf Windaus (1876-1959)	Germany	sterol and vitamin chemistry
1929	Sir Arthur Harden (1865-1940)	Great Britain	biochemistry
	Hans von Euler-Chelpin (1873-1964)	Germany/ Sweden	molecular biology
1930	Hans Fischer (1881-1945)	Germany	organic chemistry
1931	Carl Bosch (1874-1940)	Germany	industrial and high-pressure chemistry
	Friedrich Bergius (1884-1949)	Germany	high-pressure chemistry
1932	Irving Langmuir (1881-1957)	United States	surface chemistry
1934	Harold Clayton Urey (1893-1981)	United States	isotopic separations/ geochemistry/ cosmochemistry
1935	Frédéric Joliot (1900-1958)	France	radioactivity/ radioisotopes/ nuclear fission
	Irène Joliot-Curie (1897-1956)	France	radioactivity/ radioisotopes/ nuclear fission
1936	Peter Debye (1884-1966)	The Netherlands/ United States	molecular structure/ X-ray diffraction
1937	Sir Walter Norman Haworth (1883-1950)	Great Britain	carbohydrate chemistry
	Paul Karrer (1889-1971)	Switzerland	structural analysis/ natural product synthesis
1938	Richard Kuhn (1900-1967)	Germany	vitamin synthesis/ stereochemistry
1939	Adolf Butenandt (1903-)	Germany	hormones/viruses/ carcinogenesis
	Leopold Stephen Ružička (1887-1976)	Croatia/ Switzerland	terpenes/natural product synthesis
1943	Georg von Hevesy (1885-1966)	Hungary/ Sweden	radioisotopic tracer techniques
1944	Otto Hahn (1879-1968)	Germany	nuclear chemistry/ radiochemistry
1945	Artturi Ilmari Virtanen (1895-1973)	Finland	agricultural and nutritive chemistry

YEAR	RECIPIENT	COUNTRY	AREA
1946	James Batcheller Sumner (1887-1955)	United States	enzyme and protein chemistry
	John Howard Northrop (1891-1987)	United States	enzyme and virus research
	Wendell Meredith Stanley (1904-1971)	United States	biochemistry and virus research
1947	Sir Robert Robinson (1886-1975)	Great Britain	organic synthesis
1948	Arne Tiselius (1902-1971)	Sweden	physical chemistry and biochemistry
1949	William Francis Giauque (1895-1982)	United States	chemical thermodynamics
1950	Otto Paul Hermann Diels (1876-1954)	West Germany	organic synthesis
	Kurt Alder (1902-1958)	West Germany	organic synthesis
1951	Edwin Mattison McMillan (1907-)	United States	nuclear chemistry/ nuclear physics
	Glenn Theodore Seaborg (1912-)	United States	nuclear chemistry
1952	Archer John Porter Martin (1910-)	Great Britain	biochemistry
	Richard Laurence Millington Synge (1914-)	Great Britain	physical chemistry/ biochemistry
1953	Hermann Staudinger (1881-1965)	West Germany	macromolecular chemistry
1954	Linus Pauling (1901-)	United States	structural chemistry/ molecular biology
1955	Vincent du Vigneaud (1901-1978)	United States	organic synthesis/ molecular biology
1956	Sir Cyril Norman Hinshelwood (1897-1967)	Great Britain	chemical kinetics
	Nikolai Semenov (1896-1986)	Soviet Union	chemical kinetics
1957	Sir Alexander Robertus Todd (1907-)	Great Britain	vitamins/coenzymes/ nucleic acids
1958	Frederick Sanger (1918-)	Great Britain	protein structure
1959	Jaroslav Heyrovský (1890-1967)	Czechoslovakia	electrochemistry/ polarography
1960	Willard Frank Libby (1908-1980)	United States	nuclear chemistry
1961	Melvin Calvin (1911-)	United States	photosynthesis
1962	Max Ferdinand Perutz (1914-)	Great Britain	biochemistry/ molecular biology
	John Cowdery Kendrew (1917-)	Great Britain	structural chemistry/ molecular biology

YEAR	RECIPIENT	COUNTRY	AREA
1963	Karl Ziegler (1898-1973)	West Germany	organometallic and polymer chemistry
	Giulio Natta (1903-1979)	Italy	polymer chemistry/ chemistry education
1964	Dorothy Crowfoot Hodgkin (1910-)	Great Britain	X-ray crystallography/ biomolecular structure
1965	Robert Burns Woodward (1917-1979)	United States	synthesis of natural materials
1966	Robert S. Mulliken (1896-1986)	United States	structural chemistry
1967	Manfred Eigen (1927-)	West Germany	electrolyte theory/ fast reactions
	Ronald G. W. Norrish (1897-1978)	Great Britain	photochemistry/ reaction kinetics
	George Porter (1920-)	Great Britain	photochemistry/ reaction kinetics
1968	Lars Onsager (1903-1976)	Norway/United States	electrolyte theory/ irreversible thermodynamics
1969	Derek H. R. Barton (1918-)	Great Britain	conformational analysis/organic synthesis
	Odd Hassel (1897-1981)	Norway	conformational analysis/X-ray crystallography
1970	Luis F. Leloir (1906-1987)	Argentina	carbohydrate chemistry/ biochemistry
1971	Gerhard Herzberg (1904-)	Canada	molecular spectroscopy/ structure determination
1972	Christian B. Anfinsen (1916-)	United States	molecular biology/ biochemistry
	Stanford Moore (1913-1982)	United States	protein chemistry/ analytical biochemistry
	William H. Stein (1911-1980)	United States	protein chemistry
1973	Ernst Otto Fischer (1918-)	West Germany	organometallic chemistry
	Sir Geoffrey Wilkinson (1921-)	Great Britain	structural and organometallic chemistry

YEAR	RECIPIENT	COUNTRY	AREA
1974	Paul J. Flory (1910-1985)	United States	macromolecular physical chemistry
1975	John Warcup Cornforth (1917-)	Australia	organic synthesis/ stereochemistry
	Vladimir Prelog (1906-)	Switzerland	organic synthesis/ stereochemistry
1976	William N. Lipscomb (1919-)	United States	borane chemistry/ X-ray crystallography
1977	Ilya Prigogine (1917-)	Belgium	thermodynamics/ statistical mechanics
1978	Peter D. Mitchell (1920-)	Great Britain	biochemistry/ bioenergetics
1979	Herbert C. Brown (1912-)	United States	boron compounds/ organic synthesis
	Georg Wittig (1897-)	West Germany	reaction mechanisms/ organic synthesis
1980	Paul Berg (1926-)	United States	microbiology/ biochemistry
	Walter Gilbert (1932-)	United States	molecular biology/ biophysics
	Frederick Sanger (1918-)	Great Britain	molecular biology
1981	Kenichi Fukui (1918-)	Japan	electronic structure/ organic reactions
	Roald Hoffmann (1937-)	United States	electronic structure
1982	Aaron Klug (1926-)	South Africa/ Great Britain	structural molecular biology
1983	Henry Taube (1915-)	United States	reaction kinetics/ inorganic synthesis
1984	Robert Bruce Merrifield (1921-)	United States	protein and peptide synthesis
1985	Herbert A. Hauptman (1917-)	United States	X-ray crystallography
	Jerome Karle (1918-)	United States	X-ray crystallography
1986	Dudley R. Herschbach (1932-)	United States	molecular reaction dynamics
	Yuan T. Lee (1936-)	China/United States	molecular reaction dynamics/ photochemistry
	John C. Polanyi (1929-)	Canada	molecular reaction dynamics

YEAR	RECIPIENT	COUNTRY	AREA
1987	Donald J. Cram (1919-)	United States	molecular recognition/ host-guest chemistry
	Jean-Marie Lehn (1939-)	France	molecular recognition/ host-guest chemistry
	Charles J. Pedersen (1904-)	United States	macrocyclic polyethers (crown ethers)
1988	Johann Deisenhofer (1943-)	West Germany	X-ray crystallography/ structural analysis
	Robert Huber (1937-)	West Germany	X-ray crystallography/ structural analysis
	Hartmut Michel (1948-)	West Germany	macromolecular structure/protein chemistry
1989	Sidney Altman (1939-)	Canada/United States	molecular biochemistry
	Thomas R. Cech (1947-)	United States	molecular biochemistry

1901

Chemistry
Jacobus Henricus van't Hoff, The Netherlands

Physics
Wilhelm Conrad Röntgen, Germany

Physiology or Medicine
Emil von Behring, Germany

Literature
Sully Prudhomme, France

Peace
Jean Henri Dunant, Switzerland
Frédéric Passy, France

JACOBUS HENRICUS VAN'T HOFF
1901

Born: Rotterdam, The Netherlands; August 30, 1852
Died: Steglitz (modern Berlin), Germany; March 1, 1911
Nationality: Dutch
Areas of concentration: Stereochemistry, chemical dynamics, and chemical equilibrium

A pioneer in the fields of chemical equilibrium and chemical dynamics, van't Hoff was one of the early investigators to seek theoretical explanations for the observations that had accumulated. He formulated a theory of osmotic pressure by drawing an analogy between the behavior of gases and that of solutions

The Award
Presentation
The presentation speech for Jacobus Henricus van't Hoff's award was made by Dr. Carl Theodor Odhner, former Rector of the National Swedish Archives, President of the Royal Swedish Academy of Sciences, and a member of the first Nobel Committee.

Odhner heralded van't Hoff's theoretical discoveries as the most important made since John Dalton proposed the atomic theory in 1802. Three specific aspects of van't Hoff's work drew attention from Odhner. The first was van't Hoff's pioneering work in chemical dynamics, then his ideas about osmotic pressure of solutions, and last the theory of the asymmetry of carbon atoms, which led to the founding of stereochemistry. It was to the field of molecular theory that the majority of Odhner's attention was given.

A law, named for Amedeo Avogadro, states that the number of gas molecules in a set volume at a set pressure and temperature is the same for all gases. Van't Hoff showed that this law also applies to substances in solution. Thus, the concept of the molecule was found to be valid in general and not restricted to gases alone. Osmotic pressure exerted in solutions is the same as the pressure of gases, and this concept allowed van't Hoff to make significant progress in considering problems in chemical equilibrium.

Odhner concluded by drawing the audience's attention to the great practical consequences foretold by these investigations by pointing out that chemical reactions occur most widely in solution and, in fact, that the metabolic functions of living beings depend on solution phase reactions.

Nobel lecture
Van't Hoff's lecture, entitled "Osmotic Pressure and Chemical Equilibrium," was delivered on December 13, 1901; it described the investigations that resulted in van't Hoff's being awarded the Nobel Prize. Van't Hoff defined osmotic pressure by

describing an experiment. When a sugar solution is separated from pure water by a membrane capable of passing the water but not the sugar, the water forces its way through the membrane into the solution. The process results in a greater pressure on the side of the membrane toward the solution. That pressure is osmotic pressure.

Early studies of osmosis were conducted by botanists, because of the connection of this effect with the flow of water through the membranes of plants. The importance of the osmotic effect to fluid movement in animal cells was discovered at a later date. Biologists developed a method to determine how concentrated a solution must be to have the same osmotic pressure that exists in plant or animal cells. This method, when applied in chemistry, measured the strength of the attraction that binds water of crystallization in crystals. Scientists could measure the pressure but could not find a correlation between its magnitude and the concentration or temperature of the solution.

Van't Hoff recognized that, when working with dilute solutions, the osmotic pressure was the same as the pressure the dissolved substance would exert as a gas. That is, just as in the gas state molecules move and collide with the container to exert pressure, the molecules of the dissolved substance move in the solution and collide to cause a pressure. Using this idea, van't Hoff calculated osmotic pressure that compared well with actual measured values.

Next followed a brief mathematical excursion, during which van't Hoff brought together the equation for osmotic pressure with equations describing chemical equilibrium and its temperature dependence and equations describing the amount of work done by a chemical reaction. After stating these, van't Hoff turned to the results that were obtained from the equations.

The first result was that it was now possible to calculate the molecular weights of substances in the liquid and solid states as well as the gas. The calculations showed that, in general, the same molecule existed in the different states—not different combinations of molecules, as had been thought. Another result was an exact replication of the law of mass action, which had been formulated previously on a different basis. The calculations also provided a link between the heat evolved by a reaction and the equilibrium constant and showed how the equilibrium constant of a reaction varied with temperature. Finally, they set the relationship between the equilibrium constant and work done by a reaction. Van't Hoff concluded by returning to the role that osmotic effects play in biological and medical fields and predicting that further great discoveries along this line would be made.

Critical reception

This was the first year of the Nobel awards, and they did not attract much attention outside Sweden. *The New York Times* did not mention the awards at all, and *The Times* of London had only slight coverage. Following a list of the recipients, *The Times* classed the science winners as "extremely distinguished men of science in Germany whose work was accomplished 5 to 15 years previously." The only discussion that surfaced was an exchange of letters to the editor in *The Times* that centered on the way that people were nominated for the awards and decried the lack of any British winners. The letters in reply described the nomination process and assured the original writer that there had been input from British scientists.

As can be seen in the quote above, the Nobel Foundation had already recognized that it would need to interpret the conditions of Alfred Nobel's will quite broadly. The will called for the award to be made "to those who, during the preceding year . . . shall have made the most important chemical discovery or improvement." The statutes of the Nobel Foundation interpret this as the "most recent results." They recognized that they were required to compromise between timeliness and the need for a discovery to have its impact proven. For example, van't Hoff's work on stereochemistry was, by now, proven, but it was too old for consideration, as he had gone on with the newer work in thermodynamics.

The Nobel Committee sent out three hundred letters seeking nominations for the Nobel Prize and received responses from only twenty proposers. Eleven of these proposed van't Hoff, and the others were scattered among several individuals. Indeed, the explosive development of chemistry within the previous decade made the matter of the choice more a consideration of the order in which several individuals would be chosen rather than who would be chosen. The overwhelming response from those scientists making nominations settled the question, and van't Hoff was selected.

The standing that van't Hoff had with his peers is clearly indicated by the fact that he had already been awarded the Davy Medal of the Royal Society of London eight years before, was appointed Chevalier of the Legion of Honor in 1894, served as president of the German Chemical Society in 1901, and had been elected member or honorary member of the Chemical Society of London, the Royal Academy of Sciences of Göttingen, and the American Chemical Society. Earlier in the year 1901, he was awarded honorary doctorate degrees from the University of Chicago and from both Harvard and Yale universities. The Harvard degree read that it was being presented to "the greatest living physical chemist."

Biography

Jacobus Henricus van't Hoff was the third of seven children born to Jacobus Henricus and Alida Jacoba Kolff van't Hoff in Rotterdam, The Netherlands, on August 30, 1852. Following the usual primary and secondary education, van't Hoff enrolled at the polytechnic school at Delft as an engineering student in 1869. He finished the three-year program in two years and received the highest score on the final examination. These years left him with an interest in mathematics, philosophy, and poetry and a great interest in chemistry, inspired by the lectures of Jean-Abraham-Chrétien Oudemans.

During the next years, van't Hoff studied at several institutions. In 1871 he enrolled as a mathematics student at the University of Leiden, transferring to the University of Bonn in 1872 to study chemistry. He transferred again, in 1874, to the University of Paris and finally, later that year, enrolled at the University of Utrecht to finish the work for his doctorate. He completed that degree in 1874 and remained in Utrecht, taking a position as an instructor in the veterinary school in 1876. In 1877 he was appointed lecturer (later professor) at the University of Amsterdam, where he remained for eighteen years. Van't Hoff married Johanna Francina Mees of Rotterdam in 1887; they had two daughters and two sons. He left Amsterdam in 1896 to accept a research professorship at the University of Berlin and remained there until his death on March 1, 1911.

Scientific Career

Van't Hoff's professional career began while he was still a schoolboy. This early step took the form of chemical demonstrations performed for an audience of his parents and their friends. The young van't Hoff charged the audience an admission fee for the privilege. From that point until his death at fifty-eight years of age, van't Hoff's primary interest was chemistry, particularly the mathematical treatment of theoretical aspects of the science.

Van't Hoff's parents prevailed upon him to train as an engineer at Delft, speculating that there were more opportunities in that field than in a research career. This two-year pause in his chemical training was fortuitous in that it allowed him to develop mathematical skills and a love of mathematics that would provide the backbone of his later chemical work. During the summers of this same time period, van't Hoff worked in a sugar factory, and this experience found its way into his chemistry as well: In a tribute to van't Hoff in 1952, the Sugar Division of the American Chemical Society listed six theoretical and experimental contributions that he had made which had direct impact on that industry.

After taking his degree in engineering in 1871, van't Hoff entered the University of Leiden as a mathematics student. During that year his interest in chemistry was rekindled by his attendance at the chemistry lectures of Oudemans, and he left Leiden to study organic chemistry with Friedrich August Kekulé at the University of Bonn. After two years of study there, he moved to Paris to study with Charles-Adolphe Wurtz. He was finally ready to settle down, and he returned to the Netherlands and the University of Utrecht to complete work on his doctorate. He received his doctorate, summa cum laude, in 1874, by presenting an uninspired dissertation concerning a routine study dealing with cyanacetic and malonic acids. This was later seen as taking the safe way to his degree, because he had been at work on a much more important, and more controversial, subject during this same time.

Four months before presenting his doctoral dissertation, van't Hoff had published an eleven-page pamphlet that was to create a major controversy in the chemistry world. He first published it in Dutch and later translated the work into French so that it would become more widely available. The pamphlet later grew into the well-known book *La Chimie dans l'espace* (1875; chemistry in space) and, for the first time, lifted molecules from the flat, two-dimensional world into three dimensions. This publication ushered in the field of stereochemistry, the study of spatial relationships of atoms and molecules. In arriving at this point, van't Hoff was greatly influenced by Kekulé's formulation of the quadravalent carbon. Van't Hoff's concept was able to explain the existence of numerous different compounds all having the same molecular formula, an explanation not possible with the two-dimensional structural ideas then in use. Also, using his concept of an asymmetrical carbon, he explained the existence of a class of isomers (substances with identical formulas but different structures) called optical isomers. Optical isomers are materials with the ability to change the angle of polarization of polarized light. An asymmetrical carbon atom occupies the center of a tetrahedron that has four different atoms or groups occupying the corners. Exchange of atoms or groups on two corners results in a second molecule with the same chemical composition and properties but with different optical activity. Knowing that these ideas would be controversial, van't Hoff did not submit this work as his dissertation. Joseph-Achille Le Bel, who had been a student with van't Hoff at Bonn, working independently in France, published these same ideas two months after van't Hoff's original pamphlet. The field of molecular structure was in turmoil for some time, but eventually this view, largely through its promotion by established chemist Johannes Adolph Wislicenus, became the foundation of modern structural chemistry. The importance of this work is such that it has been said that had there been a Nobel Prize to be granted at the time, van't Hoff surely would have received it.

During the years that the controversy continued, van't Hoff taught private chemistry students for a time and then won an appointment to teach physics at the Royal Veterinary School in Utrecht. As his stereochemical ideas became more widely acknowledged, his fame spread, and he was appointed to a position at the University of Amsterdam in 1877. The first year there, he was a lecturer, and the next, at the age of twenty-six, he was chairman of the chemistry department. From this position, over the following eighteen years, van't Hoff did most of his groundbreaking theoretical work on chemical dynamics and equilibrium.

It was an exhausting pace that he set. He gave five lectures a week in organic chemistry and one each in mineralogy, crystallography, geology, and paleontology, and he supervised the chemistry laboratory and its graduate students. He also found time to write the two-part *Ansichten über die organische Chemie* (1878-1881; views of organic chemistry). As time passed, he was able to devote more of his attention to the developing field of physical chemistry, which, together with Wilhelm Ostwald and Svante Arrhenius, van't Hoff was building. The building blocks of physical chemistry supplied by van't Hoff were the relationship between the rates of chemical reactions and the concentrations of the materials reacting, the relationship between the physical and chemical concepts of energy, and the relationship between the biological concept of osmosis and the chemical state of substances in solution. In 1887, van't Hoff cofounded and coedited the *Zeitschrift für physikalische Chemie* (journal of physical chemistry) with Ostwald.

Van't Hoff applied his mathematical background to the matter of chemical reaction rates and was able to describe the concentration-time relationships displayed by reactions. He classified these relationships as unimolecular, bimolecular, or trimolecular and described the differences in behavior as caused by the number of molecules participating in the reaction. He was able to determine experimentally the orders of a number of reactions.

The relationship between the physical and chemical concepts of energy led van't Hoff into the study of chemical equilibria. Again utilizing his mathematical abilities, van't Hoff applied the principles of thermodynamics, developed to describe the energy changes occurring in a steam engine, to the chemical process. The concepts of conservation of energy and of the second law of thermodynamics proposed by Nicolas-Léonard-Sadi Carnot were the main points of the application. This resulted in van't Hoff's concept of a dynamic equilibrium that shifted its balance point in response to temperature changes. These ideas were published in 1884 in *Études de dynamique chimique* (studies in dynamic chemistry) and resulted in bringing together the three founders of physical chemistry.

Biologists had been able to measure, but not explain, the phenomenon of osmosis for several years when van't Hoff took up the problem. His successful explanation resulted from his drawing an analogy between the movement of the molecules of a gas and the movement of the molecules of a dilute solution. The explanation, however, failed with solutions that were able to conduct an electrical current. The publication of these results, with the electrolytes called an anomaly, came to the attention of Arrhenius, who used this point to develop his revolutionary theory of electrolytic dissociation. In this same area of study, van't Hoff was able to show, using the principles of thermodynamics, that the lowering of the freezing point of a solution was proportional to the osmotic pressure of that solution. That opened up new possibilities for measuring the molecular weights of both solids and liquids.

As his stature in chemistry grew, other universities tried to attract van't Hoff away from Amsterdam. For a time that was prevented by the fact that Amsterdam provided him with a new physical chemistry institute built expressly for him. The time came, however, when an offer was made that van't Hoff was ready to accept. It came from the University of Berlin, where he would have a completely equipped, private laboratory and would be asked to give only one lecture per week in physical chemistry. The attractiveness of the offer, coupled with van't Hoff's admission that he was tired of teaching, was enough to overcome the attachment of eighteen years. The most renowned physical chemist of the day relocated to the University of Berlin in 1896 as professor of experimental physics.

Van't Hoff's first ten years at Berlin were almost a retirement for him. Relieved of his rigorous lecture schedule, he took the opportunity to travel throughout Europe and to America. These trips served to enhance his reputation as he lectured at the major universities of the Western world. He was still very active in research, but the publications, according to a contemporary chemist, "show a van't Hoff grown tired, living on one of his former ideas and expanding it indefinitely." It nevertheless remained important work. The prolonged project was the study of a single problem: the mineral equilibria underlying the formation of the Permian marine salt deposits of Germany. This project had practical importance, because these deposits were the prime source of potash used industrially for the manufacture of ceramics, detergents, soaps, glass, and fertilizer. With thirty collaborators and a number of students, van't Hoff published fifty-two papers in which chemistry was first applied in a systematic, methodical way to a geological problem. This was a classical case of developing practical value from idealized theory. The conclusions reached by van't Hoff stand, with little change, even now.

Van't Hoff emerged from this period in 1908, seemingly revitalized and ready to generate new ideas as he once had. During his last years, he directed his work toward the role of enzymes as biological catalysts. He published only a few papers in this time period, but they were full of possibilities and showed his old flair for developing new ways of thinking about a problem.

His last publication, fittingly, was on the same subject as his first. A few months prior to his death in 1911 he wrote the entry "Stereoisomerism" for the latest revision of the *Encyclopædia Britannica*.

Bibliography

Primary
CHEMISTRY: *La Chimie dans l'espace*, 1875; *Ansichten über die organische Chemie*, 1878-1881; *Études de dynamique chimique*, 1884; *Lois de l'équilibre chimique dans l'état dilue, gazeux ou dissous*, 1886; *Dix années dans l'histore d'une théorie*, 1887; *Vorlesungen über Bildung und Spaltung von Doppelsalzen*, 1897; *The Arrangement of Atoms in Space*, 1898; *Lectures on Theoretical and Physical Chemistry*, 1899-1900; *Über die Theorie der losungen*, 1900; *Physical Chemistry in the Service of the Sciences*, 1903; *Zur Bildung der ozeanischen Salzablagerungen*, 1905-1909; *Die Lagerung der Atome im Raume*, 1908; *Die chemischen Grundlehren nach Menge, Mass, und Zeit*, 1912; *Untersuchungen über die Bildungsverhältnisse der ozeanischen Salzablagerungen insbesondere des Stassfurter Salzlagers*, 1912.
BIOGRAPHY: *Gedachtnisrede auf Hans Heinrich Landolt*, 1910.

Secondary
Cohen, Ernst J. *Jacobus Henricus van't Hoff: Sein Leben und Werken*. Leipzig: Akademische Verlagsgesellschaft, 1912. This is the only known full-length biography of van't Hoff.
Eugster, Hans P. "The Beginnings of Experimental Petrology." *Science* 173 (August 6, 1971): 481-489. This article treats van't Hoff's work on marine salt deposits in the context of his whole career and in the context of the industrial importance of these deposits.
Harrow, Benjamin. *Eminent Chemists of Our Time*. 2d ed. New York: Van Nostrand, 1927. Two chapters in this book are devoted to van't Hoff. This first is mainly biographical, and the second treats his accomplishments and their meaning.
_____. "The Meeting of Ostwald, Arrhenius, and van't Hoff." *Journal of*

Chemical Education 7 (1930): 2697-2699. Using Ostwald's autobiography as his source, Harrow describes the closeness among these three scientists and their impact on one another.

Holleman, A. F. "My Reminiscences of van't Hoff." *Journal of Chemical Education* 29 (1952): 379-382. Holleman was a student of van't Hoff at the University of Amsterdam, where he worked in van't Hoff's private laboratory. Holleman recalls both the man and his work in this article.

Hudson, Claude S. "The Basic Work of Fischer and van't Hoff in Carbohydrate Chemistry." *Journal of Chemical Education* 30 (1953): 120-121. A presentation, given at a memorial celebration of the centennial year of van't Hoff's birth, which outlines his contributions in the field of sugar chemistry.

Moore, Forris J. *A History of Chemistry.* 3d ed. New York: McGraw-Hill, 1939. This classic history of chemistry presents an overall view of van't Hoff's work as a part of the development of chemistry.

Kenneth H. Brown

1902

Chemistry
Emil Fischer, Germany

Physics
Hendrik Antoon Lorentz, The Netherlands
Pieter Zeeman, The Netherlands

Physiology or Medicine
Sir Ronald Ross, Great Britain

Literature
Theodor Mommsen, Germany

Peace
Élie Ducommun, Switzerland
Charles Albert Gobat, Switzerland

EMIL FISCHER
1902

Born: Euskirchen, Prussia; October 9, 1852
Died: Berlin, Germany; July 15, 1919
Nationality: German
Areas of concentration: Carbohydrate and purine chemistry

Fischer synthesized glucose and at least thirty other sugars. He showed that in biological systems the shapes of these molecules were more important than their structures. He also synthesized more than 150 compounds known as purines. He then synthesized purine itself and showed its biological importance

The Award

Presentation

Professor Hjalmar Théel, a geologist and President of the Royal Swedish Academy of Sciences, presented Emil Fischer for the Nobel Prize in Chemistry in December, 1902. In his address, Théel asserted that one of the main tasks of organic chemistry is to investigate and reproduce the processes found in living matter; Emil Fischer, he said, pioneered many of the techniques that made this objective possible. Previous studies of the carbohydrates had been fraught with difficulty because the materials were intractable viscous liquids. Using phenylhydrazine as a chemical instrument, Emil Fischer made beautiful crystalline derivatives of many sugars, enabling him to characterize and synthesize more than thirty of these materials.

In 1874, Jacobus van't Hoff and Joseph-Achille Le Bel formulated a theory of the tetrahedral carbon atom. Their ideas concerned the spacial arrangement of atoms in a molecule. Fischer soon applied this theory to his effort to determine molecular shapes. He showed that the structure attributed to glucose could have at least sixteen different shapes, but only one of them could be glucose itself. Then, in a brilliant series of experiments, he synthesized glucose. He also showed that chemical transformations in living organisms are dependent upon the geometrical configuration of the molecules as well as on their composition.

The group of compounds now known as purines had been found in numerous natural products, such as urine and animal feces. Common stimulants such as theophylline, theobromine, and caffeine are also purines and are found in tea, cocoa, and coffee. Fischer brought order and clarity to this field of study by showing that they are derivatives of one parent substance. He then synthesized the parent compound and named it purine. This work gave strong support to the theory that the purines, such as uric acid, originated in the nucleic acids of the cell nucleus.

Nobel lecture

On December 12, 1902, Fischer gave his Nobel lecture, entitled "Syntheses in the Purine and Sugar Group." He showed a remarkable awareness that, although the practical achievements of chemistry may be evident to the public eye, the methods, abstractions, and language of the subject are seldom understood by those outside the discipline. His presentation was in clear and simple terms and included some speculation about the future.

Fischer noted that his general subject, organic chemistry, once confined itself to the study of materials originating in plants or animals. After 1828, however, it gradually became clear that one could synthesize these materials from substances that did not originate in life forms. In addition, new structural concepts and synthetic techniques opened vistas for the creation of materials for which there were no counterparts in nature. This boon to late nineteenth century medicine and commerce opened new doors to the understanding of nature itself. To illustrate this point, he used his knowledge of the purines and carbohydrates to show how organic chemistry solved some of the great problems of biology.

Speaking to a Swedish audience, he pointed out that the Swede Carl Scheele had discovered uric acid in urinary calculi and that it was the cause of gout. Materials of similar composition were found in the excrement of snakes, in the depot food of insects, and in the manure of sea birds. Fischer named these substances purines and showed that all of them shared a skeletal structure that was found in the cell nucleus. The biological significance became evident, and Fischer went on to synthesize the parent compound, purine itself.

Among the purines that Fischer found in vegetable matter were the stimulants caffeine (coffee), theobromine (cocoa), and theophylline (tea). He synthesized all these materials from uric acid and noted their value to medicine. They could now be made cheaply and in quantity. Observing that brewed coffee was stimulating and pleasant to drink, but that it was also expensive, Fischer suggested that scientists could now synthesize the ingredients responsible for the taste and aroma of coffee, and, after adding synthetic caffeine and hot water, one could have an inexpensive, savory, and refreshing drink.

Fischer went on to discuss his work with sugar molecules. In spite of the fact that the carbohydrates were abundant in plants and animals, early studies were severely hampered by experimental difficulties. The carbohydrate glucose had been found in fruit juices, and it was known that carbohydrates such as starch and cellulose were molecules composed of glucose units. Systematic knowledge beyond these simple facts, however, was almost nonexistent.

It was apparent to Emil Fischer that glucose was the most important simple sugar. After a long series of remarkable experiments, he synthesized not only glucose but also many other sugars. He showed that their chemistry and biological significance were dependent on their geometric shape. He also showed that biological catalysts, the enzymes, owed their capacity to bring about very specific chemical changes to their unique geometry. He used the analogy of a key fitting only one lock to explain how an enzyme (the key) "fits" a given substrate (the lock). It was now apparent that the process of photosynthesis follows a stereochemical pathway—a process quite different from what takes place in a test tube.

Critical reception

In 1902, knowledgeable scientists were not surprised when Emil Fischer received the Nobel Prize. They fully expected it. Fischer's name had been familiar to the world of chemistry even before he had completed his professional education in 1882. Before that date, he had started work on the purines and published his discovery of phenylhydrazine. He also drew the attention of the German dye industry by determining the structure of the rosaniline dyes. Between 1882 and 1902, he gained a worldwide reputation for his research on the purines and his classical research on the carbohydrates.

An examination of the newspapers published in December, 1902, reveals that the Nobel Prizes, although prestigious, had not yet acquired the importance that is attached to them today. The Peace Prize was the only one mentioned in *The New York Times*. *The Times* of London, December 9, 1902, contained only one short article, merely listing each laureate, his field, and place of origin. Articles reporting the chemistry award in the Stockholm newspapers are deposited in the Bancroft Library of the University of California, Berkeley. The notices are brief, but they do include a few phrases from Fischer's Nobel lecture.

Not all Nobel awards are free of controversy, but the award to Fischer seems to have been one of them that was. Richard Willstätter, himself a Nobel laureate in 1915, described Emil Fischer as being at the top of his profession. Fischer's associates and students held him in the highest esteem. He won the Davy Medal of the Royal Society of London, the Prussian Order of Merit, and the Maximilian Order for the Arts and Sciences, and he served as president of the German Chemical Society. Sixty-eight honorary doctorates were eventually conferred upon him, and the German Chemical Society created the Emil Fischer Medal to perpetuate his name.

Biography

Emil Fischer was born on October 9, 1852, in Euskirchen, a Rhineland village close to Cologne. His father, though lacking in formal education, was a successful businessman, and his mother was the former Julie Poensgen, a devout Protestant. Fischer was the youngest of six children, five of whom were girls. First educated by tutors but later attending public schools, Fischer completed his college preparatory program at the top of his class. He was two years younger than his compatriots. He wanted to become a physicist or a mathematician but was denied permission from his father, who knew a few people in these professions—all of whom were poverty-stricken. After Emil's unsuccessful apprenticeship in business, however, his father compromised by allowing him to study chemistry.

In the spring of 1871, he enrolled in the University of Bonn. In 1872 he transferred to Strassburg, where he earned a doctorate in 1874, studying with Adolf von Baeyer. He then followed von Baeyer to Munich to continue his studies. While at Munich he extended his phenylhydrazine studies and did further research on dyes. Fischer had become financially independent because of an early bequest from his father, which enabled him to wait patiently for a desirable position. He refused a lucrative offer to direct research in the dye industry and declined an invitation to direct the Chemistry Institute at the University of Aachen. He sought the independence to pursue his own research that only academic life could provide. He accepted the chair at Erlangen in 1882 and began a truly meteoric career.

Fischer moved to Würzburg in 1885, where he gained worldwide fame by revealing the secrets of carbohydrate molecules. Students came from foreign countries to study with him, and he published papers at a prodigious rate. In 1888 he married Agnes Gerlach, the daughter of an anatomy professor at Erlangen. He was offered the directorship of the Chemistry Institute of the University of Berlin in 1892 and, with some reluctance, he accepted the position. In 1895 he lost his wife to illness and was left with three sons, the oldest being only six years of age. When Fischer received the Nobel Prize in 1902, he became one of the best-known scientists in the world. He served Germany during World War I by directing the management of raw materials. Losing two of his three sons during the war, exhausted by his own efforts during the conflict, disillusioned by events in his country, and afflicted with cancer, he died in Berlin on July 15, 1919.

Scientific Career

Emil Fischer's first publication (in 1875) concerned derivatives of hydrazine. Fischer himself named the parent compound hydrazine, though that compound had not yet been made. The well-known diazonium compounds were related to hydrazine, and they had been formulated by August Kekulé. The diazonium compounds, however, were unstable, and because Kekulé's proposed formulations were similar to the stable azo compounds, the whole matter was controversial. Fischer solved the problem by confirming the work of Kekulé and establishing the structure of phenylhydrazine, a compound that would later have great value for him. Many of his hydrazine derivatives became useful for the dye industry. In 1886 he discovered a method for making derivatives of indole, a process that became widely known as the Fischer indole synthesis.

In 1884, Fischer learned that phenylhydrazine was a powerful instrument for investigating aldehydes and ketones because the reaction products were readily identifiable crystalline solids. Later he learned that carbohydrates, which are polyhydroxy aldehydes and polyhydroxy ketones, reacted with phenylhydrazine to form osazones. These beautifully crystalline compounds enabled him to elucidate the chemistry and structure of the carbohydrates.

Fischer's doctoral thesis concerned the chemistry of dyestuffs and colors. In 1862 August von Hofmann, who in later years would be his predecessor at the University of Berlin, had prepared an important dye called rosaniline. The structure of the dye had been studied but was not known with certainty. In 1878, Emil Fischer, along with his cousin Otto, showed that rosaniline and related dyes were triphenylmethane derivatives—information which was of great interest to the fledgling dye industry of Germany.

In 1881, Emil Fischer began a study of uric acid and its derivatives that continued until 1914, when he made theophylline-D-glucoside phosphoric acid, the first synthetic nucleotide. Nucleotides are biologically important substances that are found in the nuclei of animal cells. In 1882, he suggested formulas for uric acid, caffeine, theobromine, xanthine, and guanine, but he was not yet certain that he was correct. He synthesized theophylline and caffeine in 1895 and uric acid in 1897. In 1897, he proposed that uric acid and similar substances were oxygen compounds of a hypothetical base, which he named purine. Finally, in 1898, he demonstrated the correct structures by making purine itself, the parent substance. By 1900, he had synthesized about 130 derivatives, including hypoxanthine, xanthine, theobromine, adenine, and guanine. Fischer's laboratory methods became the basis for the industrial production of caffeine, theophylline, and theobromine by the German drug industry.

In 1903, he made 5,5-diethylbarbituric acid, a hypnotic and sedative known under the trade names Barbital, Veronal, and Dorminal. The parent compound, barbituric acid, had been made earlier by Emil Fischer's preceptor, Adolf von Baeyer. The phenylethyl derivative was made in 1912, and it became widely known under the trade names Luminal and Phenobarbital, gaining worldwide use as a sedative and sleeping aid.

Emil Fischer started his classic work on the carbohydrates in 1884 at Erlangen. It was principally for this contribution that he received the Nobel Prize. One cannot overestimate the importance of this work, since the carbohydrates are of fundamental importance to all plant and animal life. At the time, only four simple sugars were known: glucose, galactose, fructose, and sorbose. Three sugars that were combinations of simpler sugars were also known: sucrose, maltose, and lactose. Glucose, also called dextrose, was of special importance to him because of its wide occurrence.

From the work of Le Bel and van't Hoff, he knew that the structure then attributed to glucose could have at least sixteen different molecular shapes, yet only one of these molecular shapes could be that of glucose. In a notable series of experiments, he synthesized most of these molecules, including glucose. It was here that his earlier discovery of phenylhydrazine proved indispensable. Using phenylhydrazine as a reagent, he was able to identify and characterize the components of the various intractable and viscous syrups encountered in this branch of chemistry.

He suffered many illnesses during this period as a result of continuous exposure to phenylhydrazine. He had not yet learned that phenylhydrazine was quite toxic and was the main cause of his distress. While he was a student of von Baeyer, he had been poisoned by a mercury compound and was reprimanded for being careless. These experiments eventually led him to take important steps toward improving laboratory safety. He pioneered the widespread use of the fume hood, a device to protect laboratory workers from poisonous vapors. He designed laboratory buildings at Würzburg and at Berlin that incorporated greatly improved safety features, especially improved ventilation.

In 1894 Emil Fischer studied the action of enzymes on some sugars. He noted that the enzymes were very specific in their action. For example, the enzyme maltase caused the breakdown of α-methyl glucoside but not β-methyl glucoside. Meanwhile, the enzyme emulsin decomposed β-methyl glucoside but not α-methyl glucoside. The two glucosides were found to be mirror-image molecules: They were related to each other as the right hand is related to the left hand. That is, they were different just as each glove in a pair of gloves is different from the other. He reasoned that an enzyme was active as a catalyst only if it had a specific configuration that would "fit" the molecule on which it was to act. He used the analogy of a lock and key to explain this, comparing an enzyme with a key that would fit only one lock.

In 1899, Emil Fischer started his work on the proteins. The proteins were known to be essential to all forms of life. They were chainlike molecules, the links of which were amino acids. Fischer knew that thirteen different amino acids had been obtained by decomposing various proteins. First, he proceeded to synthesize many of them.

Proteins obtained from living systems produce only one form of each amino acid, a form that Fischer designated as the L-form, from the Latin word *laevus*, meaning left or left-handed. He learned, however, that laboratory syntheses of these materials produced not only the L-form amino acids but also the D-form, named from the Latin *rectus*, meaning right or right-handed. Thus it became necessary for him to separate the L-form from the D-form in order to obtain the same amino acids that were found in nature. He succeeded in this by converting each product of a laboratory synthesis to a mixture of salts. The salts were separated by fractional crystallization. The purified L-form amino acids were then separated from their individual salts.

In 1901, he modified a method devised by Theodor Curtius to separate mixtures of amino acids obtained by decomposing proteins. The amino acids themselves could not be separated by distillation without causing them to decompose. Fischer solved this dilemma by converting the mixtures of amino acids to esters, volatile compounds that could be distilled. He then obtained each amino acid from its purified ester. Using this method, he identified valine, proline, and hydroxyproline. By 1907, he had developed a method for combining amino acids to form segments of proteins known as peptides. He succeeded in making a peptide consisting of eighteen amino acids, an amazing feat for that time. He recognized that the proteins were very complex and that even simple peptides could have large numbers of different amino acid sequences. He showed that the characterization of the proteins required the identity, the number, and the sequence of the constituent amino acids. He also recognized a pitfall called the Walden inversion and then used it to advantage in synthesizing amino acids.

Like his mentor, Adolf von Baeyer, Emil Fischer relied upon experimental data and had a distrust of theoretical approaches. Although he did not disdain theory, he feared that he might be misled and was distrustful of whatever he considered to be preconceived. He wanted nature itself to speak to him through laboratory data. He became a skilled analyst and learned to conduct most laboratory procedures with very simple equipment. His research was so thorough and complete that it remains essentially unchallenged. Except for some work on specific heats that caused him to consult with Albert Einstein, and a brief theoretical encounter with the Walden inversion, Fischer's methodology was essentially pragmatic. His published research was written in such an exceptionally clear and lucid style that many students and established scholars were attracted to his Berlin laboratories through reading one of his publications. From 1882 until 1914, he published an average of twelve articles each year. At least one hundred of his students became university professors, and many had distinguished careers as industrial chemists. He promoted the establishment of the Kaiser Wilhelm Institutes, later known as the Max Planck Institutes. These organizations permitted scholars to pursue their research unburdened by teaching or other obligations.

Emil Fischer devoted most of his career to the study of natural products. In the nineteenth century, his understanding of the importance of the shape of molecules gave impetus to the movement that culminated in the twentieth century understanding of the genetic code. Thus he has been called the father of modern biochemistry. In Fischer's autobiography, *From My Life*, Richard Willstätter says of him, "He was the unmatched classicist, master of organic chemical investigation with regard to analysis and synthesis, and as a personality a princely man."

Bibliography

Primary

CHEMISTRY: *Untersuchungen über Kohlenhydrate und Fermente von Emil Fischer*, 1906-1923; *Untersuchungen über Aminosäuren, Polypeptide, und Proteine von Emil Fischer*, 1906-1923; *Untersuchungen in der Puringruppe (1882-1906) von Emil Fischer*, 1907.

AUTOBIOGRAPHY: *Aus meinem Leben*, 1922.

MISCELLANEOUS: *The Emil Fischer Papers*, on deposit in the Bancroft Library of the University of California (14 vols.; includes correspondence between 1876 and 1919, scientific writings, patent litigations, manuscripts, copies of published works, laboratory notebooks, and building plans).

Secondary

Darmstädter, Ludwig. "Emil Fischer." *Journal of Chemical Education* 5, no. 1 (1928): 37-42. Provides a good account of the history of carbohydrate chemistry. The author gives a historical perspective on Fischer's work that lends significance to Fischer's scientific legacy. There is also a personal biography, describing Fischer's leadership in societies. The account of Fischer's discovery of the barbiturates is excellent.

Farber, Eduard. "Emil Hermann Fischer." In *Dictionary of Scientific Biography*, vol. 5, edited by Charles Coulston Gillispie. New York: Charles Scribner's Sons, 1972. Farber offers a brief biography, followed by an account of Fischer's discovery of phenylhydrazine and the indole synthesis. There is a fine summary of his research on the purines, the carbohydrates, the amino acids, and the proteins. Primary and secondary bibliographies are also provided.

_____, ed. *Great Chemists*. New York: Interscience, 1961. A short, nontechnical biography of Fischer: his youth and education, his professional training, and his first research efforts. Fischer's tenure at Erlangen and Würzburg and the first great tragedy of his life are related. An excellent account of the man's personal life and the major accomplishments of his career.

Forster, Martin Onslow. "Emil Fischer Memorial Lecture." *Journal of the Chemical Society* 117 (1920): 1157-1201. A tribute to Fischer by one of his former students, incorporating a lucid summary of his scientific work. Delivered before London's Royal Society, the lecture includes some rare anecdotes about Fischer and provides insights into his scientific methodology. Although the treatment of Fischer's scientific work is necessarily technical, the general reader will enjoy reading this warm account by one who knew Fischer personally.

Nobelstiftelsen. *Nobel Lectures: Chemistry, 1901-1921*. New York: Elsevier, 1966. The presentation speech by Professor Hjalmar Théel and Fischer's Nobel lecture are reprinted here. The lecture is presented in simple terms for its general audience, with many historical references to place the laureate's work in perspective. Fischer explains how one person can no longer rely solely on personal efforts, but must proceed with careful planning and the collaboration of many colleagues.

John J. Lucier

1903

Chemistry
Svante August Arrhenius, Sweden

Physics
Antoine-Henri Becquerel, France
Pierre Curie, France
Marie Curie, Poland and France

Physiology or Medicine
Niels R. Finsen, Denmark

Literature
Bjørnstjerne Bjørnson, Norway

Peace
Sir William Cremer, Great Britain

SVANTE AUGUST ARRHENIUS
1903

Born: Castle of Wijk, Uppsala, Sweden; February 19, 1859
Died: Stockholm, Sweden; October 2, 1927
Nationality: Swedish
Areas of concentration: Physical chemistry, immunology, and atmospheric physics

Arrhenius applied the research methods of physics to the chemical problem of electrolysis in extremely dilute solutions. He developed a new theory of electrolytic dissociation that proved powerful in explaining a wide range of chemical phenomena

The Award

Presentation

Dr. H. R. Törnebladh, President of the Royal Swedish Academy of Sciences, presented the Nobel Prize in Chemistry to Svante August Arrhenius on December 10, 1903. Törnebladh related Arrhenius' work historically to that of Jöns Jakob Berzelius, a fellow Swede who had sought an electrical explanation of chemical phenomena. Conflicting evidence led to the rejection of Berzelius' theory and the acceptance of heat as the cause of chemical reactions. Increasing difficulties with thermochemical explanations, however, made a new alternative attractive by the time Arrhenius began to pursue doctoral work in the 1880's.

Arrhenius' research centered upon the chemical consequences of passing electrical current through dilute solutions. He offered a new explanation of electrolysis, founded on the concept that salts placed in solution dissociate into positively and negatively charged components called ions, regardless of whether a current is present. Törnebladh attributed to Arrhenius the ability to deduce from his new perspective all the known laws governing chemical reactions.

Arrhenius' theory, because of its controversial nature, underwent a lengthy ten-year process of adoption by chemists and caused a great amount of effective research to be undertaken, which established much closer ties between physics and chemistry. Törnebladh believed that the uniting of physics and chemistry implicit in Arrhenius' work would lead to a more productive future for both sciences.

Nobel lecture

On December 11, 1903, Arrhenius delivered his Nobel lecture, entitled "Development of the Theory of Electrolytic Dissociation." His lecture included a historical sketch of the forerunners of his theory, a discussion of his experiments, a survey of their explanatory power, and a summary of the corroborating evidence.

Arrhenius briefly traced the history of atomism from Democritus to John Dalton. A second source of his theory was the idea of dissociation, which he found rooted in experimental problems with the gas laws, where anomalies suggested that some dissociation into separate molecules was taking place. A third formulative stand for his theory was the work of Rudolf Clausius on the electrical conductivity of salts in solution. Clausius held that dissociation was partial and temporary but that possibly it was taking place when no current was passed through the solution. By 1884 Arrhenius, using methods for measuring the conductivity of salts developed by Friedrich Kohlrausch, established that conductivity does not increase indefinitely, but approaches a limit. In addition, he established that the acids and bases with the greatest conductivity were the strongest and that the most active acids and bases electrically were also the most chemically active.

The theory of dissociation had broad explanatory power. An unexpected result of Arrhenius' research was that extremely dilute solutions approach a state of complete activity—that is, they approach the strength of the strongest acids, a prediction verified by experiments conducted by Wilhelm Ostwald in Germany. Arrhenius also believed that the most significant result in support of his theory was the simplicity of his explanation of the amount of heat given off whenever an acid and a base neutralize. Further, Jacobus Henricus van't Hoff suggested that molecules in extremely dilute solutions obeyed the gas laws, with gas pressure being replaced by osmotic pressure (the pressure against the surface) in fluids. A much higher osmotic pressure than expected resulted when DeVries carried out experiments, which Arrhenius explained in 1887 as the result of partial dissociation in solution. He similarly explained depressed freezing points of solutions. The experiments which Arrhenius conducted and the writing which he and Ostwald did from 1884 to 1890 were directed toward demonstrating that the theory of dissociation was consistent with experiments conducted by other physicists.

Ostwald and Arrhenius worked diligently to marshal additional evidence. Ostwald applied the theory to absorption spectra and demonstrated its usefulness in explaining the ratio in which two competing acids divide a base (avidity). Arrhenius conducted experiments concerning changes in heat during dissociation and internal friction in solutions.

Arrhenius alluded in his conclusion to opponents who suggested that his theory was not true, but was only a useful working hypothesis. He suggested that since explanatory power indicated the validity of his theory, he would hold it until a more powerful one appeared. Arrhenius also regarded his theory as significant because it brought chemistry and physics closer together. In 1903 he could hardly know that within twenty years he would be regarded as a founder of the interdisciplinary science of physical chemistry.

Critical reception

In 1903, when Arrhenius received the third Nobel Prize awarded in chemistry, there was still no established pattern in the public reaction to the awards. While the prizes were immediately the largest science awards monetarily and were gaining prominence as a result, the scientific world was still waiting to see who received awards to determine the long-term reputation of the prizes as the epitome of recognition. As a consequence, there was little public commentary on the prizes. *The Times* of London carried a brief notice with no critical comment, as did the scientific journal *Nature*. Failing to mention Arrhenius at all, the *Scientific American Supplement* incorrectly stated that Pierre and Marie Curie and Henri Becquerel shared the chemistry prize (they actually shared the physics prize that year). The editors of *Science* complained that three of the four (actually six) recipients were Scandinavian and that half the income had been diverted to local use by the Nobel Institute, against the express wishes of the will of Alfred Nobel. This comment became an American theme for the next four years, restated with variations by *The Independent*, *The Outlook*, and *Popular Science Monthly*. The journals emphasized that the prizes were not being awarded for invention during the previous year. Such comments demonstrated both a lack of appreciation of theoretical science and the difficulties of assessing what would have future importance. The complaints disappeared when Americans began to gain recognition.

Without extensive public comment, establishing reaction to Arrhenius' worthiness was difficult until the records of the Nobel Institute became matters of public record. Only then did it become clear that significant behind-the-scenes political maneuvering occurred for and against Arrhenius. His poor relationship with the experimental physicists of the University of Uppsala who dominated the physics selection committee resulted in Arrhenius' receiving the prize in chemistry even though he was a physicist. Arrhenius, a member of the physics selection committee, removed himself from the deliberations in 1902 and 1903.

By 1903 Arrhenius, who had studied extensively abroad and who corresponded extensively with German and French scholars, was the best-known and most highly regarded Swedish scientist. He had received nominations for both the physics and chemistry prizes in the two previous years and received seven in physics and twelve in chemistry in 1903. By 1903 the chemistry committee felt that it was unconscionable to wait any longer to recognize Arrhenius, so it proposed to the physics committee that half of each prize be awarded to Arrhenius. The reluctant physics committee said that the effect of giving Arrhenius a full prize and the others only a half prize would imply that Arrhenius' work was the most significant, and some members were not willing to admit that.

The chemists countered that Arrhenius' work was indeed significant, that he was a physicist using physical research methods, and that he should receive the entire physics prize. The physicists had another agenda, however—that of claiming the field of radioactivity for themselves. They consequently nominated the Curies, who were chemists, along with Becquerel. At this point, the chemists, fearing the loss of the discovery of new elements to the physicists, nominated William Ramsay by a vote of three to two, but the chemistry section of the Academy voted to support Arrhenius seven to three.

The tension between Uppsala physicists and Arrhenius was well enough known in the tightly knit European science community that the awarding of the chemistry prize to Arrhenius drew no critical comment from other chemists. His important role in aiding the formulation of policy for awarding the prizes was known to some, and by 1903 his importance (along with that of van't Hoff and Ostwald) in physical chemistry was widely recognized.

Biography

Svante August Arrhenius was born February 19, 1859, at the castle of Wijk, near Uppsala, Sweden. His family had engaged in farming for several generations, but his father was a surveyor who became a superintendent of grounds for the University of Uppsala.

At the age of three, Arrhenius taught himself to read, and at the cathedral school in Uppsala he displayed promise in mathematics and physics. He enrolled at seventeen in the University of Uppsala to study physics, but his instructors were strongly committed to experimental physics and resisted the rapid developments in theoretical physics. Thus, in 1881, he moved to Stockholm to study with Erik Edlund. By 1884, Arrhenius had submitted his doctoral dissertation to the University of Uppsala, but, the significance of his research being missed, he was granted the lowest possible honor above an outright refusal.

Wilhelm Ostwald, recognizing the importance of Arrhenius' theory, influenced Uppsala to grant a lectureship to Arrhenius in November of 1884, and Edlund encouraged the Swedish Academy to award a travel grant in 1886 so that Arrhenius could study further in Europe. In 1891 Arrhenius accepted a lectureship at the Högskola, the technical high school in Stockholm, where he became a professor from 1895 until 1904 and rector from 1897 until 1902. In 1902 and 1903, he studied in Denmark and Germany, working on physiological problems in serum therapy. He spent part of 1904 in the United States and then, in 1905, became the director of the Nobel Institute for Physical Chemistry near Stockholm, a post he held until a few months before his death in 1927.

Married in 1894 for two years to former laboratory assistant Sofia Rudbeck, he had a son, Olaf Wilhelm, who became a noted soil scientist and botanist. His second marriage in 1905 to Maria Johansson produced a son, Sven, and two daughters, Ester and Anna-Lisa. Following a short illness, Arrhenius died on October 2, 1927.

Scientific Career

Arrhenius, disappointed by the reception of his doctoral work by Per Teodor Cleve, whom he admired, began a campaign to win acceptance for his theory by sending copies of his dissertation to several scholars throughout Europe. His work was favorably received by Sir William Ramsay in England and by Wilhelm Ostwald in Russia. When Ostwald came to Sweden to visit Arrhenius, his influence secured the lectureship that would not have been forthcoming without his help.

With his Swedish Academy travel grant, Arrhenius worked from 1886 to 1891 with some of the finest physicists of Europe. During this time, however, his ionization theory met with extensive passive resistance. Incomplete atomic theory contributed to the difficulty of accounting for the formation and stable existence of the ions involved, and certain strong solutions remained anomalous, but Ostwald advocated the fruitfulness of the new theory, demonstrating that it could account for a wide variety of chemical phenomena. When Ostwald joined with van't Hoff to found the *Zeitschrift für physikalische Chemie* (journal of physical chemistry), Arrhenius published a vastly improved version of his electrolytic dissociation theory in the first issue. The three scholars stimulated and refined one another's theories and research projects, creating a formidable association promoting the theory of ionization. They were informally called the "wild ionians."

When he moved to the Högskola in 1891, Arrhenius found the environment stimulating. Many of the outstanding faculty were doing creative work in a free environment, but the school was always inadequately funded and equipped. Arrhenius, who was still burning with the frustration of not being recognized by the physicists in Sweden, wished, with some of the other faculty, to turn the Högskola into a degree-granting institution that would surpass Uppsala. While informally called the University of Stockholm as early as 1904, the Högskola was only gradually transformed, formally becoming the university in 1966.

Arrhenius, ever the activist, moved on to other projects. Beginning in 1897, he participated in formulating policy governing the great bequest of Alfred Nobel and served on the physics selection committee from 1900 until his death in 1927. He campaigned actively for certain scholars who supported atomic theory and blocked others, most notably Walther Nernst (who was awarded the chemistry prize for 1920), all in accord with an agenda to establish the Nobel Prizes as the premier science awards in the world, keeping them on the very edge of scientific progress. Though often a minority member on the committee, he was also a political adept who frequently won.

During the 1890's, Arrhenius continued research in electrolytic conductivity, the viscosity of solutions, and the effects of temperature upon reaction velocity. He also began to expand his interests into other fields of study by investigating the problems of atmospheric magnetism, conductivity, and solar radiation. The results of his research appeared in many European scientific journals, in systematic fashion in *Lärobok i theoretik Electrochemi* (1900; *Text-book of Electrochemistry*, 1902), and in *Lehrbuch der kosmischen Physik* (1903; treatise on cosmic physics).

After the turn of the century, Arrhenius' interdisciplinary interests continued to expand. Following time in Germany and Denmark, during which he studied serum therapy, he brought together the results of his work in 1904 in a series of lectures delivered at the University of California on principles of physical chemistry applied to toxins and antitoxins. These lectures appeared as *Theorien der Chemie* (1906; *Theories of Chemistry*, 1907) and *Immunochemistry* (1907).

Assuming the position of director of the Nobel Institute, he began a period of intense and productive work. By 1907 cosmologists became aware of his expanding interests through *Das Werden der Welten*, a German translation of *Världarnas utveckling* (1906; *Worlds in the Making*, 1908). Arrhenius became concerned with cosmological problems because the astronomers were applying the second law of thermodynamics in a fashion that seemed to point to the exhaustion of heat and motion in the universe. Since Arrhenius believed the universe was eternally self-renewing, he sought to discount the concept of heat exhaustion by proposing that deteriorating solar objects were replaced by new stars arising from nebulae that were increasing in temperature.

During this intense period of effort he also published *Människan inför världsgåtan* (1907; *The Life of the Universe*, 1909), which included a variation in the older debate on the plurality of worlds (life on other planets). He supported those who argued that life was universally diffused throughout the universe. While Arrhenius presumed innumerable habitable planets, he argued that appropriate initial conditions for life to arise and evolve would be uncommon. He reasoned that life was more likely to arise from spores that were exuded from already inhabited planets and spread through space to planets that had evolved to a habitable state. Arrhenius intended his argument as an alternative to Sir William Thomson's claim that meteorites were the means of seeding the planets with life. These proposals have since been given the name panspermia, and while they were high in explanatory value, they have held little other than historical interest since the discovery of intense ultraviolet radiation in space.

The most productive portion of Arrhenius' career occurred from 1890 to 1910. From 1891 to 1900, fifteen international scholars came to pursue postdoctoral studies with Arrhenius—an unprecedented number for a Swedish scientist. After the turn of the century, the quality of his work was widely recognized, and honors began to accumulate. He was elected to more than twenty scientific societies, most of them outside Sweden. While many of his peers believed that the recognition was tardy, the Swedish Academy of Sciences finally granted Arrhenius membership in 1901. It was followed in 1902 by receipt of the Davy Medal of the (English) Royal Society. The keystone of his career, the theory of electrolytic dissociation, won for him the Nobel Prize in 1903. In 1905 he attained associate member status in the German Chemical Society. On his visit to the United States in 1911, he received the first Willard Gibbs Medal and became an associate of the American Academy of Science. The Royal Society elected him as a foreign member in 1912, and he received the Faraday Medal of the English Chemical Society in 1914. He was awarded honorary doctorates by the universities of Birmingham, Cambridge, Edinburgh, Greifswald, Groningen, Heidelberg, Leipzig, and Oxford.

After his return from the American trip in 1911, although Arrhenius continued to conduct research and to write, his pace began to slow, and his ideas were less fruitful and dramatic. In 1915 he made a further contribution to biochemistry with his *Quantitative Laws in Biological Chemistry*. He returned to cosmological interests and published *Stjärnornas Öden* (1915; *Destinies of the Stars*, 1918). Despite Arrhenius' interest in extraterrestrial life and his confidence in its existence, he refrained from excesses. He was disturbed by Percival Lowell's claims concerning life on Mars and suggested that Lowell imagined much more than could be proven.

Most of the writing of the last decade of his life was dedicated to short articles and the editing of previous works. One result of this effort was *Kemien och der moderna livet* (1919; *Chemistry in Modern Life*, 1925). In 1926 he published his last major work, *Erde und Weltall*, a revision and combination of his earlier books on cosmology. In the spring of 1927, when it was obvious that his health was failing, he resigned from the directorship of the Nobel Institute. His reduced workload did not restore him, however, and he died on October 2, 1927.

Arrhenius' most significant work was the fortunate collaboration with Ostwald and van't Hoff in promoting atomic theory and ionization. The activities of these three men led to the establishment of the field of physical chemistry, which has expanded magnificently in the decades since. More regrettable is the popular memory of Arrhenius that causes him to be cited for one of his less enduring ideas, that of the spread of life through panspermia. He is more justly remembered for reducing interdisciplinary barriers, thus contributing to a fruitful period of research in both physics and chemistry.

He was devoted to the development of Swedish science, which he wished to internationalize both through the influence that the Nobel Prize selection process would have upon Swedish academics and through the importance that Swedish scientists would assume as the curators of the most significant scientific prizes. His leading role in writing the regulations governing the awarding of the prizes contributed greatly to the realization of his dual objective.

Outside physical chemistry, his most notable accomplishments include his satisfactory explanation of the aurora borealis and his contributions toward the theory of light pressure from the Sun. His relations with scientists around the world, with the exception of the Uppsala physicists, were warm and good-humored. He was popular at international conventions because of his fluency in French, German, and English. His very genuine concern for his fellow scientists was perhaps best expressed in his work to free German and Austrian scientists from prisoner-of-war camps at the end of World War I, even though he had favored the Allies during the war.

Bibliography

Primary
CHEMISTRY: *Lärobok i theoretik electrochemi*, 1900 (*Text-book of Electrochemistry*, 1902); *Lehrbuch der kosmischen Physik*, 1903; *Theorien der Chemie*, 1906 (*Theories of Chemistry*, 1907); *Immunochemistry*, 1907; *Theories of Solutions*, 1912; *Quantitative Laws in Biological Chemistry*, 1915; *Kemien och der moderna livet*, 1919 (*Chemistry in Modern Life*, 1925).
COSMOLOGY: *Lehrbuch der kosmischen Physik*, 1903; *Världarnas utveckling*, 1906 (*Worlds in the Making*, 1908); *Människan inför världsgåtan*, 1907 (*The Life of the Universe*, 1909); *Stjärnornas Öden*, 1915 (*Destinies of the Stars*, 1918); *Erde und Weltall*, 1926.

Secondary

Crawford, Elisabeth T. *The Beginnings of the Nobel Institution: The Science Prizes, 1901-1915*. New York: Cambridge University Press, 1984. This significant scholarly work with index and bibliography presents a comprehensive and detailed account of the early history of the awarding of the science prizes; it gives extensive detail of Arrhenius' involvement in the organizing of the prizes and his actions in promoting and blocking particular recipients.

Farber, Eduard. *The Evolution of Chemistry: A History of Its Ideas, Methods, and Materials*. New York: Ronald Press, 1952. While providing minimal biographical information, this book contains a brief but clear explanation of Arrhenius' theory of dissociation, which was his most original work and the foundation of his receiving the Nobel Prize.

Jaffe, Bernard. *Crucibles: The Story of Chemistry from Ancient Alchemy to Nuclear Fusion*. New York: Simon & Schuster, 1948. One chapter contains a popular and dramatic account of Arrhenius' career, depicting him as a hero who overcame great opposition from entrenched science, finally triumphing to receive well-deserved recognition.

Larson, Cedric A. "Svante August Arrhenius." *Science Digest* 46 (August, 1959): 83-89. This is a readily available, brief, and accurate biography. Since it is a popular account of his life, the explanations of the science with which Arrhenius was involved are quite readable. The account of his life is somewhat more personal than the other available sources.

Nobelstiftelsen. *Nobel: The Man and His Prizes*. 3d ed. New York: Elsevier, 1972. This work contains extended discussion of Arrhenius' role in the development of policy and his activities in promoting and blocking the selection of Nobel winners in physics and chemistry. An underlying theme is his conflict with the traditionalists at Uppsala.

Palmær, Wilhelm. "Svante Arrhenius, 1859-1927." In *Great Chemists*, edited by Eduard Farber. New York: Interscience, 1961. This is a translation and abridgment of an article that first appeared in 1929. The chapter is thorough, accurate, and one of the more authoritative English sources. As with most of the available material on Arrhenius, there is little about his private life.

Ivan L. Zabilka

1904

Chemistry
Sir William Ramsay, Scotland

Physics
Lord Rayleigh, Great Britain

Physiology or Medicine
Ivan Pavlov, Russia

Literature
José Echegaray y Eizaguirre, Spain
Frédéric Mistral, France

Peace
Institute of International Law

SIR WILLIAM RAMSAY
1904

Born: Glasgow, Scotland; October 2, 1852
Died: Hazlemere, near High Wycombe, Buckinghamshire, England; July 23, 1916
Nationality: Scottish
Area of concentration: Physical chemistry

Ramsay startled the scientific world by discovering five new elements that are constituents of air: argon, helium, krypton, neon, and xenon, the so-called inert or noble gases. In addition to identifying and isolating these new elements, Ramsay determined their characteristics and their place in the periodic table of elements

The Award

Presentation

The Nobel Prize in Chemistry was presented to Sir William Ramsay by Professor J. E. Cederblom, President of the Royal Swedish Academy of Sciences, on December 10, 1904. Cederblom began his address by acknowledging the link between physics and chemistry by which "almost invariably" a discovery made in one field will affect the other. Thus, the work of Lord Rayleigh (John William Strutt) on the density of nitrogen, which earned for him the 1904 Nobel Prize in Physics, inspired the work of his fellow scientist, British chemist William Ramsay. Their subsequent collaboration led to the discovery of argon, the first of the "rare" gases to be identified. It was so named because of its unusual property of chemical inertness or inactivity (the word "argon" is from the Greek word meaning "inactive").

Cederblom related how Ramsay's search for sources of argon led to his discovery of helium, an element of the sun that was thought not to occur on the earth and that, like argon, is chemically inert. The word "helium" is from the Greek word for sun, *helios*. Ramsay later went on to discover three more inert gases: krypton (meaning "hidden"), neon (new), and xenon (strange). Ramsay called them "noble gases" because of their supposed "aristocratic" characteristic of not associating or forming compounds with the more common elements. He showed that these gases formed a natural family of elements, and he determined where they "fit" in the periodic table of elements.

According to Cederblom, the discovery of an entirely new group of elements was an "utterly unique" event in the history of chemistry, made all the more remarkable by the discovery that these elements are constituents of the earth's atmosphere. Moreover, their property of chemical inertness was startling. Previously it was thought that the ability to react chemically and combine was basic to all elements. The existence of elements for which this was not true required, according to Cederblom, a broadening of the very definition of an element.

Cederblom concluded his address with an account of Ramsay's work with radium, in particular his discovery that helium is a by-product of the radioactive decay of radium. Cederblom speculated that this discovery would have scientific implications "the full extent of which it is now impossible to foresee."

Nobel lecture

Ramsay delivered his Nobel lecture, entitled "The Rare Gases of the Atmosphere," on December 12, 1904. In it, he traced the sequence of events leading to the discovery of the rare gases, beginning with his personal historical antecedents. Ramsay's paternal grandfather had been a chemical manufacturer, and his maternal grandfather had been a "medical man." Ramsay believed he had thus inherited his "taste for chemistry" from both sides of his family.

Early in his career, Ramsay had become interested in physical chemistry, that branch of chemistry which deals with the study of chemical properties and phenomena. Ramsay briefly described his early work in physical chemistry that led to the discovery of argon. Of the discovery of argon he said little. The major portion of his lecture was devoted to the discovery of the other inert gases: helium, krypton, neon, and xenon.

Ramsay was an accomplished public speaker and lecturer, and his account of the means by which he and his assistants isolated, identified, and determined the physical and chemical properties of the inert gases, showing them all to be members of a new family of inert elements and all to be constituents of the earth's atmosphere, was characteristically straightforward and precise.

Throughout his address, Ramsay graciously gave credit both to his predecessors and to the contemporaries upon whose work he drew, as well as to his own assistants. Ramsay concluded his lecture with a brief history of the discovery of natural radioactivity and the work being done in this new field, in particular his and Frederick Soddy's investigation of the radioactive element radium. Their research into the properties of the gas generated by the radioactive disintegration of radium eventually led to Ramsay's announcement in 1910 of the discovery of a sixth inert gas, now known as radon.

Critical reception

By the time Ramsay was awarded the Nobel Prize, there was little controversy about his work on the inert gases; his earlier discoveries and conclusions were generally accepted. At the time of its announcement, however, the discovery of argon generated great excitement and controversy. Many scientists found it difficult to believe that, after all the work that had been done to determine the composition of the air, there could still be an undiscovered constituent. An editorial in *Scientific American* on March 2, 1895, stated that it was "decidedly singular" that argon had "been so long overlooked," and warned that any "theory of its characteristics must be accepted with extreme caution." *The Times* of London had reported earlier, in December, 1894, that there were "grave uncertainties brooding over" the discovery.

The matter soon became the subject of public satire in the press. The February 28, 1895, issue of *The Electrical Review* carried an article whose title, "Argon: The Supposed New Element in the Atmosphere," parodied the title of Ramsay and Lord Rayleigh's paper announcing their findings: "Argon: A New Constituent of the Atmosphere." In early April, an article appeared in *The Electrical Review* entitled "The Argon Myth."

Ramsay was apparently indifferent to the criticism. In response to it, he is said to have retorted: "They say! Let them say!" Lord Rayleigh, on the other hand, who was a scrupulous experimenter, was angered by suggestions that the weighing of nitrogen had been "fudged." Rayleigh's son later recalled that for his father "the discovery of argon as a whole" caused him "more pain than pleasure." Eager to "get back again from chemistry to physics," Rayleigh left it to Ramsay to investigate argon further.

Controversy also arose among those who accepted the discovery. Some believed that Ramsay was taking too much of the credit. The matter became the subject of bitter and heated dispute, though not between the two principals involved. Rayleigh and Ramsay had much respect for each other; both had successfully isolated the gas, and it was Rayleigh who suggested that they publish their results jointly. Finally, both men received Nobel Prizes in 1904 for their work on the inert gases, Rayleigh in physics and Ramsay in chemistry.

Biography

William Ramsay was born in Glasgow, Scotland, on October 2, 1852, the only child of William Ramsay, an engineer, and Catherine Ramsay, née Robertson. In 1866, at the age of fourteen, Ramsay entered the University of Glasgow, where he received a classical education that emphasized the study of Latin, Greek, and philosophy. He showed an early interest in chemistry, however, and in 1869 went to work in the laboratory of the Glasgow city analyst. There he acquired a general working knowledge of chemistry and a considerable analytical skill.

In 1870, having decided to make chemistry his profession, Ramsay traveled to Germany to complete his studies, first at Heidelberg with Robert Bunsen, and later in Tübingen with Rudolf Fittig. Under Fittig's direction, he completed his dissertation on the toluic acids in 1872. Soon afterward, Ramsay returned to Glasgow to take a junior post in the chemistry department of the University of Glasgow. Until this time, he had been primarily interested in organic chemistry, but around 1876 his interests turned to physical chemistry.

In 1880, at the age of twenty-eight, he was appointed professor of chemistry at the University College of Bristol. In 1881, he married Margaret Buchanan and was promoted to principal of the college. He succeeded Alexander Williamson in the chair of chemistry at the University College of London in 1887, a position he held until his retirement in 1912.

William Ramsay was knighted in 1902 and in 1904 was awarded the Nobel Prize in Chemistry. He died of a cancerous tumor on July 23, 1916, at the age of sixty-four.

Scientific Career

Ramsay was fond of saying that science was in his blood. He had an uncle who was a famous geologist and an aunt who was a botanist. His paternal grandfather, the founder and first president of the Glasgow Chemical Society, had been a chemical engineer, and his mother's father had been a physician and the author of several textbooks on chemistry and anatomy for medical students.

Despite this scientific and technical background, Ramsay's mother wished him to become a minister, and his early education was devoted to the study of classical languages, English, moral philosophy, and logic. He first became interested in chemistry while recovering from a broken leg, when he read Thomas Graham's *Elements of Chemistry* (1838) in order to learn how to make fireworks. His father gave him some apparatus and chemicals and, with a friend, Ramsay soon began conducting chemical experiments in his bedroom.

In 1869, Ramsay went to work for the Glasgow city analyst, from whom he gained valuable practical experience in analytical work. The following year, he attended the chemistry lectures of Professor Thomas Anderson at the University of Glasgow. His plans to continue his studies in Germany were frustrated by the outbreak of the Franco-Prussian War, so he continued to work in his laboratory at home and attended the lectures of Sir William Thomson (later Lord Kelvin) in Glasgow.

After the Franco-Prussian War, Ramsay traveled to Germany, where he secured a position in the laboratory of the analytical chemist Robert Bunsen at the University of Heidelberg. The German physicist Gustav Kirchhoff, Bunsen's friend and colleague, had shown that a chemical element, when heated, gave off light that could be passed through a prism to produce a unique pattern of colored lines. An element's spectrum, as this pattern was called, was like a fingerprint: No two were exactly alike. Working together, Bunsen and Kirchhoff developed a piece of equipment, called a spectroscope, that could generate and compare these line patterns. The invention of the spectroscope was a major breakthrough in identifying new elements, and the use of spectral analysis was to play an important role in Ramsay's later work on the inert gases.

Ramsay stayed in Heidelberg only a short time. On the advice of friends, he moved to Tübingen in the spring of 1871 to study organic chemistry with the German chemist Rudolf Fittig. Fittig was interested in the aromatic compounds, and under his direction Ramsay conducted an investigation of the toluic acids that became the basis for his doctoral dissertation.

Ramsay returned to Glasgow in the fall of 1872 as an assistant in the chemistry department of the University of Glasgow. Still primarily interested in organic chemistry, he began a series of investigations of the pyridine bases and their derivatives. In 1876, however, he turned to the physical side of chemistry after he met and began working with the English chemist J. B. Hannay. Together they studied the solubility of gases in solids.

While he was professor of chemistry at the University College of Bristol and later its principal (1880-1887), Ramsay developed a method for determining the volumes of liquids at their boiling points. Since much of his time was taken up with administrative matters, Ramsay relied for help in conducting experimental research on a series of able assistants, beginning with Sydney Young, who joined the faculty of the college in 1882. The two men undertook an investigation of the thermal properties of solids and liquids, with Young doing much of the laboratory work.

In 1887, Ramsay was appointed professor of chemistry at the University of London. During his tenure there, which ended with his retirement in 1913, he made the discoveries that earned for him international fame and recognition, and eventually the Nobel Prize.

The English physicist Lord Rayleigh had been working on determining the atomic weights, or densities, of certain elements. He had successfully weighed the gases hydrogen and oxygen and had turned to the problem of weighing nitrogen. To obtain a sample of the pure gas for this purpose, he prepared nitrogen from air from which he had removed what he supposed were all of its other constituents: oxygen and hydrogen. He removed the oxygen using red-hot copper and the hydrogen using copper oxide. Rayleigh was an extremely careful and thorough experimenter. To confirm his results, he also used a different method of preparing the nitrogen, this time from ammonia mixed with air and passed over heated copper. To his surprise, he discovered that the atmospheric nitrogen was heavier than the nitrogen prepared from the ammonia.

Puzzled, he wrote a letter to the editors of the scientific journal *Nature* in 1892, detailing his results and soliciting theories as to the cause of the discrepancy in densities. Ramsay read the letter and became interested in the problem. Meanwhile, Rayleigh continued his research, and in 1894 he presented a paper to the Royal Society of London entitled "An Anomaly Encountered in the Determination of the Density of Nitrogen," in which he presented his data but refrained from drawing any conclusions. Soon afterward, Ramsay wrote to Rayleigh asking for his permission to investigate the matter. Ramsay suspected that the atmospheric nitrogen was mixed with a small quantity of a heavier, hitherto unknown gas. First preparing nitrogen, then using magnesium to absorb the nitrogen, he successfully isolated enough of the residual gas to submit it to spectral analysis. Its spectrum, made up of red, green, and blue lines, was found to be distinct from that of nitrogen or any other known element. Ramsay concluded that it was a new gas.

Ramsay and Rayleigh announced the discovery in Oxford on August 13, 1894, at the annual meeting of the British Association, where the new element was christened "argon." On January 31, 1895, they presented their findings in a joint paper before the Royal Society of London. The news was greeted with curiosity mixed with skepticism. In investigating the properties of the new gas, Ramsay had discovered that argon was chemically inert (hence the name, which means "inactive"). Repeated experimentation failed to produce any evidence of chemical change or interaction.

Ramsay continued his investigation of argon. He had heard of the work of

William F. Hillebrand, a chemist with the U.S. Geological Survey who in 1888 had reported obtaining a gas from the mineral uraninite. Thinking that uranium might be a source of argon, Ramsay and his assistant Morris William Travers successfully extracted from cleveite, an ore of uranium, a gas that spectroanalysis showed contained not only argon but also the element helium, recognizable by the distinct bright yellow line in its spectrum.

Helium had first been observed in the sun's spectrum by the French astronomer Pierre Janssen in 1868 and was subsequently analyzed and named by the British astronomer J. Norman Lockyer. Janssen's and Lockyer's discovery was generally dismissed by chemists, however, who insisted on chemical confirmation of a new element, and so helium was largely forgotten. Ramsay's announcement of the discovery of terrestrial helium at the annual meeting of the Chemical Society on March 27 created a sensation. Most scientists had doubted its existence anywhere, and those who did not believed that it did not occur on the earth. Equally astounding, Ramsay showed that, like argon, helium was chemically inert.

Ramsay now had two inert gases. Where did they belong in the periodic table of elements? The periodic table of elements was the work of the Russian chemist Dmitry Mendeleyev, who had conceived a scheme for arranging chemical elements by placing them in the order of their increasing atomic weights. He found that they naturally fell into groups, or families, of elements with shared characteristics. Ramsay boldly suggested that argon and helium were the first two in a new group of elements characterized by their unique chemical stability. He predicted that there were at least two more inert gases waiting to be discovered. Rayleigh and Ramsay had determined the atomic weight of argon to be 40. Helium, much lighter than argon, had an atomic weight of 4. Ramsay predicted that the two other inert gases would have atomic weights of 20 and 80, respectively.

In June, 1898, Ramsay and coworker Morris Travers announced the discovery of a new gas, which they had isolated from air brought to a liquid state at low temperature and high pressure. They called the new gas krypton. It had an atomic weight of 82. A fortnight later, they discovered yet another gas, with an atomic weight of 20, which they called neon. By allowing a large quantity of liquid air to evaporate and then removing oxygen and nitrogen from the residue, Ramsay and Travers in July obtained a mixture of argon and krypton in which they detected still another gas. Its spectrum consisted of brilliant blue lines. They named it xenon and determined its approximate atomic weight to be 130. Like helium and argon, all three of these newest gases were chemically inert. Moreover, they were all found to be constituents of the earth's atmosphere.

In 1896, radioactivity was discovered by the French physicist Antoine-Henri Becquerel, who demonstrated that the heavy metal uranium gave off radiation. Two years later, in 1898, the French chemist Marie Curie, continuing the work begun by Becquerel, showed that the heavy metal thorium also gave off radiation. With her husband Pierre, she isolated two new elements, both of which were radioactive. The first they named polonium, for Madame Curie's native country of

Poland. The second they called radium.

The physical and chemical properties of these radioactive elements, as they came to be called, attracted a large number of investigators. Ramsay became interested in radioactivity and with Frederick Soddy undertook a series of experiments on radium. Ramsay and Soddy showed that helium was continually being generated by radium, a discovery that eventually led to an understanding of the process of radioactive disintegration.

In 1900, Friedrich Dorn discovered that radiation gave off a radioactive gas that was inert. In 1910, Ramsay and his assistant Robert Whytlaw-Gray succeeded in weighing the gas and announced it to be the sixth, and last, of the inert gases. Its density is approximately 222, making it the heaviest gas. Because of the brilliant glow it gave off when liquefied, Ramsay called it niton, after the Latin word for "shining." It has since come to be known as radon.

At the time of their discovery, the inert gases were believed to be both extremely rare and chemically inert. Further research showed that at least some of them, such as argon, helium, and neon, are in fact quite common, and both xenon and radon form compounds with the element fluorine. For the most part, though, the inert gases are characterized by their exceptional chemical stability. None of them interacts with oxygen, which makes them nonflammable. It is this nonflammable characteristic that makes helium a safe gas for filling dirigibles. Similarly, argon is used to provide a chemically nonreactive environment for such operations as cutting, welding, and refining certain metals. Argon is also used in electric lights; xenon and neon are found in fluorescent lamps. Medical applications of the inert gases include the use of xenon mixed with oxygen as an anesthetic and the use of the highly radioactive radon in cancer therapy.

Ramsay was an extremely able experimenter, and much of his success can be attributed to his skill in the laboratory. More important, however, was his scientific imagination and insight, which allowed him to recognize something new and to see connections that others had overlooked. According to Robert John Strutt, Lord Rayleigh's son and biographer, both Rayleigh and Ramsay stood out from their contemporaries as "the two men who alone realized the significance of the apparent discrepancy in the densities of nitrogen." Early in their correspondence and very early in their work on the problem of the difference in the densities of nitrogen, Ramsay had written to Rayleigh, asking him: "Has it occurred to you that there is room for gaseous elements at the end of the first column in the periodic table?"

Bibliography

Primary
CHEMISTRY: *A System of Inorganic Chemistry*, 1891; "Argon: A New Constituent of the Atmosphere," *Transactions of the Royal Society of London*, vol. 186, 1895 (with Lord Rayleigh); *The Gases of the Atmosphere: The History of Their Discovery*, 1896; "Helium and Argon: Experiments Which Show the Inactivity of These Elements," *Nature*, vol. 54, 1896 (with J. Norman Collie); "The Recently Dis-

covered Gases and Their Relation to the Periodic Law," *Science*, vol. 9, 1899; *Modern Chemistry*, 1900; "Experiments in Radio-activity and the Production of Helium from Radium," *Nature*, vol. 68, 1903 (with Frederick Soddy); *Introduction to the Study of Physical Chemistry*, 1904; "Ancient and Modern Views Regarding the Chemical Elements," *The Smithsonian Institution Annual Report 1911*, 1912; *Elements and Electrons*, 1913.
EDITED TEXT: *Seventh International Congress of Applied Chemistry*, 1910 (with William Macnab).

Secondary

Asimov, Isaac. *The Noble Gases*. New York: Basic Books, 1966. Well-written account of the history of the inert, or noble, gases, which, as Asimov points out in his introduction, "has consisted of one astonishing and unexpected event after another." The book traces man's interest in the air from the Greek philosophers to the late nineteenth century discovery of the noble gases. Asimov presents much interesting information on the properties and uses of the noble gases.

Farber, Eduard. *Milestones of Modern Chemistry*. New York: Basic Books, 1966. A collection of historic papers associated with what the author calls the "dramatic turning points" in the development of modern chemistry. Chapter 6, "Adventures in Methodology," briefly describes the means by which various scientists throughout history have sought to determine the composition of the air. The chapter describes the methodological approach that Rayleigh and Ramsay took to solve the problem of the difference in densities between atmospheric nitrogen and chemical nitrogen, the solution of which led to the discovery of argon. The abstract of the paper Rayleigh and Ramsay presented to the Royal Society on January 31, 1895, is reproduced in its entirety.

Ramsay, Sir William. *The Gases of the Atmosphere: The History of Their Discovery*. 4th ed. London: Macmillan, 1915. Ramsay wrote this book for the general reader. In it, he tells of the development of man's ideas about the nature of air, which, according to him, included the entire history of chemistry and physics up to that time. Beginning with the mythological notion that air was semi-spiritual in nature, Ramsay records the development of the experimental method and discusses the contributions and personalities of the early researchers of air. Placing himself within this tradition, Ramsay relates his own contribution to the study of the earth's atmosphere: the discovery of the inert gases, their properties, and their relationship to the other elements.

Strutt, Robert John. *Life of Lord Rayleigh*. Rev. ed. Madison: University of Wisconsin Press, 1968. A biography of Lord Rayleigh written by his son, who was also a physicist. Chapter 11, "The Discovery of Argon," describes the discovery of the inert gases in clear and, for the most part, nontechnical language. The chapter also portrays the characters of Rayleigh and Ramsay. The focus is on Rayleigh, and his son's version of the story is slightly different from other sources, including Ramsay's published accounts. Included is the Rayleigh-

Ramsay correspondence from this period, when the two men wrote to each other on almost a daily basis.

Tilden, Sir William Augustus. *Sir William Ramsay: Memorials of His Life and Work*. London: Macmillan, 1918. Tilden was asked by the chemistry department of the University of Glasgow to write this biography of Ramsay, which covers Ramsay's childhood and youth, his university years, teaching career, scientific achievements, and retirement. Contains extensive quotations from Ramsay's letters, as well as from letters and reminiscences of Ramsay's friends, family, and associates. Also includes photographs, a list of the honors presented to Ramsay, and an index.

Travers, Morris William. *The Discovery of the Rare Gases*. London: Arnold, 1928. This book is based on Ramsay's scientific papers, which Travers, Ramsay's longtime assistant, undertook to arrange in 1927 at the request of Ramsay's wife. It provides a detailed and technical description of Ramsay's experimental work involving the inert gases. Original drawings and text are reproduced from Ramsay's notebooks, describing the apparatus and procedures he used in his experiments.

Weeks, Mary Elvira, and Henry M. Leicester. *Discovery of the Elements*. 7th ed. Easton, Pa.: Journal of Chemical Education, 1968. Chapter 18, "The Noble Gases," gives a historical account of the discovery of the inert gases as well as biographical information on the scientists involved in the endeavor. Includes photographs of Ramsay, Rayleigh, Rudolf Fittig, Pierre Janssen, J. Norman Lockyer, and Morris William Travers, as well as a list of references to the scientific publications of Ramsay, Rayleigh, and Travers, among others.

Nancy Schiller

1905

Chemistry
Adolf von Baeyer, Germany

Physics
Philipp Lenard, Germany

Physiology or Medicine
Robert Koch, Germany

Literature
Henryk Sienkiewicz, Poland

Peace
Bertha von Suttner, Austria

ADOLF VON BAEYER
1905

Born: Berlin, Prussia; October 31, 1835
Died: Starnberg, Oberbayern, Germany; August 20, 1917
Nationality: German
Areas of concentration: Organic dyes and organic structural analysis

Baeyer stimulated the development of the chemical dye industry through his investigations of indigo and the phthaleins, and he advanced theory through his extensive empirical research. He developed the strain theory for carbon compounds and made a systematic study of hydroaromatic compounds

The Award

Presentation

Illness prevented Adolf von Baeyer from attending the 1905 Nobel Prize presentation ceremonies, and the German ambassador received the award for him. Professor A. Lindstedt, President of the Royal Swedish Academy of Sciences, spoke briefly during the ceremonies of December 10, 1905, about Baeyer's work and its significance. Noting the close relationship between science and technology, he commented on Baeyer's contributions to the development of the coal-tar dyestuff industry, an industry unimaginable fifty years earlier. Baeyer provided a foundation for this industry through his research on the triphenylmethane dyestuffs and the composition of indigo.

The colorfastness and beautiful color of indigo made it one of the most important of the organic pigments, and reproducing it by synthetic methods was an inviting problem for chemical research. The synthesis of indigo was, however, a very difficult task. Skilled as he was, Baeyer devoted years of careful work to determining the structure of indigo and synthesizing the pigment from simpler constituents. Adapting the laboratory methods to large-scale industrial production then required additional years of effort by those involved (Baeyer himself did not participate in the industrial development). When synthetic indigo became available, it competed successfully with natural indigo and produced dramatic economic benefits, especially in Germany.

In 1871, Baeyer discovered a new group of colored compounds called phthaleins and showed that they were related to triphenylmethane, an aromatic hydrocarbon. This work led to a new concept of the chemical composition of pigments as well as to a better understanding of how molecular structure affects the optical properties of organic compounds.

Baeyer also studied the hydroaromatic compounds. These substances provide a transition between the two main classes of organic compounds—aromatic, on the one hand, and aliphatic (or "fatty") on the other. By extending these concepts and methods to the terpenes and camphor, he opened up previously inaccessible fields for synthetic work.

Nobel lecture

Baeyer was unable to attend the Nobel Prize ceremonies as a result of an unspecified illness. Thus, he did not deliver a Nobel lecture.

Critical reception

When Baeyer received the Nobel Prize, he was seventy years old and had an international reputation. An outstanding experimenter, he was the most eminent organic chemist in Germany during the latter part of the nineteenth century and the early part of the twentieth century. Consequently, the announcement that he had won the Nobel Prize, reported without fanfare in the United States, did not appear to generate any controversy.

The New York Times of December 10, 1905, did not comment on the Nobel chemistry awardee or his career, except to note that "Adolph von Boeyer," professor at Munich, was to receive the chemistry award for researches leading to the evolution of organic chemistry and the development of the chemistry industry. *Scientific American* of December 23, 1905, reporting that King Oscar had distributed the awards on December 10, used essentially the same wording as *The New York Times* and transliterated the name as "Adolph von Böyer." A longer article in *The Independent* of December 14, 1905, provided a few biographical details and some comments about Baeyer's work, noting his strain theory and his extensive work on aniline dyes. The article concluded with an observation that Baeyer's synthesis of indigo had given Germany a new industry worth millions of dollars a year. *The Outlook* of December 16, 1905, recognized the international importance of the annual Nobel awards, pointing out that the awards are open to worthy individuals of all nations in recognition of work that is generally of international value. The editorial then lamented the fact that as of 1905 no American had received an award, but at the same time made it clear that the awards committee was making fair and impartial decisions. According to the article, the 1905 prizewinner in chemistry was "Professor Adolph von Beyer," who had done remarkable work in organic chemistry.

Shortly before Baeyer was awarded the Nobel Prize, his friends and students decided to honor him on his seventieth birthday (October 31, 1905) by publishing his scientific papers in book form. There were nearly three hundred of these papers, covering the period from 1857 to 1905. In an introduction, Baeyer provided an account of the chief events of his life and of the main trend of his scientific work, and Emil Fischer (winner of the 1902 Nobel Prize in Chemistry) wrote a sketch about life in Baeyer's Strasbourg laboratory. A review of this two-volume collection of Baeyer's papers appeared in *Science* on August 17, 1906. Although it is not a direct reaction to Baeyer's Nobel award, it is an assessment of Baeyer and his work, published shortly after such reaction would have been anticipated. The reviewer suggests that a thorough study of Baeyer's scientific publications reveals an admirable love and respect for truth for its own sake and that this characteristic, in combination with his unusual experimental ability, explains his marked influence on the development of organic chemistry. This assessment was based on personal contact, since the reviewer, John Ulric Nef, was one of Baeyer's Ph.D. students. The closeness of this relationship could perhaps have made the review more favorable than otherwise, but the comments are consistent with evaluations of Baeyer and his work by many others.

Biography

Johann Friedrich Wilhelm Adolf (von) Baeyer was born in Berlin on October 31, 1835. His father, Johann Jacob Baeyer, was a lieutenant general in the Prussian army, and his mother, Eugenie (née Hitzig), was the daughter of a criminologist. Baeyer began his studies at the Friedrich-Wilhelms Gymnasium, and he attended the University of Berlin for two years (1853-1855), concentrating on mathematics and physics. After a year of military service, he turned to experimental chemistry. In 1856, he began a two-year period of study at Heidelberg with Robert Wilhelm Bunsen, and from there he moved to August Kekulé's private laboratory, also in Heidelberg. He earned the Ph.D. degree in 1858 at Berlin with a thesis on organic arsenic compounds, work which had been done in Kekulé's laboratory.

When Kekulé went to Ghent in 1858, Baeyer followed, but he returned to Berlin two years later. He had investigated uric acid while at Ghent, and with this study, he qualified as a university teacher. In the same year he became a lecturer in organic chemistry at the Gewerbe Institute (later the technical high school at Charlottenburg). Six years later, the University of Berlin appointed him to the unpaid position of senior lecturer.

Baeyer married Adelheid (Lida) Bendemann in 1868, and they had three children: Eugenie, Hans, and Otto. In 1872, he became professor at the new university at Strasbourg, and three years later, the University of Munich called him to succeed Justus von Liebig. He remained at Munich for more than forty years. Baeyer died after a brief illness on August 20, 1917, at his country house in Starnberg.

Scientific Career

Baeyer's maternal grandfather, Julius Eduard Hitzig, was an authority on criminal law and a student of the history of literature. His house had been a center of Berlin's literary life, a gathering place for poets and many others interested in literature. This environment had no effect on Baeyer, however, who developed no interest in literature. He was much more inclined toward natural phenomena, and even as a young boy he performed simple chemical experiments. He was only twelve when he made his first chemical discovery—a new double carbonate salt of copper and sodium.

Baeyer acquired a thorough foundation in science and mathematics at the Friedrich-Wilhelms Gymnasium, and he concentrated on mathematics and physics during his first two years at the University of Berlin. After a year of military service, he knew that he wanted to study chemistry, and in 1856 he entered Bunsen's laboratory at Heidelberg. There, in 1857, he published the results of his studies on methyl chloride, the first of his many papers.

Baeyer soon became dissatisfied with the applied physical chemistry emphasis in Bunsen's laboratory, and in 1857 he moved to August Kekulé's laboratory, where he could devote himself almost exclusively to organic chemistry. Kekulé's laboratory in Heidelberg was just getting under way, and Baeyer was Kekulé's first student. The laboratory, which was extremely modest and primitive, had no fume outlets, except for the draft from the fireplace. During his work on arsenic compounds, Baeyer suffered a slight but permanent injury when he accidentally inhaled fumes of the highly toxic arsenic monomethyl chloride. In 1858, Kekulé accepted a call to Ghent, and Baeyer went with him. On the way to Ghent, Baeyer met Adolf Schlieper, a factory owner who had once worked with Justus von Liebig on uric acid. Schlieper still had samples of his preparations, which he gave to Baeyer for further investigation. These studies on uric acid led Baeyer to his discovery of barbituric acid, the parent compound of the barbiturate family.

Baeyer returned to Berlin in 1860 and held various teaching positions, including an appointment in organic chemistry at the Gewerbe Institute, where he had a roomy laboratory. He spent the next twelve years at this location, continuing his studies on uric acid and attracting a group of capable young chemists such as Karl Graebe, Karl Liebermann, and Victor Meyer.

Baeyer began his studies of indigo during this period in Berlin. His interest in the blue pigment had begun years earlier when, at age thirteen, he purchased a lump of indigo and began to investigate its properties. As early as 1841, Auguste Laurent had found that oxidation of the pigment introduced oxygen atoms and essentially split the molecule into two equal parts, producing isatin. Baeyer attempted to reverse the Laurent process by reducing isatin—replacing the two oxygen atoms of isatin with hydrogen—in an effort to obtain the compound from which indigo itself is derived. The usual reduction procedures introduced hydrogen but removed only one of the oxygen atoms; Baeyer finally was able to remove the second oxygen atom by a new method—distillation over hot zinc dust. Thus, he had prepared the parent compound of indigo, which he named indole, and he was then able to propose a structure for indigo based on the structure of indole. As early as 1870, Baeyer had accomplished the complete reversal of Laurent's process, the conversion of isatin all the way to indigo; consequently, when he synthesized isatin from phenylacetic acid in 1878, he demonstrated the possibility of a complete synthesis of indigo from common chemicals. Nevertheless, it was not until 1897 that synthetic indigo appeared on the market at a price below that of the natural product. Baeyer chose not to take an active part in eliminating difficulties associated with the commercial production of indigo, and this resulted in some ill feeling on the part of the dye industry.

Baeyer's new method of zinc dust distillation was also used with success by his students Graebe and Liebermann in their studies of alizarin, the pigment obtained from the madder plant. Madder was used to dye the red caps and trousers of French soldiers and the red fox-hunting and army coats of the British. In 1868, Graebe and Liebermann reduced alizarin with zinc dust and obtained the parent compound, anthracene. This work led them to the structure of alizarin and a technically feasible synthesis of the pigment. The economic impact of this development was almost immediate, and in only a few years natural madder from France had been driven off the market.

In 1870, Baeyer published his views on condensation reactions—reactions involving the removal of water from materials containing carbon, hydrogen, and oxygen. In many of these reactions the water is formed by joining together a hydrogen atom from one substance and a hydroxyl group from another. Baeyer considered all cases of this type and described the types of organic compounds that might be formed by such a reaction. In one investigation, he used phthalic anhydride as a dehydrating agent to assist in removing water from several naturally occurring phenols, but found that the phthalic anhydride reacted directly with the phenols to form phthaleins, a series of compounds which became important as dyestuffs. Included among the phthaleins are phenolphthalein, widely used as an acid-base indicator and as a laxative, and the related compounds fluorescein and eosin. Baeyer showed that these compounds, as well as the rhodamine dyes derived from them, could be classified as derivatives of the hydrocarbon triphenylmethane, also the parent compound of the previously known rosaniline dyes.

Baeyer entered a more comfortable stage of his professional career in 1872, when he became head of the laboratory at the newly founded University of Strasbourg. Among his collaborators at Strasbourg were Emil Fischer (winner of the 1902 Nobel Prize in Chemistry) and his cousin Otto Fischer. Emil had wanted to study physics, but Otto persuaded him to go to the University of Strasbourg, where he decided, under the influence of Baeyer, to devote his life to chemistry. Fischer earned his Ph.D. at Strasbourg in 1874 with a thesis on fluorescein and orcinphthalein.

When Justus von Liebig died in Munich on April 18, 1873, Liebig's chair was first offerd to Kekulé, who did not wish to leave Bonn. Eventually, Baeyer was selected for this professorship, and he moved to Munich in 1875, teaching there until his retirement forty years later.

At Munich Baeyer began his studies on acetylene and polyacetylene compounds, which led to his famous "strain theory" of cyclic or ring compounds. He began with existing structural theory, assuming that the four chemical bonds of carbon (the valence bonds) are directed in space as though toward the corners of a regular tetrahedron. With this shape, the angle between any two bonds is 109.5 degrees. Baeyer assumed that these directed valences would resist any deflection from this normal direction, and that if the deflection occurred, strain would be introduced. Deflections of this type would be expected with carbon atoms joined by double or triple bonds and when connected in rings of alicyclic (saturated) compounds. According to this approach, a ring containing three carbon atoms would have valence bond angles of 60 degrees. The difference between this angle and the normal angle (109.5 degrees) would measure the angle strain, but since two bonds are deflected at each angle, the angle difference must be divided by two to determine the deflection per bond. Thus, the valence bond deflection for the three-membered ring is

24.75 degrees. Similar calculations show that very little strain (less than 1 degree) would be introduced in forming a five-membered ring, perhaps accounting for the frequency with which five-membered rings are found. Although Baeyer's approach explained the behavior of a number of compounds, it also led to many contradictions. The problem with Baeyer's theory was his assumption that the rings of carbon atoms are planar regular polygons; a much better explanation of experimental behavior has been provided since Baeyer's time by assuming that the rings are nonplanar and puckered, especially in the case of five- and six-membered rings.

Baeyer also contributed to organic structural theory through his research on the constitution of benzene. At the time, several different structures had been proposed for benzene, and Baeyer began a series of experiments that he thought would lead to a suitable representation. Rather than work with benzene itself, he chose to work with benzene derivatives, such as the phthalic acids (the dicarboxylic acids of benzene). He tried to prepare reduced forms of these compounds (compounds with additional hydrogen atoms attached to the ring) by heating them with zinc dust, the technique he developed with his work on indigo. He thought that the locations of the added hydrogen atoms would reveal the extra valence positions on the carbon atoms of the ring. The results of these studies were not always anticipated, and they did not settle the issue concerning the constitution of benzene. However, this work did lead to a thorough, systematic study of the chemistry of the di-, tetra-, and hexahydrobenzenes, as well as other hydroaromatic compounds. This work also provided a bridge between the two main divisions of organic chemistry—aromatic and aliphatic—and led Baeyer into the field of terpene chemistry. He spent eight years working on terpenes, determining the structures of many of them and synthesizing some of the simplest representatives of the series. Much of this terpene work was done in collaboration with Victor Villiger; nearly a century later, the Baeyer-Villiger oxidation is still an important and useful reaction.

Baeyer was sixty-six when he conducted his investigations of peroxides and peracids. In these studies he showed that the weakly basic character of oxygen is not limited to certain types of organic compounds but is exhibited in all oxygen-containing organic compounds. He called the salt-like products formed in these reactions "oxonium compounds." Baeyer's final studies on triphenylmethane and triphenylmethane derivatives resulted in a new era of understanding about the relationship between molecular constitution and color.

In addition to his extensive research activities, Baeyer made significant contributions as a teacher of organic chemistry. Following in the footsteps of Jöns Jakob Berzelius and Justus von Liebig, he founded a teaching laboratory for chemists and achieved a position in the chemical world similar to the positions formerly occupied by these two pioneers. No one since Berzelius and Liebig had exerted such an influence on chemical teaching and research as did Baeyer—almost half the important professorships in Germany and many in foreign countries were filled by his students. He was not a brilliant or eloquent teacher, but he excelled in presenting the content of his lectures in a clear and simple manner. His laboratory teaching methods instilled in his students the importance of thinking independently.

Baeyer maintained a simple life, even in his later years when he was the recipient of many honors and recognitions, including the Liebig Medal, awarded by the Berlin Chemists Congress, and the Davy Medal, presented by the Royal Society. He belonged to many scientific societies, including the Berlin Academy of Sciences and the German Chemical Association. When he was fifty, he was raised to the hereditary nobility and thereafter was called von Baeyer. He appreciated the honor but did not otherwise place much value on this distinction.

Baeyer continued to teach and lecture at Munich for four decades, until he finally yielded to physical ailments forced upon him by old age. He was still young in spirit, and his mind remained clear until his death a few years later at his country house in Starnberg on August 20, 1917.

Bibliography

Primary

CHEMISTRY: *Gesammelte Werke*, 1905 (2 vols., including 278 of Baeyer's papers, from 1857 to 1905, and an autobiographical account of the first half of his scientific career).

Secondary

Beer, John J. *The Emergence of the German Dye Industry*. Urbana: University of Illinois Press, 1959. This is a scholarly but readable account of the development of the dyestuff industry. It also covers significant developments in Britain, France, and Switzerland.

Farber, Eduard, ed. *Great Chemists*. New York: Interscience, 1961. The article on Adolf von Baeyer in this book includes a picture of Baeyer and roughly a dozen pages of text describing Baeyer's career, personality, and philosophy. It is a translation of an earlier article by Richard M. Willstätter, a Baeyer Ph.D. student and the winner of the 1915 Nobel Prize in Chemistry.

Gienapp, Ruth Anne. "Adolf von Baeyer." In *Dictionary of Scientific Biography*, vol. 1, edited by Charles Coulston Gillispie. New York: Charles Scribner's Sons, 1970. Von Baeyer is one of the scientists profiled in this valuable reference work. The article contains details about his life and a discussion of his scientific contributions and their significance. Includes brief primary and secondary bibliographies.

Henrich, Ferdinand. "Adolf Von Baeyer (1835-1917)." *Journal of Chemical Education* 7 (1930). This eighteen-page article discusses Baeyer's major scientific contributions (some knowledge of chemistry is helpful, but not absolutely essential) and provides biographical information and insights into his personality. Also included are several photographs showing Baeyer, a gathering of Baeyer's friends (including several important scientists), Baeyer's laboratory at Munich, and various artworks honoring Baeyer.

Nef, J. U. "Baeyer's Work in Chemistry." *Science* 24 (August 17, 1906): 211-213. This

WITHDRAWN

COLORADO COLLEGE LIBRARY
COLORADO SPRINGS
COLORADO

two-page article discusses *Gesammelte Werke*, the two-volume collection of Baeyer's scientific papers that was published in 1905 in honor of his seventieth birthday. Although it begins as a book review, most of the article is a discussion of Baeyer's work and his scientific contributions.

Partington, James Riddick. *A History of Chemistry.* 4 vols. New York: St. Martin's Press, 1961. This is a four-volume scholarly treatment of the history of chemistry. It includes brief biographical sketches of important chemists, including Baeyer. Discussions of the chemists' scientific contributions generally assume some knowledge of chemistry. The articles include selected references to original publications.

Richard B. Bennett

1906

Chemistry
Henri Moissan, France

Physics
Sir Joseph John Thomson, Great Britain

Physiology or Medicine
Camillo Golgi, Italy
S. Ramón y Cajal, Spain

Literature
Giosuè Carducci, Italy

Peace
Theodore Roosevelt, United States

HENRI MOISSAN
1906

Born: Paris, France; September 28, 1852
Died: Paris, France; February 20, 1907
Nationality: French
Areas of concentration: Fluorine chemistry and high-temperature reactions

Moissan distinguished himself as one of the foremost inorganic chemists of his day by the isolation of fluorine, the investigation of fluorine compounds, and the study of reactions at high temperatures. He also produced microscopic artificial diamonds by heating and cooling iron containing carbon

The Award

Presentation

The Royal Swedish Academy of Sciences awarded the 1906 Nobel Prize in Chemistry to Henri Moissan for his isolation of fluorine and the introduction of the electric furnace to scientific investigations. These contributions opened new areas of both scientific and industrial pursuits. The award was presented by Professor Johan P. Klason, President of the Royal Swedish Academy of Sciences. In his presentation address, Professor Klason outlined the history of halogen chemistry, beginning with Antoine-Laurent Lavoisier's antiphlogiston theory. This was followed by a description of Sir Humphry Davy's work on isolation of new elements through electrolysis. The additional work of Karl Wilhelm Scheele and Jöns Jakob Berzelius led to the conclusion that hydrofluoric acid must contain a halogen that had not yet been isolated. After the failures of others, Moissan finally, through clever experimental efforts, isolated this element in appreciable quantities.

Professor Klason went on to describe Moissan's efforts to prepare minerals through the use of high temperatures made possible by an electric arc. Moissan's electric furnace made it possible to exclude side effects in these syntheses. Professor Klason highlighted Moissan's production of synthetic microscopic diamonds. The process involved melting pig iron containing carbon in an electric furnace and crystallizing graphite into diamond by very rapid cooling of the melted iron. Professor Klason concluded his remarks by referring to the "mighty wave unleashed [by Moissan] into the world of technology," which, he said, had not yet attained its full height.

Nobel lecture

No lecture was delivered by Moissan.

Critical reception

In 1906, the Nobel Prizes were only in their sixth year. In these early years, the science prizes generated little interest in the press. The public at large was still

The Nobel Prize Winners

relatively unfamiliar with the awards, and the scientific community did not yet consider them to be particularly prestigious, since there were other honors and awards with longer histories of distinguished winners.

Moissan died less than a year after receiving the Nobel Prize, and *Scientific American*, in an article after his death, called him "one of the greatest of modern chemists, certainly one of the best known." The article likened his work to that of the Curies, in that it was "spectacular in the extreme." It also noted that Moissan never obtained patents for his discoveries, but rather considered his work to be for the benefit of human knowledge.

The announcement of Moissan's preparation of fluorine had been made some twenty years earlier, to the French Academy of Sciences on June 28, 1886. The president of the academy appointed a committee of three eminent scientists to investigate Moissan's claim to the isolation of fluorine. Moissan's first attempt to demonstrate the preparation of fluorine in the presence of this illustrious group met with failure. The following day, however, the substitution of new chemicals resulted in a successful attempt in front of the committee, and Moissan's claim to isolating fluorine was legitimized.

The isolation of fluorine resulted in Moissan's being known throughout the scientific world, and the later preparation of artificial diamonds made the name of Moissan a household word. The popular press spoke of diamonds becoming so plentiful that the companies mining the natural diamonds would go out of business.

Biography

Henri Moissan was born September 28, 1852, in Paris, to a family of modest means. The family moved to the small city of Meaux in 1864. There Moissan attended the municipal school and came under the influence of an excellent teacher by the name of James, who taught natural sciences and mathematics. James provided Moissan with free private instruction and aroused in him an interest in chemistry. Moissan also received instruction in chemistry from his father.

In order to support himself as well as to continue to study chemistry, Moissan traveled to Paris in 1870, where he accepted a position in an apothecary's shop. His duties left him with little time to study, and Moissan, wanting to become a university student, abandoned the position in December of 1872 to begin studying chemistry under Frémy at the Musée d'Histoire Naturelle. He supported himself by giving private instruction and was awarded the bachelor's degree in 1874. He was awarded the diploma of Pharmacien de Première Classe in 1879 and received the degree of Docteur des Sciences Physiques in 1880. Moissan procured his first academic position in 1879 at the Agronomic Institute at Paris. In 1886 he became a professor of toxicology at the School of Pharmacy and in 1889 became a professor of chemistry at the Sorbonne.

At the age of thirty, Moissan married Léonie Lugan, the daughter of the pharmacist at Meaux. The marriage was very successful and lasted until Moissan's death. Moissan's father-in-law gave the couple an income that removed any concern for finances and allowed Moissan to apply himself full-time to scientific efforts. Although Moissan's creative efforts were mostly in the field of chemistry, his interests also included French literature, painting, sculpture, and the national economy. As a young man, he wrote a play that came close to being produced.

Moissan died February 20, 1907, after suffering from an acute case of appendicitis. There is little doubt that his scientific efforts shortened his life. He is quoted as having said that "fluorine has taken ten years of my life." Moissan's only child, Louis, died in battle on August 10, 1913.

Scientific Career

The work that led to the first great scientific accomplishment of Henri Moissan, the isolation of fluorine, began in the year 1884. To appreciate his achievement fully, one must know something about the nature of this chemical element.

Fluorine is a member of a group of elements known as the halogens (from the Greek words meaning "formers of sea salts"). Compounds of fluorine occur mostly as insoluble minerals such as fluorspar, a compound of calcium and fluorine. Fluorine never occurs in the uncombined state. In addition to fluorine, the halogen family includes the elements chlorine, bromine, and iodine. All but fluorine can be conveniently isolated from their naturally occurring compounds by reactions with other chemicals; however, there is no chemical sufficiently reactive to extract fluorine from any of its naturally occurring compounds, because fluorine is the most reactive substance known. It reacts with every element except oxygen, nitrogen, and some of the rare gases. Fluorine reacts violently with cold water in several simultaneous reactions. The products of these reactions include oxygen, oxygen difluoride, hydrogen peroxide, ozone, and hydrogen fluoride.

Fluorine will react with all substances that are not protected by a covering of binary (two-element) compounds of fluorine. Even fireproof materials, such as asbestos and glass, can be made to burn in fluorine. Because of its extreme reactivity, fluorine is a very dangerous material. At moderate temperatures, however, some metals, such as iron, copper, nickel, and cobalt, form adhering binary compounds of fluorine that protect the metals from further reaction.

Because of its extreme reactivity, fluorine was the last of the halogens to be isolated. In 1774, chlorine was isolated by Karl Wilhelm Scheele by action of hydrochloric acid on manganese dioxide; however, he did not recognize it as an element. Chlorine was finally recognized as an element by the English chemist Sir Humphry Davy after he was unsuccessful in his attempt to decompose it into simpler substances. Iodine was first isolated in 1811 by Bernard Courtois, a French chemist, and was recognized as an element in 1813 by Joseph-Louis Gay-Lussac. Antoine-Jérôme Balard recognized bromine as an element in 1826; yet, it was probably first produced by the German organic chemist Justus von Liebig some time before that date. The isolation of these elements from naturally occurring compounds convinced the early investigators of the existence of fluorine in analogous compounds.

If there are no substances sufficiently reactive to extract fluorine from its compounds, how was the element to be isolated? The answer to this question eluded chemists for nearly a century. Davy turned to the use of an electric current. Early experiments led to the discovery that some substances decompose when a current is passed through them. This process is called electrolysis. The similarity of hydrogen chloride and hydrogen fluoride convinced Davy that fluorine was present in the latter compound. He attempted to isolate fluorine through electrolysis of hydrogen fluoride, but his efforts were fruitless.

Others followed Davy in similar attempts. Thomas Knox, a Scot, suffered severely from inhaling toxic vapors in his attempts to isolate fluorine. Another investigator, Paulin Lauyet, lost his life in an attempt to isolate this ferocious element. Several problems were encountered in these efforts. Anhydrous (water-free) hydrogen fluoride, a gas, is a nonconductor of current. When dissolved in water, it becomes a poor conductor; however, because fluorine reacts vigorously with water, it could never be isolated through electrolysis of an aqueous solution. Also, because fluorine reacts with almost everything, there was the problem of what to use in the construction of the apparatus to be used in the effort. Frémy, one of Moissan's teachers, came the closest to isolating fluorine (before Moissan), through the electrolysis of fused salts (consisting of charged particles that are conductors). At the high temperature required to melt these compounds, however, fluorine reacted with the apparatus and returned to the combined state before it could be isolated.

Moissan succeeded where others had failed. He obtained fluorine by passing a current through a mixture of potassium hydrogen fluoride and liquid anhydrous hydrogen fluoride at low temperatures. Potassium hydrogen fluoride is a salt (made up of charged particles), and hence, the mixture was able to conduct a current. Finally, on June 26, 1886, Moissan succeeded in bringing about the electrolytic decomposition of hydrogen fluoride. From the positive pole, a pale yellow-green gas flowed, which exhibited the extreme reactivity expected of fluorine. It set fire to silicon and reacted with water to form ozone. It did not, however, react appreciably with the apparatus, which was constructed of a platinum and iridium alloy—a very expensive but unreactive combination. Moissan later learned that ordinary copper could be used in the apparatus, since it forms a tightly adhering copper fluoride coating that protects the copper from further reaction with fluorine. He also found that if fluorine is absolutely dry, it does not attack glass.

Moissan went on to prepare and describe the properties of many new fluorine compounds. His comprehensive research on the combination of fluorine with other substances led him to the study of compounds of fluorine and carbon. He had a vague idea that the extreme reactivity of fluorine could bring about the crystallization of carbon in the form of a diamond. Interest in the composition of diamonds goes back to Lavoisier. In 1830, he demonstrated, by burning a diamond in oxygen, that it consisted of nothing but carbon. That is, in terms of its chemical composition, diamonds are no different from graphite, coke, lampblack, and other forms of elements of carbon. The term "allotropism" is used by chemists to refer to the phenomenon in which an element exists in more than one form.

Often the differences between allotropic forms are manifested in crystal structure. A diamond is a perfect network solid. It contains carbons, atoms tetrahedrally bonded to one another. The strength of these bonds gives diamonds their high melting points. Since the bonds are directional and rigid, they produce a hard, rigid crystal. The crystalline regularity of the diamond is also responsible for its renowned beauty.

Graphite, the most prevalent allotropic form of carbon, is black, slippery, and soft. It is less dense than carbon. It is easy to convert diamond to graphite, but the reverse is extremely difficult. It occurred to the early investigators that high pressures would be expected to change graphite (which has a large volume and low density) to diamond (small volume, high density). It appears that R. S. Marsden did produce some small diamond crystals by heating charcoal with silver-platinum alloy and subsequent cooling; however, his effort received little attention.

Moissan's approach to the problem was to attempt to produce the conditions of high pressure and high temperature that exist in red-hot meteorites passing through the earth's atmosphere. Diamond-bearing meteorites consisting mostly of iron with graphite embedded in them had been discovered. Moissan reasoned that the sudden cooling of the very hot meteorite with the embedded graphite created a sufficiently high pressure to result in the crystallization of carbon in the form of diamond. That is, the sudden cooling of the outer portion of the meteorite resulted in a contraction that produced, in the interior of the meteorite, the necessary pressure to create the diamond.

To produce experimentally the conditions that exist in the interior of the meteorite required very high temperatures. To meet this need, Moissan again turned to electricity. He built a unique electric-arc furnace. The electric-arc furnace was not a new concept with Moissan, but the skill with which he used this device in his research effort resulted in his generally being regarded as the founder of high-temperature chemistry.

On February 6, 1893, Moissan succeeded in producing small artificial diamonds. Essentially, this involved melting iron at about 4,000 degrees Celsius in the electric furnace, dissolving carbon in the molten iron, and cooling the molten mixture in cold water. The outer surface cooled more quickly than the inner portion, bringing about the necessary pressure to cause the carbon to crystallize in the form of diamonds. Most of the diamonds were black and not of gem quality. The largest one was 0.7 millimeter long and colorless.

Moissan's electric furnace became a valuable and widely used research tool and was often called the Moissan furnace. Using this device, he isolated a number of uncommon metals, including manganese, columbium (niobium), tantalum, and thorium. He also prepared numerous binary compounds of boron, silicon, and carbon. The most notable of these compounds, calcium carbide, reacts with water to form acetylene gas.

Moissan's whole life was one of scientific achievement, even though he originated no new laws and formulated no new theories. He was essentially an experimentalist. As a result of his experimental efforts, he solved two of the most difficult and perplexing problems of his day—the isolation of fluorine and the preparation of artificial diamonds. Moissan began his work when European chemists had largely abandoned the field of inorganic chemistry, believing it to be barren of interesting problems, and devoted their research efforts to organic chemistry. Moissan's isolation of fluorine resulted in the revival of research in inorganic chemistry. His electric furnace was a valuable incentive in this effort and opened the whole new field of high-temperature research. The demand for acetylene gave rise to the calcium carbide industry, which rapidly became a burgeoning business.

Bibliography

Primary
CHEMISTRY: *Le Four électrique*, 1897; *Le Fluor et ses composés*, 1900; *Traité de chimie minérale*, 1904-1906.

Secondary
Farber, Eduard, ed. *Great Chemists*. New York: Interscience, 1961. A collection of biographies of 110 eminent chemists. Among these is an English translation of a biography originally written in German by Alfred Stock, a student of Moissan. Although this biography was written by a chemist for chemists, it contains much information that can be understood by the nonchemist.
Harrow, Benjamin. *Eminent Chemists of Our Time*. 2d ed. New York: Van Nostrand, 1927. A collection of biographies of great chemists including that of Henri Moissan. It is written in a popular, interesting style, and includes an excellent discussion of the scientific work of Moissan.
Ihde, Aaron J. *The Development of Modern Chemistry*. New York: Harper & Row, 1964. This is a one-volume work on the history of chemistry, containing numerous references to Moissan and his work. Pages 366-369 are of particular interest, although the index must be consulted for all the references to Moissan's research efforts.
Partington, James Riddick. *A History of Chemistry*. 4 vols. New York: St. Martin's Press, 1961. A comprehensive treatise on the history of chemistry. This is a scholarly, well-documented, authoritative work, but is not easy to read.

B. R. Siebring

1907

Chemistry
Eduard Buchner, Germany

Physics
Albert Abraham Michelson, United States

Physiology or Medicine
Alphonse Laveran, France

Literature
Rudyard Kipling, Great Britain

Peace
Ernesto Teodoro Moneta, Italy
Louis Renault, France

EDUARD BUCHNER
1907

Born: Munich, Bavaria (modern West Germany); May 20, 1860
Died: Focsani, Romania; August 13, 1917
Nationality: German
Areas of concentration: Fermentation and enzyme chemistry

Buchner discovered the cell-free fermentation of sugar. His demonstration that living yeast cells were not essential for fermentation marked the beginning of modern enzyme chemistry

The Award

Presentation

Count K. A. H. Mörner, President of the Royal Swedish Academy of Sciences, did not deliver his presentation text orally, because the death of King Oscar II two days earlier had caused the cancellation of the presentation ceremony.

Mörner began his text by noting that scientists regard as particularly significant any research that opens to investigation phenomena hitherto shrouded in mystery because they occur within living organisms. Scientists knew so little of the inner course of events in organisms that such events were regarded as expressions of the life of living cells. Among these mysterious life processes was fermentation, which involved the decomposition of substances under the influence of agents called "ferments" or "enzymes." These agents were of unknown nature; none had ever been isolated in pure form. They were known only by the effects they produced.

Mörner then gave the prevailing view of fermentation at the time of Buchner's studies. Since fermentation took place only in the presence of living cells, the connection between fermentation and the live yeast seemed so essential that the process was viewed as an expression of the vital activity of the cells.

When Eduard Buchner's work appeared in 1897, the effect was sensational. He had succeeded in obtaining the fermenting agent free from live yeast cells and demonstrated its fermenting power on various types of sugar. This discovery of cell-free fermentation had freed the study of fermentation from its association with life forces and opened it to physical and chemical research. In the ten years since 1897, Mörner noted, many important chemical investigations had been conducted, opening vast new prospects in the understanding of biological processes. Mörner concluded with the observation that the nature and constitution of the enzyme that caused fermentation was still unknown and that a solution to this puzzle might well be the subject of a future Nobel Prize.

Nobel lecture

Buchner delivered his Nobel lecture, "Cell-Free Fermentation," on December 11, 1907. The first half was entirely historical; the second half was an account of his research. He began by mentioning a series of investigations on ferments during the 1830's that demonstrated that yeast consisted of the live cells of a microscopic plant. Leading chemists, such as Jöns Jakob Berzelius and Justus von Liebig, rejected the proposition that fermentation was the result of the life activity of a microorganism. They regarded all processes in animals and plants as physical and chemical ones, not acts of life. To Berzelius, yeast was merely a catalyst. The vitalistic viewpoint triumphed, however, following the studies of Louis Pasteur during the 1850's. Pasteur established the presence of live yeast in several kinds of fermentation; if there was no live yeast present, there was no fermentation.

Buchner noted that the chemical viewpoint never died but found adherents throughout the nineteenth century. Plant physiologists, however, countered the claims of chemists by arguing that all attempts to separate a chemical agent from yeast cells had failed, including attempts by Pasteur himself. Two decades of negative results had resolved the matter in favor of the vitalistic theory of fermentation.

After his historical sketch, Buchner gave an account of his own work. He began with a description of the yeast cell and noted his desire to study all of its contents chemically by breaking open the cell. He considered earlier attempts at pulverizing yeast before presenting the method that he and a coworker, Martin Hahn, had developed. They mixed sand and diatomaceous earth with yeast and ground the mixture. They then wrapped the doughy mass in strong canvas and squeezed out the liquid with a hydraulic press. The yellow liquid so obtained had fermenting power when it was added to a sugar solution. Buchner considered a variety of experiments which eliminated the possibility that some intact yeast cells or pieces of live protoplasm were the producers of the fermentation. After much experimentation, he concluded that he had separated the enzyme from the yeast cells and that the fermentation was cell-free, caused by an active agent which he named zymase.

Buchner's lecture continued with a briefer presentation of his research after 1897. He tried to isolate zymase as a pure substance, but this direction was not successful. A second direction—the study of the chemical processes in cell-free fermentation—did produce some positive results, although he acknowledged that others were more successful than he in determining intermediate products. Buchner concluded by commenting on the lack of understanding of both the details of alcoholic fermentation and the nature of zymase. Nevertheless, now that fermentation had been separated from the life of organisms, scientists could study enzymes and their activities in various physiological processes, and a vision had recently emerged of the cell as a chemical factory which produced a variety of reactions and products under the direction of enzymes.

Critical reception

The reaction to Buchner's Nobel Prize in 1907 was slight, indeed almost nonexistent outside Germany. *The New York Times* made no mention of him. *The Times* of London mentioned his name only in its story on the award winners for 1907, whereas the physics, physiology or medicine, literature, and peace prizes received ample coverage. *The Nation* carried a story on the Nobel Prize winners in its January 2, 1908, edition, providing accounts of the literature, physics, and physiology or medicine awards but not mentioning Buchner at all. The lack of interest in Buchner stood in contrast not only to the other 1907 prizewinners but also to the major controversy his work created among scientists, which raged for about five years after the 1897 discovery of zymase. Major scientists debated the merits and meanings of Buchner's claims, and a large literature developed concerning the chemical versus vitalistic views of fermentation. The controversy ended with the vindication of Buchner's chemical interpretation. One can conjecture that this controversy had already drawn the attention of those scientists most likely to comment on Buchner's findings. The Nobel award may have evoked no further reaction because there was little more to say that had not already been expressed.

Biography

Eduard Buchner was born in Munich on May 20, 1860, into a Bavarian family that had produced scholars over many generations. His father, Ernst Buchner, was a professor of forensic medicine and obstetrics at the University of Munich and was the editor of a medical journal. His mother, Friederike (née Martin) Buchner, was the daughter of a clerk in the royal treasury. Eduard's older brother, Hans, became a distinguished scientist in the fields of bacteriology, immunochemistry, and hygiene. His father died in 1872, forcing the boy to earn a livelihood with no further education likely. Hans, however, saw to his brother's education in Munich schools. In 1877, he served in the field artillery of the German army before entering the Munich Technical University to study chemistry. Financial difficulties led to his withdrawal, however, and for four years he worked in canning factories.

In 1884, Buchner resumed his studies with the aid of a three-year scholarship, working with Adolf von Baeyer, one of Germany's leading organic chemists, in the organic chemistry section of the Bavarian Academy of Sciences in Munich. He received a Ph.D. in 1888 from the University of Munich. In 1890, he became Baeyer's assistant, and in 1891 he was a lecturer at the university. With funds obtained by Baeyer, he established a small laboratory for research in the chemistry of fermentation, an interest of Buchner's stemming from his years in the preserve and canning industry.

In 1893, Buchner left Munich for the University of Kiel; in 1896, he joined the faculty of the University of Tübingen. In 1898, he was in Berlin as professor of general chemistry at the College of Agriculture and director of the Institute for the Fermentation Industry. In Berlin he was active in the German Chemical Society and became its president in 1904. He married Lotte Stahl, daughter of a Tübingen mathematician, in 1900, and they had two sons and a daughter. His reputation for high-spiritedness manifested itself on his wedding night, which he spent in a police station after his arrest for loud singing in the streets of Tübingen. Missing teaching at a university, he left Berlin after ten years for the University of Breslau in 1909.

His last academic appointment was at the University of Würzburg in 1911.

With the outbreak of World War I, Buchner volunteered for military duty, serving for eighteen months between 1914 and 1916 as captain of an ammunition supply unit in France, Prussia, and Poland; he was awarded the Iron Cross. In 1916, he received a promotion to major. He returned to Würzburg to resume his teaching, but with the entrance of the United States into the war in 1917 he once again volunteered to defend his country and served as head of a unit supplying munitions to troops in Romania. On August 11, shrapnel struck him, and he died two days later in a military hospital.

Scientific Career

Buchner's research career began in Adolf von Baeyer's organic chemistry laboratory in the 1880's. His first studies were in preparative organic chemistry under the guidance of Baeyer's assistant, Theodor Curtius, a master of the chemistry of organic nitrogen compounds. Although his biochemical research on fermentation would overwhelm this early work with Curtius, their studies disclosed a new group of azo compounds in 1883. From 1885 to 1905, Buchner experimented independently and produced forty-eight papers on the preparation of organic nitrogen compounds, especially on pyrazole and the use of diazoacetic ester in synthesis.

It was, however, Buchner's studies on the chemistry of fermentation and enzymes that brought him fame and the Nobel Prize. Fermentation had intrigued Buchner from his days in the canning industry. His first purely independent research was on the influence of oxygen in fermentation in 1885. Yet in his small laboratory in Munich, he produced only one paper on the subject before his departure for Kiel in 1893, and his colleagues thought so little of his work that they told him to abandon the field, since it seemed to have been thoroughly exploited already, and nothing was likely to come from this research.

While living in Kiel and Tübingen between 1893 and 1898, Buchner would return to Munich on holidays to work with his brother Hans, who was a professor at the university and director of the Institute of Hygiene. Eduard adored him; ever since the early death of his father, Hans had been his "father" and mentor. It was at the institute that the celebrated discovery of cell-free fermentation occurred. The circumstances of the discovery were unusual, because the subject of the experiments was not fermentation, and the discovery was unexpected; it was a surprising by-product of the real purpose of the research.

The research was in Hans Buchner's field of bacteriology and immunology. He had developed a chemical theory of immunity in which proteins of blood plasma were the agents that combated harmful bacterial toxins in the blood. The search for antibacterial proteins was his major concern in the 1890's. He also began to look for antitoxic proteins in bacteria themselves. The experiments with Eduard were an attempt to extract and isolate immunologically active proteins from bacterial cells.

As early as 1893, the brothers tried to break open yeast cells by grinding in order to extract proteins from inside the cells. The yeast experiments were merely a trial run for work on bacterial cells, because yeast was inexpensive and readily available. Eduard's task was to develop a sand-grinding method to open the yeast cells. If it worked, they would move on to bacteria.

When Buchner was in Kiel and Tübingen, the grinding work was continued by Hans's assistant, Martin Hahn. It was Hahn, not Eduard Buchner, who made the breakthrough. He found that the addition of diatomaceous earth to the sand made the sticky paste obtained from ground yeast consistent enough to be workable. Hahn wrapped the paste in canvas cloth and pressed it in a hydraulic press, obtaining a yellow press juice consisting of undiluted intracellular juice rich in dissolved cellular materials.

Hahn reported to Hans Buchner the results of his successful method and also noted that the juice rapidly decomposed, advising him that a preservative should be added. When Eduard returned to Munich during an autumn holiday in 1896, Hahn went on his vacation. Buchner resumed the experiments and decided to use a concentrated cane-sugar solution as a preservative. He observed the generation of bubbles in the press juice. To his surprise, the juice was apparently fermenting the cane sugar. Subsequent experiments revealed that alcoholic fermentation of sugar was indeed occurring. Hans told him that this result must be attributable to fragments of living protoplasm in the juice that had passed through the grinding and pressing process, but further work by Eduard indicated that the juice was free of cells.

Buchner realized the significance of the surprise discovery. He had accomplished something that others had tried to do for decades, with negative results: He had extracted the active agent of fermentation from living cells. The original purpose of the research—to extract therapeutic agents from inside cells—was now abandoned in order to pursue cell-free fermentation.

In 1897, Buchner's paper on cell-free fermentation appeared, with his conclusion that the process was caused by a specific chemical substance, an enzyme, which he named zymase. Over the next five years, he published eighteen papers devoted to experiments which consolidated his evidence as well as explaining and defending his work and claims. In 1903, the two brothers and Martin Hahn coauthored a comprehensive presentation of the subject in book form as *Die Zymase-Gärung* (fermentation by zymase).

Buchner's 1897 publication caused both a sensation and an intense controversy over the next five years. Since 1897, writers have focused on the importance of Buchner in resolving the nineteenth century debate between chemical and vitalist theories of the nature of alcoholic fermentation. Was fermentation a vital act of living yeast or a purely chemical act by a substance within yeast? Buchner resolved the question in favor of the chemical view. This version of history, however, does not adequately reflect the issue as it existed in the 1890's. The controversy from 1897 to 1902 reflected developments from the 1870's more than it did the earlier vitalist-chemical dispute.

By the 1870's, several ferments had been obtained as extracts from organic

116   *The Nobel Prize Winners*

sources. These functioned outside living cells and were mostly digestive ones—digesting protein, carbohydrate, or fat. For example, trypsin is a protein-splitting ferment that was first obtained in the 1830's from stomach juices. By the 1870's, ferments had been divided into two categories, and a dualistic scheme appeared which effectively ended the chemical-vitalist debate. Ferments were either "organized" or "unorganized." The former functioned inside the cells of organisms and were responsible for all complex physiological processes, such as respiration, synthesis, and fermentation. These organized ferments were the living substance, the protoplasm, of cells. Unorganized ferments, however, were purely chemical agents, and the physiologist Wilhelm Kühne in 1876 gave them the name "enzyme." They were extractable from organic sources and functioned outside living cells.

This dualistic scheme seemed a reasonable resolution to the debate. One ferment represented the vital activity of living protoplasm, the other the chemical action of an enzyme. In the 1890's, all known enzymes were restricted to simple splitting of organic materials. The more intricate intracellular processes were the province of living protoplasm. Enzymes functioned extracellularly; ferment, intracellularly.

Buchner's 1897 publications appeared in this context. He had discovered cell-free fermentation; an agent inside the cell had been forcibly separated from the cell and caused fermentation outside the cell. In disbelief, the advocates of protoplasm argued that it had to be fragments of living protoplasm that were present in the pressed juice. Buchner's zymase upset the respectable dualism of Kühne, and a new controversy began.

The argument over experimental evidence was what concerned Buchner in the eighteen papers published during the next five years. He had to redo all of his work more carefully, try to eliminate loopholes, and overcome criticism. The stakes were considerable; zymase was the first enzyme to carry out a complex physiological reaction, the first strictly intracellular enzyme. Thus, when reports appeared asserting either that his experiments could not be repeated or that the press juice was not really cell-free, Buchner had to respond with more experiments and present a stronger case for the existence of zymase.

He demonstrated that fermentation occurred even at the temperature of an ice chest; the press juice was active even after two weeks in the cold temperature. He added antiseptics to the juice, which were expected to kill any fragments of protoplasm. Nevertheless, fermentation continued. He checked to make sure no yeast cells got through the process from beginning to end. By adding alcohol and ether to the juice, he got a precipitate. He preserved it as a dry powder; it, too, retained its effectiveness. He prepared sterile juice. He vacuum-dried and desiccated his samples. Protoplasm could not survive such treatments.

Buchner did reveal the presence of another enzyme, one that made the cell-free juice inactive after prolonged storage by destroying the zymase. He also disclosed other enzymes, but attempts to separate these from zymase were not successful. He studied other types of fermentation between 1902 and 1909: lactous, acetous, citrous, and butyrous fermentations. This work was helpful in confirming the idea that fermentation was a series of enzyme-catalyzed reactions. Other scientists entered the controversy on his side, some of whom became the pacesetters, obtaining more impressive results than Buchner managed to achieve.

Experimentally, there were challenges, but many reports appeared substantiating Buchner. Ideologically, those already committed to enzymes sided with him; those committed to protoplasm took the other side. By the end of the debate, zymase had been accepted as a true intracellular enzyme. Furthermore, the Buchner-Hahn method of breaking open cells led to the discovery of more enzymes in the juices of both yeast and bacteria.

When the tide turned in Buchner's favor, he became the hero to a new generation of chemists interested in the chemical study of biological processes. His work coincided with the birth of the field of biochemistry at the beginning of the twentieth century, and enzymes became the central concern of biochemists. His work also had important implications for the brewing industry, for it offered the promise of purely enzymatic fermentation free of the diseases and problems associated with living yeast.

The vindication of Buchner was important for the future of science. It gave self-awareness and energy to the new biochemistry. The potential of an enzyme chemistry that would focus on biological processes at the chemical level raised the hope that enzymes would be found, isolated, and studied, and that the life processes that they mediate would be understood in terms of chemical structures and reactions.

Bibliography

Primary

CHEMISTRY: "Alkoholische Gährung ohne Hefezellen," *Berichte der deutschen chemischen Gesellschaft*, vol. 30, 1897 ("Alcoholic Fermentation Without Yeast Cells," in *Great Experiments in Biology*, 1955); *Die Zymase-Gärung*, 1903 (with Hans Buchner and Martin Hahn).

Secondary

Dixon, Malcolm. "History of Enzymes and Biological Oxidation." In *The Chemistry of Life*, edited by Joseph Needham. Cambridge, England: Cambridge University Press, 1970. Dixon provides a succinct survey of the history of enzymes in this collection of essays on the history of biochemistry. His account is not very profound but does contain much valuable information.

Fruton, Joseph S. *Molecules and Life: Historical Essays on the Interplay of Chemistry and Biology*. New York: John Wiley & Sons, 1972. This is the best secondary source on the history of biochemistry. The first chapter provides a detailed exposition of the history of enzyme research and culminates with a penetrating analysis of Buchner's studies based on the author's vast knowledge of the literature.

Kohler, Robert. "The Background to Eduard Buchner's Discovery of Cell-Free Fermentation." *Journal of the History of Biology* 4 (Spring, 1971): 35-61. Kohler, a historian of science, provides a perceptive account of the experiments and ideas during the sixty years preceding Buchner's work, enabling the reader to understand the sources of Buchner's own studies and his ideas.

_____. "The Enzyme Theory and the Origin of Biochemistry." *Isis* 64 (June, 1973): 181-196. This article is concerned with the rise and early development of biochemistry at the beginning of the twentieth century. Kohler shows how this development is connected to the enzyme research of the 1890's and how Buchner's discovery of zymase provided a major impetus to the emergence of biochemistry.

_____. "The Reception of Eduard Buchner's Discovery of Cell-Free Fermentation." *Journal of the History of Biology* 5 (Fall, 1972): 327-353. This comprehensive historical study of the controversy surrounding Buchner's research is the most illuminating available.

Moore, Ruth. *The Coil of Life*. New York: Alfred A. Knopf, 1962. This is a popular account of discoveries in biochemistry and allied sciences from Lavoisier to the discoveries associated with DNA in the twentieth century. The author, one of the best-known popular science writers, devotes one chapter to a lucid presentation of Buchner's discovery of zymase.

Albert B. Costa

1908

Chemistry
Ernest Rutherford, New Zealand

Physics
Gabriel Lippmann, France

Physiology or Medicine
Paul Ehrlich, Germany
Ilya Mechnikov, Russia

Literature
Rudolf Christoph Eucken, Germany

Peace
Klas Pontus Arnoldson, Sweden
Fredrik Bajer, Denmark

ERNEST RUTHERFORD
1908

Born: Spring Grove, near Nelson, New Zealand; August 30, 1871
Died: Cambridge, England; October 19, 1937
Nationality: New Zealander
Areas of concentration: Radioactivity and nuclear physics

Rutherford revolutionized atomic theory by demonstrating that radioactivity results from the disintegration of atoms, which had previously been regarded as immutable. His research also led to an understanding of the various types of radiation

The Award

Presentation

On December 10, 1908, K. B. Hasselberg, President of the Royal Swedish Academy of Sciences, presented Ernest Rutherford with the Nobel Prize in Chemistry. Hasselberg began his speech by noting the connection between Rutherford's work and that of several Nobel laureates who preceded him—Sir Joseph John Thomson's identification of the electron, Antoine-Henri Becquerel's discovery of naturally occurring radioactivity, Pierre and Marie Curie's discovery of various radioactive elements and their examination of the properties of these substances. Rutherford distinguished two types of emissions from radioactive materials, alpha and beta rays, and demonstrated that the former were particles rather than waves. Further research showed that radioactive elements produce an emanation, which Rutherford proved was a gas, itself radioactive and subject to the same laws of transformation and decay as its parent.

These changes, Rutherford and Frederick Soddy concluded, were not molecular but atomic in origin, the result of one element spontaneously changing itself into another. Rutherford and Soddy speculated that this transmutation involved the production of helium; Sir William Ramsay and Soddy soon confirmed the fact that radium does give off helium. Such discoveries are important, Hasselberg stated, but even more significant are the possibilities that they suggest for further examination of the structure of the atom that, barely a decade earlier, had been regarded as indivisible, the smallest building block of matter.

Hasselberg digressed briefly from his account of Rutherford's work to explain why a physicist was being awarded the prize designated for original research in chemistry. The sciences, he remarked, are interrelated, and Rutherford's work had so extensive and obvious an importance to chemists that he well deserved this recognition.

Nobel lecture

On December 11, 1908, Rutherford delivered his Nobel lecture, "The Chemical Nature of the Alpha Particle from Radioactive Substances," in which he reviewed a decade of research into this product of atomic disintegration. He began by observing that he was the first to recognize that radiation was not uniform but rather consisted of at least two types, which he labeled alpha and beta; shortly afterward, Paul Villard found a third variety, which he called gamma rays. Because alpha rays were the least penetrating of the three, most researchers ignored them, but Rutherford noted that they contained most of the energy produced by radioactive substances. Hence, he sought to understand this ray. Work by Lord Rayleigh and Sir William Crookes indicated that alpha rays might carry a positive charge and so could be affected by a magnetic field. When Rutherford secured a sufficiently active source of radiation in 1902, he confirmed this hypothesis. He also measured their speed at 2.5×10^9 centimeters per second (15,500 miles per second), or one-twelfth the speed of light; their charge-to-mass (e/m) ratio he found to be 5,000 electromagnetic units. Since the hydrogen atom has an e/m ratio of 9,650 electromagnetic units, if the alpha particle carried a single charge it must have a mass of two hydrogen atoms. Even before Rutherford could identify the exact nature of this particle, he recognized that it must come from within the atom of a radioactive substance and that, as a result of its expulsion, the element must be transformed.

In 1903, Pierre Curie reported that radium produces a large amount of heat, which Rutherford attributed to the alpha particles' movement within the element, the energy of motion being converted into that of heat. As Rutherford remarked, "These experiments brought clearly to light the enormous energy . . . which was emitted" during the disintegration process. Although Rutherford did not pursue the thought, his discovery of the source of heat in radium—energy of motion— confirmed the law of conservation of energy that radiation, with its seemingly unending production of energy, had threatened. At the same time, his observation suggested the possibility of harnessing the energy for peaceful or military purposes.

Responding to the discovery that radium emanation produces helium, Rutherford speculated that the inert gas came from the alpha particles. Indeed, he proposed that the alpha particles were helium atoms carrying a double charge. Measurements showed that the alpha particle had twice the charge of a hydrogen atom; because the e/m ratio was half that of hydrogen, the particle must have a mass of 4, like helium.

Experiments showed that alpha particles from radium, thorium, and actinium are identical, and, as Rutherford noted, "the atomic weights of many elements differ by four." He therefore concluded that the alpha particle must be one of the fundamental constituents of the elements. Still uncertain about the structure of the atom, he speculated that the alpha particle acquired its charge by losing two electrons. Rutherford's later recognition of the nucleus, Niels Bohr's refinement of this model, and James Chadwick's discovery of the neutron corrected this view of the disintegration process and the way atoms are constructed. Rutherford's observation that the loss of an alpha particle reduced an element's atomic weight by four nevertheless provided useful confirmation of the atomic weight of radium and lent strong support to Bertram B. Boltwood's hypothesis that lead is the end product of uranium disintegration, for if uranium were to lose eight alpha particles, it would yield an element with the atomic weight of 206.5, close to lead's 207.19. Rutherford, who always insisted on experimental evidence for any theory, characteristically added, "The coincidence of numbers is certainly striking, but a direct proof of the production of lead from radium will be required before this conclusion can be considered as definitely established."

Critical reception

By 1908, Rutherford had earned the admiration of the world's scientific community. In 1904, Ernest Merritt had predicted that he would soon receive the Nobel Prize. When this prophecy was fulfilled, Rutherford's former mentor at the Cavendish Laboratory, J. J. Thomson, himself a Nobel laureate and among those who had nominated Rutherford for the award, wrote to his former student, "It is indeed splendid news . . . , no one ever deserved it more and I am sure the award will meet with universal approbation." From Yale, Bertram B. Boltwood wrote in an equally enthusiastic manner:

> I am *perfectly delighted* over it, although I have believed for some time that they could not possibly pass you by very many times. . . . I think that it was very fine their giving you the "chemistry" prize, for you certainly have done a great thing for the chemists in more ways than one, but I think that they might have thrown in the physics prize too without overdoing it.

Thomson and Boltwood were both friends of Rutherford, but those who knew only his work and not the man himself were also pleased. Swedish mathematician M. G. Mittag-Leffler, who hosted Rutherford in Copenhagen on December 12, 1908, praised his research and correctly anticipated that he would continue to make other important discoveries, though his expectation that Rutherford would win a second Nobel was never realized. Svante August Arrhenius, perhaps the world's most eminent chemist of the period and a fellow Nobel laureate, and the Dutch physicists Heike Kammerlingh Onnes and Hendrik Antoon Lorentz added their voices to the chorus of praise.

Although Rutherford had occasionally published in popular journals and had presented numerous lectures, he remained less well known to the general public than other pioneers in the field of nuclear physics, such as the Curies. Determining the charge carried by an alpha particle lacked the appeal of finding a new element. Newspaper and magazine accounts of the award were consequently less exuberant than colleagues' letters, often reporting the fact without comment. *The New York Times* for December 11, 1908, seems to have expressed the sentiments of the non-scientific community when it said that the Swedish Academy's selections were satisfactory because "no claimants of larger general repute were available." Faintly praising the recipients of the Nobel Prizes for chemistry and physics, it remarked that Rutherford and Gabriel Lippmann "are scholars whose attainments in their special field may be equaled by some others, but are probably not surpassed."

While the scientific community applauded and the general public yawned, Rutherford was somewhat surprised—not so much at receiving the award as at its being for chemistry. For Rutherford, the word "chemist" was synonymous with "fool." Still, he accepted his metamorphosis in good humor, observing to his Swedish hosts that he had witnessed the transformation of elements, but no mutation had been as rapid as his own from physicist to chemist. More soberly, he consciously added the word "chemical" to the title of his Nobel address. The Swedish Academy, too, may have harbored doubts about the appropriate label to attach to Rutherford's work, since, as Hasselberg noted in his presentation, the sciences were no longer divided and distinct. There could be no doubt, though, that Rutherford's discoveries merited the recognition they received; the category of the award is curious but finally irrelevant.

Biography

Ernest Rutherford, whom biographer David Wilson called "the greatest experimental scientist of his age," was born in Spring Grove (later renamed Brightwater), thirteen miles south of Nelson, in the South Island of New Zealand, on August 30, 1871. His father, James Rutherford, was a farmer, wheelwright, and miller; his mother, Martha Thompson Rutherford, was a schoolteacher. After attending public school at Foxhill and Havelock, Rutherford won a Board of Education scholarship to Nelson College, a secondary school. Two years later another scholarship allowed him to attend Canterbury College, Christchurch; because he was one of twelve children, money was not otherwise available. At Canterbury, Alexander William Bickerton, professor of chemistry, encouraged his interest in research.

For most of his college career Rutherford lived in the house of Mrs. Arthur de Renzy Newton, whose eldest daughter, Mary, became his wife in 1900. After receiving his bachelor of arts (1893), master of arts (1894), and bachelor of science (1894) degrees from Canterbury College, he traveled halfway around the world, thanks to an 1851 Exhibition Scholarship, to the Cavendish Laboratory in Cambridge, England. His work so impressed J. J. Thomson that at the age of twenty-seven Rutherford was recommended for the physics professorship of McGill University in Montreal. There he made his discoveries about the alpha and beta particles and nuclear disintegration that won for him the Nobel Prize. In his decade at McGill, he published seventy papers and three books, about as many as he would produce during the rest of his career.

Rutherford spent the next twelve years (1907-1919) at Manchester University, before becoming director of the Cavendish Laboratory in 1919. In 1922, he received the Copley Medal, the Royal Society's highest honor, and from 1925 to 1930 he served as president of that body. Elevated to the peerage in 1931—he had been knighted in 1914—he took the title of Baron Rutherford of Nelson, after the New Zealand town near his birthplace. Until his death he remained active in research and continued to promote important work by colleagues and students at the Cavendish. As president of the Academic Assistance Council in the 1930's, he helped relocate hundreds of scholars fleeing Germany. Rutherford died, after a brief illness, on October 19, 1937, and was fittingly buried at Westminster Abbey, near Sir Isaac Newton and Lord Kelvin.

Scientific Career

Recommending Rutherford for the 1851 Exhibition Scholarship in 1894, Alexander William Bickerton commented, "From the first he exhibited an unusual aptitude for experimental science and in research showed originality and capacity of a high order." The work to which Bickerton referred concerned magnetism and radio waves; when Rutherford went to the Cavendish Laboratory in 1895, he intended to continue his investigation of this subject. Taking with him the radio-wave detector he had built—he was a master at designing equipment—he soon held the world record for broadcasting and receiving radio signals: half a mile. Even after J. J. Thomson redirected Rutherford's research, Rutherford did not completely abandon his first interest. In Canada he became the first person to send radio signals to and from a train in motion, and his 1923 presidential address to the British Association was the first to be simultaneously broadcast to the audience at the meeting and to six distant stations.

Although in 1895 he was well ahead of Guglielmo Marconi in his work on the radio, Rutherford willingly agreed to turn his attention to the newly discovered Röntgen rays and radioactivity. Over the next two years, he published five papers on this topic. The last of these, which appeared in 1899, clearly demonstrated that the radiation given off by uranium was of at least two types. By the time this work was published, Rutherford had assumed the professorship at McGill University, where his research revealed that the radioactive thorium oxide gave off a mysterious "emanation" that was itself radioactive and that made radioactive any material that it touched. The radioactivity of this emanation proved to be more penetrating than that of the thorium; also, unlike that of its parent, it did not remain constant but instead decayed exponentially with time.

To understand the nature of this emanation, Rutherford enlisted the help of the chemist Frederick Soddy. Although they had disagreed before about the nature of the atom and were to fall out again, their brief collaboration produced eight papers that changed the way the world looked at matter. For a century, John Dalton's atomic theory had claimed that each element was composed of indivisible atoms unique to itself, so that an atom of lead differed from that of gold. J. J. Thomson's discovery of the electron had proved the existence of a subatomic building block common to all elements; Rutherford would apparently subvert Dalton's view even more dramatically. Soddy determined that the emanation is an inert gas, now called thoron. Here, then, was an element, thorium, producing another. Rutherford was warned not to publish such a heretical idea, and he was cautious about reporting his findings. In "The Radioactivity of Thorium Compounds, II" (1902), he referred to "sub-atomic chemical change" rather than transmutation of elements, and he attributed to this process the energy given off by radioactive materials.

Having identified the chemical nature of the emanation, Rutherford began to consider the radiation it produced. Thoron yielded beta rays, while thorium gave off alpha rays. Here was conclusive evidence that alpha rays were not, as previously suspected, produced by beta rays but were created independently. Rutherford also determined that alpha rays were in fact particles at least as large as hydrogen atoms. Though several more years of research were necessary to identify the alpha particle as a helium nucleus, it was already apparent in 1902 that radioactivity was the process by which an element gives off energy and matter and thereby transforms itself into a different substance. In "The Cause and Nature of Radioactivity" (September and November, 1902), Rutherford and Soddy published their conclusions. "Radioactive Change" (May, 1903) was even more explicit: "In radioactive change the chemical atom must suffer disintegration." Speaking at the Sheldonian Theatre, Oxford, on June 12, 1903, Sir Oliver Lodge observed, "Assuming the truth of this strange string of laboratory facts, we appear to be face to face with a phenomenon quite new in the history of the world."

In that same year, Rutherford was elected to the Royal Society, and in 1904 he published *Radioactivity*, the standard text on the subject and one that H. A. Bumstead of Yale rightly predicted would become a classic. With his reputation growing in the scientific community, Rutherford was invited to give numerous talks, including the 1905 Silliman Lectures at Yale, published in 1906 as *Radioactive Transformations*. In this work he maintained that recent discoveries did not negate the theory that the atoms of each element are unique; scientists were merely learning how complex these atoms are.

While at McGill, Rutherford had been offered a number of professorships in America, but he wanted to return to England to be near the major centers of atomic research. In 1906 Sir Arthur Schuster, professor of physics at Manchester, asked Rutherford to take his post, and the next year Rutherford did so. During his tenure there, Rutherford would make his laboratory second only to Cavendish, as he produced what David Wilson describes as "a series of discoveries . . . unmatched by any other scientist at any other time."

Rutherford already knew that alpha radiation is particulate, relatively large, and positively charged. Sir William Ramsay and Soddy observed that when radon, the emanation of radium, decays, it produces helium, and helium is present in all radioactive materials. Rutherford deduced that the alpha particle must be a helium atom carrying a double charge, and a series of experiments confirmed this view. In the process of determining the ratio of charge to mass of the alpha particle, Rutherford arrived at a figure of 9.3×10^{-10} electrostatic units (esus). Since Thomson and Robert Andrews Millikan had measured the unit charge of an electron as about 3×10^{-10} esus, Rutherford's results implied a triply charged particle. Yet his intuition told him that the alpha particle carries only two charges, and his figure of 4.65×10^{-10} esus for a unit charge agreed with Max Planck's theoretically derived number. By 1910, Millikan had accepted Rutherford's figure, as the rest of the scientific community has since.

While many of Rutherford's experiments yielded spectacular results, others were undertaken simply to rule out unlikely alternatives or to provide experience for assistants. When Hans Geiger suggested that a new researcher, Ernest Marsden, be given his own project, Rutherford suggested that he look for wide-angle scattering of alpha particles fired at a target. Small-scale scattering had been observed, but no one regarded this finding as significant, and no one expected that Marsden's work would yield positive results. Marsden fired a beam of alpha particles at a thin sheet of gold foil, and some of them bounced back. Rutherford later commented, "This is almost as incredible as if you fired a 15-inch shell at a piece of tissue paper and it came back and hit you." By the end of 1910, Rutherford had arrived at a tentative model of the atom to explain this curious finding. The alpha particles must be deflected by another highly charged particle, one containing most of the mass of the atom, leaving the rest of the atom as essentially empty space. Although this model has undergone some modification since Rutherford first proposed it in "The Scattering of the Alpha- and Beta-Rays and the Structure of the Atom" (May, 1911), it remains essentially valid.

During World War I, much of Rutherford's attention was diverted to submarine detection, but he did not abandon nuclear research. In 1914, Marsden again found an anomaly. When he fired alpha particles at a target, he could create a certain number of H-particles, or hydrogen nuclei. If he conducted the experiment in the presence of air, which should absorb some of the radiation and so allow a smaller number of H-particles to be produced, he found instead that more were generated. In late 1917, Rutherford concluded that atoms of nitrogen, which account for 80 percent of the air, were being split by the alpha particles to produce oxygen and the extra hydrogen nuclei that Marsden observed. Rutherford had artificially split the atom. Chided for missing a meeting of the international submarine warfare committee because he was engaged in this research, Rutherford replied, "If, as I have reason to believe, I have disintegrated the nucleus of the atom, this is of greater significance than the war."

In 1919, he published his startling conclusion; in that year, too, he became director of the Cavendish Laboratory at the University of Cambridge, and at once sought to modernize the facility. His request for £200,000—a figure equivalent to ten years' support from the university—would not be met until 1936, but he continued to conduct and promote important research. His international outlook on science and his generous nature prompted him to resupply Belgian university libraries destroyed during the war and to arrange for the purchase of radium from the Vienna Institute, then desperately low on funds. Through his letters he encouraged scientists around the world. Among his correspondents were Ernest Lawrence, Harold Urey, and Boltwood in the United States; Enrico Fermi in Italy; R. W. Boyle in Canada; Max Born in Germany; and Niels Bohr in Denmark. This list reads like a veritable *Who's Who* of nuclear physicists.

Speaking before the Royal Society in 1920, Rutherford demonstrated his prescience by predicting the neutron, deuteron (a hydrogen atom with a mass of two rather than one), tritium (hydrogen with mass three), and helium (with a mass of three rather than four). In 1931, Urey found the deuteron, the next year James Chadwick, Rutherford's protégé, discovered the neutron at the Cavendish Laboratory, and Rutherford's last paper announced the creation of the other two atoms. In 1922 he hypothesized the existence of a positively charged electron, the positron, and again he was proved correct. He was prescient, too, in his recognition of the need for strong government support for scientific study and of the importance of such investigations to the military. At the urging of Rutherford and Thomson, the Admiralty Research Laboratory Station was established at Teddington, England, to encourage research that would have naval applications.

Rutherford was not always correct. His 1927 article "Structure of the Radioactive Atom and the Origin of the Alpha-Ray" envisioned a charged nucleus surrounded by neutral particles that broke into alpha and beta particles. Although he quickly recognized the tremendous energy produced by nuclear fission and fusion, he doubted that these forces could be harnessed on earth. Yet biographer David Wilson is right in applying to Rutherford what the seventeenth century diarist John Evelyn said of English chemist Robert Boyle:

> It must be confessed that he had a marvellous sagacity in finding out many useful and noble experiments. Never did stubborn matter come under his inquisition but he extorted a confession of all that lay in her most intimate recesses; and what he discovered he as faithfully registered, and frankly communicated.

Perhaps Rutherford himself, though, best described his contribution to modern science. When one of his former students, A. S. Eve, jokingly remarked that Rutherford had succeeded because he had ridden the crest of the wave of nuclear physics, Rutherford replied, "Well! I made the wave, didn't I?"

Bibliography

Primary
PHYSICS: *The Cause and Nature of Radioactivity*, 1902 (with Frederick Soddy); *Radioactivity*, 1904; *Radioactive Transformations*, 1906; *The Scattering of the Alpha- and Beta-Rays and the Structure of the Atom*, 1911; *Radioactive Substances and Their Radiations*, 1913; *Radiations from Radioactive Substances*, 1930 (with James Chadwick and C. D. Ellis); *The Newer Alchemy*, 1937.

Secondary
Andrade, Edward Neville da Costa. *Rutherford and the Nature of the Atom*. Garden City, N.Y.: Doubleday, 1964. Andrade worked with Rutherford in studying the wavelength of gamma rays. He gives a firsthand account of Rutherford, and he places his work in the context of scientific research during the early years of the twentieth century.
Badash, Lawrence, ed. *Rutherford and Boltwood: Letters on Radioactivity*. New Haven, Conn.: Yale University Press, 1969. Correspondence covers the period

from 1904 to 1924. Full of scientific gossip, offering an intimate picture of the world in which Rutherford operated and many glimpses at the personality behind the researcher. One sees Rutherford getting angry at a contaminated specimen, being cautious about announcing results. The letters are extensively annotated.

Bunge, Mario, and William R. Shea, eds. *Rutherford and Physics at the Turn of the Century*. New York: Dawson and Science History Publications, 1979. A collection of nine essays that explore the scientific views that prevailed when Rutherford began his work and the ways that Rutherford helped change those ideas. John L. Heilbron and Neil Cameron pay particular attention to conditions in the laboratories of McGill and Cambridge, where Rutherford did so much of his work.

Feather, Norman. *Lord Rutherford*. Glasgow: Blackie & Son, 1940. While concentrating on Rutherford's scientific contributions, Feather also provides insights into his personality. This laudatory biography includes some fascinating photographs of equipment that Rutherford used.

Trenn, Thaddeus J. *The Self-Splitting Atom: The History of the Rutherford-Soddy Collaboration*. London: Taylor and Francis, 1977. Drawing on laboratory notebooks, letters, and other unpublished material, Trenn recounts the development of Rutherford's disintegration theory and the role that Soddy played in its formation. Although the partnership was short-lived, it produced results that led to Rutherford's Nobel Prize and the modern concept of the atom.

Wilson, David. *Rutherford: Simple Genius*. Cambridge, Mass.: MIT Press, 1983. The definitive biography. This hefty, six-hundred-page volume, with its fine bibliography and helpful notes, covers not only the scientific work but also Rutherford's efforts to encourage government support for research, to promote international scientific cooperation, and to assist those researchers suffering under Fascist and Communist oppression.

Joseph Rosenblum

1909

Chemistry
Wilhelm Ostwald, Latvia and Germany

Physics
Guglielmo Marconi, Italy
Karl Ferdinand Braun, Germany

Physiology or Medicine
Emil Kocher, Switzerland

Literature
Selma Lagerlöf, Sweden

Peace
Baron d'Estournelles de Constant, France
Auguste Beernaert, Belgium

WILHELM OSTWALD
1909

Born: Riga, Latvia; September 2, 1853
Died: Grossbothen, near Leipzig, Germany; April 4, 1932
Nationality: Latvian; later German
Areas of concentration: Catalysis, electrochemistry, and reaction kinetics

Following ideas generated during his investigations of dissociation of acids and bases and their catalytic activity, Ostwald made a systematic study of the phenomena of catalysts. His description of catalysis made the wide occurrence of the effect clear and established the basis for study of catalysis in all areas of chemistry

The Award

Presentation

Wilhelm Ostwald's Nobel Prize in Chemistry was presented by Dr. Hans Hildebrand, former Rector General of the Museum of National Antiquities and President of the Royal Swedish Academy of Sciences. In his presentation, Hildebrand traced the roots of Ostwald's accomplishment to the work of Jöns Jakob Berzelius and Svante August Arrhenius. Berzelius, in 1835, had concluded that there were substances that started chemical reactions without appearing to participate in the reaction or to be changed themselves. These substances Berzelius called catalysts. In 1884, Arrhenius theorized that acids and bases separate, to varying degrees, into ions in solution and that several of the properties of these substances depended on the extent of dissociation. In experiments designed to test Arrhenius' theory, Ostwald was drawn to the type of behavior identified by Berzelius as catalysis. Ostwald broadened the study to other types of substances that showed catalytic behavior and laid the foundation for experimental studies of reaction rates. Ostwald concluded that "catalytic action consists in the modification, by the acting substance, the catalyst, of the rate at which a chemical reaction occurs, without that substance itself being part of the end-products formed."

Hildebrand emphasized the importance of Ostwald's general understanding of catalysis and predicted that this work would lead to an understanding of the role of enzymes in biological reactions—an understanding that would be of importance to mankind. Ostwald's roles as communicator, as leader in generalizing specific chemical findings, and as innovator in experimental design who developed methods that were relied upon for years were also highlighted by Hildebrand.

Nobel lecture

Ostwald delivered his Nobel lecture from brief notes on December 12, 1909. It was entitled simply "On Catalysis" and was not a science lecture as much as a philosophical lecture about science. The lecture can be seen as making three major points, points that correspond to the succession of interests in Ostwald's life. He delivered the lecture in the Grand Hall of the Royal Swedish Academy of Sciences, in which was located a bust of Berzelius, and Ostwald acknowledged his intellectual debt to that scientist. The second point consisted of a historical overview of the development of catalysis. Finally, he philosophized about the development of science and about the development of a universal system for discovery in all sciences.

Ostwald called attention to the facts that the world was only then coming to the time when scientists were recognized for their contributions during their lifetimes and that only very recently was there recognition of purely theoretical achievements. This brought him to speak of Berzelius' role in first creating the concept of catalysis. The concept of the rate of a chemical reaction had not yet been proposed, however, and Berzelius had spoken of catalysts as causing reactions. It was an amateur scientist, Ludwig Ferdinand Wilhelmy, who first led the way to the investigation of rates of reactions. It was this path that Ostwald followed, eventually establishing the role of a catalyst as a substance that speeds up the rate of a reaction that is already occurring, but occurring slowly. Ostwald mentioned several other investigators who provided clues that he could follow and examples with which he could work in detail in his development of the concept.

In the late 1890's, Ostwald lost his capacity for carrying out experimental work because of the repeated heavy stress and strain that he had put upon himself. This disability left him looking for new avenues to explore. He entered into a study of formulating a universal system of discovery for all the sciences. This philosophical work was described in the closing of his lecture in terms of reducing the process of discovery to the mathematical solution of a series of partial equations. The solving of these equations was, for Ostwald, the process of deduction, and it proceeded through a series of steps involving making observations and searching for relationships. Catalysis, in his judgment, was a field in the first stages of development: More and more observations on more and more reactions were needed. Only later would the time come when enough would be known to enable calculating the rate of a chemical reaction before performing the reaction.

Perhaps the overall tone of Ostwald's acceptance address can best be indicated in his mentioning that he was in perfect agreement with the judgment of the Nobel Foundation in choosing to reward the aspect of his work that he himself felt was his most worthy contribution. He described the feeling of being recognized by the foundation as comparable only to his reaction to the very first public scientific recognition that he ever received.

Critical reception

The Nobel Prize was still in its early stages in 1909 and had not yet developed to the point where its announcement generated high interest. Neither *The Times* of London nor *The New York Times* carried any specific information other than an announcement of the award recipients. *The New York Times* did editorialize on December 11, 1909, that the choices, in general, would "satisfy the whole world" and that "the eminence of these men, and the value of their service, are not disputed."

Attention should be called to the fact that the Nobel Foundation was, in a way, making up for previous lack of attention given to Ostwald. The 1909 award was in recognition of work that he had published prior to 1902; Ostwald had been retired from the university and from active work in catalysis since 1906. Since that time, he had been devoting his time to painting, the measurement of colors, the role of energy, philosophy, and the organization of science.

During Ostwald's Leipzig University years, he put together the first laboratory dedicated to physical chemistry. The workers in that laboratory were scientists from all around the world, making it something of a factory for producing the world's supply of professors of physical chemistry. He was generally acknowledged by this group and by those influenced by this group as the founder of the branch of chemistry known as physical chemistry. Physical chemistry is that branch which investigates chemical changes by observing changes in physical properties. He was highly respected as the editor of the *Zeitschrift für physikalische Chemie* (journal of physical chemistry), the journal that carried the highest prestige in physical chemistry at the time, and his textbooks were widely translated and utilized at many universities.

Ostwald's death in 1932 was the occasion for many memorial articles in the scientific literature, such as the *Journal of the Chemical Society* and the *Journal of Chemical Education*. Over and over, respected physical chemists paid homage to Ostwald as the man who had provided their discipline with a solid starting point. He was termed "absolutely the right man in the right place" in a reminiscence by George Jaffe published in the *Journal of Chemical Education*.

Biography

Friedrich Wilhelm Ostwald, son of Gottfried Wilhelm Ostwald and Elisabeth Leuckel Ostwald, was born in Riga, Latvia, on September 2, 1853. (He seldom used the name Friedrich and is generally known as Wilhelm Ostwald.) He received his early education at the *Realgymnasium* there. Ostwald required seven years to complete the course normally completed in four because of his widely ranging interests, which included fireworks manufacture, amateur photography, music, and painting as well as the pursuit of chemistry in his private laboratory.

In 1872 Ostwald left Riga to attend Dorpat University, and he completed this part of his chemical education in 1875. Thereafter he took positions as an unpaid assistant, first to Arthur von Oettinger and later to Carl Schmidt. These two men Ostwald credited as the main influences on his chemistry. Following came appointments at Dorpat (1877), at the Polytechnicum in Riga (1881), and at Leipzig University as professor of physical chemistry (1887). He remained at Leipzig until his retirement in 1906, with the exception of one year (1904) in which he was the first exchange professor at Harvard University.

In 1880 Ostwald married Helene von Reyher. Their marriage produced two daughters and three sons. His son, Karl Wilhelm Wolfgang Ostwald, followed in his father's footsteps and became a prominent chemist.

In retirement, Ostwald continued to be active both in scientific life and in public service. He was a pacifist, a monist, and an education reformer; he used his position and reputation to argue against the Church's claim to power in matters of natural science. Ostwald died on April 4, 1932, at his home, "Landhaus Energie," near Leipzig.

Scientific Career

From the earliest days that are known of Ostwald, the breadth of his interests was his major characteristic. He began nurturing an interest in chemical science as a youth, honed it through schooling and activity in the laboratories of the leaders of his time, and used it to experiment, discover, correlate, conceptualize, and teach. In retirement, he went on to generalize about science; he switched fields and became prominent in a second area of science and in philosophy.

Ostwald's formal education as a teenager was slowed by the fact that he spent time equipping and working in his private chemistry laboratory. Little is known about his work at that time, but it is known that he worked in photography and fireworks manufacture.

Entering the University of Dorpat in 1871, Ostwald soon came into contact with Julius Thomsen's work on the heat effects associated with chemical reactions, an early work in thermochemistry. This contact proved to be the beginning of the creation of physical chemistry as a branch of chemistry. Ostwald reasoned that physical properties other than heat could also be used as a means of studying chemical changes. The first property that came to his mind for such use was the density of a water solution in which a reaction was occurring. He named this means of following chemical reactions "volume chemistry." He moved from that property to the use of changes in optical refraction to follow chemical change. Studies of acid-base reactions, using these two physical properties as guides, formed the basis of Ostwald's doctoral thesis in 1875. Remaining at Dorpat as an assistant, Ostwald looked into the problem of chemical affinity (the attraction between substances) and gave special attention to electrochemical reactions and to chemical dynamics, the rate at which chemical reactions occur. The work in electrochemistry led to what became known as Ostwald's dilution law and brought Ostwald to the attention of the chemical community.

This recognition won for Ostwald the post of full-time professor of chemistry at Riga in 1881. The first of many textbooks that Ostwald authored, *Lehrbuch der allgemeinen Chemie* (textbook of general chemistry), was published in 1885. It presented a completely new organization and presentation of the subject and aroused much opposition. He continued his research on the problem of chemical affinity and developed a set of affinity constants of most of the known acids. At the same time, he widened the scope of the studies and became very involved in the study of the rates of chemical reactions involving acids. In particular, he studied the splitting of esters into alcohols and organic acids and the reaction through which the structure of sucrose is modified. The speed of both these reactions was increased by the presence of inorganic acids in a way that fit exactly with the affinity constants that Ostwald had previously developed. It was also during his tenure at Riga that Ostwald first became acquainted with Svante Arrhenius and his theory of ionic dissociation.

Ostwald went to Sweden in 1884 to meet Arrhenius, with the result that Arrhenius was invited to come to Riga to work with Ostwald along these new lines of chemistry. The invitation was accepted in 1886; the two men worked closely, but on different problems, for years thereafter. The influence of Jacobus Henricus van't Hoff's publications on chemical dynamics was also being felt by Ostwald during this time, although the two did not meet until later. In his writing, Ostwald recognized and propagated the importance of the new concepts of Arrhenius and van't Hoff. The controversy generated by Ostwald's "new chemistry" brought him recognition both by those who agreed and by those who did not. With this recognition came his appointment as professor of physical chemistry at Leipzig University, one of the greatest universities in Europe, in 1887.

Leipzig University was the last stop on Ostwald's academic travels. He organized the department of physical chemistry there and spent until 1906 building and strengthening it. The department was at its prime in 1899, and it was usual to find about forty students from around the world working in Ostwald's laboratory. Doing research on such a large scale required special methods, and those developed by Ostwald are still seen in university research groups. Mature scientists acted as assistants to Ostwald and as liaison officers between Ostwald and the students. Each problem to be studied was chosen in consultation between Ostwald and the students. There were weekly seminars, during which the research progress was presented to, and discussed by, all members of the laboratory. In this way Ostwald exerted his influence on each investigation even though he did not directly participate in each one. It has been pointed out that this method worked only because of Ostwald's extraordinary memory and quickness of perception.

Many chemists who would later be famous worked in this laboratory and were greatly influenced by Ostwald and his methods. Among them were Arrhenius (Nobel Prize in 1903), van't Hoff (Nobel Prize in 1901), and Walther Hermann Nernst (Nobel Prize in 1920), and Americans Theodore William Richards, Arthur Amos Noyes, and Gilbert Newton Lewis. This succession of scientists, trained as physical chemists, constituted the birth of a new branch of chemistry which by 1899 was considered to be firmly established. Ostwald was greatly involved with communicating chemical knowledge. He published numerous texts on general chemistry, electrochemistry, and physical chemistry, and in 1887 he founded, jointly with van't Hoff, the *Zeitschrift für physikalische Chemie* (journal of physical chemistry). The first volume of this journal contains both van't Hoff's seminal paper on osmotic pressure and the analogy between solutions and gases, and Arrhenius' celebrated paper on electrolytic dissociation. Ostwald continued as editor of this publication through the first one hundred volumes, stepping down in 1922.

In 1893, under Ostwald's authorship, *Die wissenschaftlichen Grundlagen der analytischen Chemie* (the scientific foundations of analytical chemistry) appeared and revolutionized the field of analytical chemistry. From that time all analytical chemistry was taught in terms of physical chemistry, and the measurement of physical properties became the common thread in all chemistry.

Ostwald's 1901 discovery of a method of nitric acid manufacture is his most famous contribution from the commercial point of view. The process involves the combustion of ammonia in the presence of a platinum catalyst. This discovery freed Germany from dependence on foreign sources of nitrates for munitions manufacture—a very important freedom in those years as the world was building toward war. Later, as World War I proceeded, the German government nationalized the plant that Ostwald had constructed and was operating for the production of nitrates.

At the turn of the century, a confrontation was occurring between two trends in the scientific world. Ostwald was the head of the group of "energetics," and Ludwig Boltzmann was the head of the "atomistics." With both men at Leipzig University, many lively discussions ensued. Ostwald and his followers claimed to represent "science without suppositions" and demanded that science be purely descriptive and deal only with correlating observable data. As late as 1904, Ostwald did not believe in the existence of atoms and would not use them, even as models, in explaining chemical observations. Eventually he did relent and accept atoms, but he never did rely on their existence in any of his own work.

Ostwald was also deeply involved in activities outside chemical research, teaching, and publication. He published books and lectured internationally about methods of teaching, philosophy, painting, and educational reform. He also published a number of biographies. These activities caused Ostwald to be away from Leipzig much of the time and strained the relationship between Ostwald and his colleagues and administrators at Leipzig. The strain was relieved when Ostwald resigned in 1906. He admitted that he had become exhausted and, in fact, had lost all interest in doing chemistry. By this time he had written at least twenty-five books and thousands of journal articles on chemical topics. Even after his resignation he continued to edit the *Zeitschrift für physikalische Chemie* and wrote about ten more books on chemistry.

Ending his career at the university did not mean that Ostwald was going into a quiet retirement. It allowed him to travel and to continue with his broad interests without the previous pressures that had brought him close to the point of a physical breakdown. He had already shown an interest in philosophy by publishing his *Lectures on Natural Philosophy* (1902), based on a set of lectures originally given in 1900, and by founding the *Annalen der Naturphilosophie* (yearbook of natural philosophy) in 1902. Through these works, and others, Ostwald founded a branch of philosophy—natural philosophy. To stand as complete, a philosophy must include metaphysics, epistemology, and axiology (ethics and aesthetics). Ostwald thought deeply about each of these topics, as is shown by his publications such as

Moderne Naturphilosophie (1914; modern natural philosophy) and *Grundriss der Naturphilosophie* (1908; outline of natural philosophy). In this last book, Ostwald put his science and his philosophy in perspective when he said: "Natural science and natural philosophy are not two fields which oppose each other, but they belong together just as two paths which lead to the same goal. This goal is: The mastery of nature by the human being."

Ostwald was a leader in the movement for monism, a doctrine stating that there is only one kind of substance or ultimate reality and that reality is one unitary organic whole with no independent parts. To Ostwald, the ultimate was energy, as it had been in all of his chemical researches. He wrote and spoke widely on this topic from 1910 to 1914, when World War I brought the effort to an end.

He put his organizational abilities to work on the national and international scale. In Germany he founded what became the Kaiser Wilhelm Institute, a national bureau of chemistry. He served on the International Commission for Atomic Weights from 1916 to 1932. He cooperated in the founding of the International Association of Chemical Societies in 1911 and, under the auspices of this group, planned an international institute of chemistry. His work on this effort was also halted by World War I.

He donated half of his Nobel Prize to furthering work on an artificial international language that he himself devised and called Ido. He had begun this project while at Harvard by studying Esperanto. Again the advent of the war swept the effort away.

The importance of Ostwald's catalysis discoveries to the war effort is ironic, because he was an ardent pacifist. Considering war a horrible waste of energy, he regularly attended all the great peace congresses and addressed several sessions. His plea for voluntary disarmament fell on deaf ears, however, and war came. Ostwald took no part in the war and was even mentioned by some as a candidate for a second Nobel Prize, this time in peace.

The last phase of his scientific creativity was begun formally in 1914. Always interested in painting, Ostwald turned his skills to the study of color. He devised ways of measuring color, invented the instruments needed, set the standards, and wrote sixteen books that soon were accepted as the classics in the study of color. It is reported that Ostwald felt that his work on color was his greatest contribution to human culture; there were those in agreement who suggested him as a candidate for a Nobel Prize in Physics.

Ostwald's autobiography, a three-volume set, *Lebenslinien* (life's line), was published in 1926-1927.

Bibliography

Primary

CHEMISTRY: *Volumchemische Studien über Affinität*, 1877; *Lehrbuch der allgemeinen Chemie*, 1885; *Die Grundlagen der Atomtheorie*, 1889; *Über die Affinitätsgrossen organischer Sauren und ihre Beziehungen zur Zusammensetzung und Constitution derselben*, 1889; *Die wissenschaftlichen Grundlagen der analytischen Chemie*, 1894; *Elektrochemie*, 1896; *Grundriss der algemeinen Chemie*, 1899; *Dampfdrucke ternärer Gemische*, 1900; *Die Schule der Chemie: Erste Einfuhrung in die Chemie für Jederman*, 1903; *Der Werdegang einer Wissenschaft*, 1908; *Fundamental Principles of Chemistry: An Introduction to All Text-Books of Chemistry*, 1909 (translated by Harry W. Morse); *Einfuhrung in die Chemie*, 1910; *Grundlinien der anorganischen Chemie*, 1912; *Die Entwicklung der Elektrochemie*, 1916; *Die chemische Literatur und die Organisation der Wissenschaft*, 1919; *Über Katalyse*, 1923.

PHYSICS: *Die Energie*, 1908; *Beitrage zur Farbenlehre*, 1917; *Einfuhrung in die Farbenlehre*, 1919; *Farbkunde*, 1923; *Die Harmonie der Farben*, 1923; *Colour Science*, 1933 (translated by J. Scott Taylor); *Er und ich*, 1936.

PHILOSOPHY: *Individuality and Immortality*, 1906; *Energetische Grundlagen der Kulturwissenschaft*, 1909; *Monistische Sonntagspredigten*, 1911; *Der energetische Imperativ*, 1912; *Die Philosophie der Werte*, 1913; *Moderne Naturphilosophie*, 1914; *Die Pyramide der Wissenschaften*, 1929.

BIOGRAPHY: *Das Ausdehnungsgesetz der Gase: Abhandlungen von Gay-Lussac, Dalton, Dulong und Petit, Rudberg, Reynault*, 1894; *Grosse Männer*, 1909; *Auguste Comte, der Mann und Sein Werk*, 1914.

AUTOBIOGRAPHY: *Lebenslinien*, 1926-1927 (3 vols.).

Secondary

Harrow, Benjamin. *Eminent Chemists of Our Time*. New York: Van Nostrand, 1927. Although Ostwald is not treated in a separate chapter in this text, much of his impact on chemistry of his day is shown in the discussions of his contemporaries.

——————————. "The Meeting of Ostwald, Arrhenius, and van't Hoff." *Journal of Chemical Education* 7 (November, 1930): 2697-2700. Utilizing the recently published autobiography of Ostwald, Harrow concentrates on the details dealing with the way in which a remarkable friendship grew among the three founders of physical chemistry. This short article gives a close look into the meetings that led to Nobel Prizes for each of these men.

Hauser, Ernst A. "The Lack of Natural Philosophy in Our Education: In Memoriam of Wilhelm Ostwald." *Journal of Chemical Education* 28 (September, 1951): 492-494. This article concerns itself with the philosophical aspect of Ostwald's life. It contains an extensive quote translated from Ostwald's *Grundriss der Naturphilosophie*.

Jaffe, George. "Recollections of Three Great Laboratories." *Journal of Chemical Education* 29 (May, 1952): 230-238. Jaffe was the last personal student of Ostwald, and he writes of his recollections of the man and the laboratory. Jaffe also met van't Hoff and Arrhenius during this period and writes about the interrelationship of these three Nobel Prize-winning chemists.

Moore, Forris J. *A History of Chemistry*. 3d ed. New York: McGraw-Hill, 1939. Pages 377-378 present a concise biography of Ostwald, and the rest of the text in this chapter places his work in the context of the developing chemistry of that era. Wall, Florence E. "Wilhelm Ostwald: A Study in Mental Metamorphosis." *Journal of Chemical Education* 42 (January, 1948): 2-10. As the title suggests, this article follows the life of Ostwald from his earliest years through his chemical interests and on to the later eclectic years. Includes a very good listing of relevant literature.

Kenneth H. Brown

1910

Chemistry
Otto Wallach, Germany

Physics
Johannes Diderik van der Waals, The Netherlands

Physiology or Medicine
Albrecht Kossel, Germany

Literature
Paul Heyse, Germany

Peace
International Peace Bureau

OTTO WALLACH
1910

Born: Königsberg, Prussia; March 27, 1847
Died: Göttingen, Germany; February 26, 1931
Nationality: German
Areas of concentration: Alicyclic and terpene chemistry

Wallach brought order to the study of terpenes and laid the foundation for the field of alicyclic chemistry by separating, purifying, and characterizing the principal constituents of the essential oils and by establishing their mutual relationships

The Award

Presentation

The Royal Swedish Academy of Sciences awarded the 1910 Nobel Prize in Chemistry to Otto Wallach; the President of the Academy, Oskar Montelius, made the presentation. Montelius, an archaeologist and Rector General of the Museum of National Antiquities, began with a discussion of the "essential oils," the volatile and odoriferous components of plants. The hydrocarbon components of these oils were called terpenes because they were also found in ordinary turpentine oil. These substances were very difficult to study because of their instability and their similar properties—they showed little or no difference in molecular weight, composition, and boiling point. Based on differences in odor, optical properties, and chemical reactivity, however, nearly one hundred terpenes had been described. Unfortunately, chemical theory could not accommodate such a large number of isomers (substances with the same number and kinds of atoms, but in different arrangements). By developing methods for separating and characterizing various terpenes, Wallach was able to reduce the actual number of known terpenes to about eight. He proved that even the most common reagents caused the terpenes to undergo change, often resulting in a change in structure without a change in composition (isomerization). Wallach's pioneering work on terpenes and other naturally occurring alcohols, ketones, sesquiterpenes, and polyterpenes opened a new field of research in organic chemistry—the study of alicyclic compounds (cyclic or ring compounds with aliphatic or "fatty" properties). Wallach's work also contributed much to the chemical industry, both through direct application of his methods and through the indirect influence felt when his students entered industry.

Nobel lecture

Wallach delivered his Nobel lecture, "Alicyclic Compounds," on December 12, 1910. He began by paying tribute to Jöns Jakob Berzelius, the great Swedish chemist, who, according to Wallach, "sowed the seed, the fruit of which we are reaping now," and to Friedrich Wöhler, who investigated the essential oil of bitter almonds. Wöhler studied under Berzelius in 1823, and Wallach studied under Wöhler in 1867.

Wallach was later professor at Göttingen, a position previously held by Wöhler.

Essential oils had been known since ancient times in the form of herbs, spices, fragrances, and medicinals, but the scientific study of these materials was only begun much later. Beginning in 1832, Wöhler and Justus von Liebig demonstrated that the oil of bitter almonds is benzaldehyde, the common aromatic aldehyde. Later, Friedrich August Kekulé proposed his ring structure for benzene, and other investigators showed that benzene-related compounds were often responsible for the strong odor (hence, "aromatic" compounds) of various plant materials. Many essential oil components, however, are not benzene-type compounds; substances in this category are the terpenes (liquid components) and the camphors (solid components).

Initial efforts to analyze these substances encountered several problems. For one thing, most essential oils were difficult mixtures to separate. For another, because of the presence of impurities, many more terpene hydrocarbons had been described and named than actually existed. Further, the terpenes were labile and readily changed structure, often without any change in molecular formula.

Wallach was successful in finding reliable, definitive characteristics for identifying the different terpenes, and he showed that the number of different compounds was actually quite small. By converting the hydrocarbons into oxygen-containing compounds and vice versa, he was able to establish many terpene relationships and to show that many terpenes are structurally related to p-cymene (1-isopropyl-4-methylbenzene). Some terpenes have a different structural feature, however: Pinene (one of the earliest known and most widely used terpenes), camphor, and related compounds contain two mutually interlaced rings and are known as bicyclic compounds. Still other compounds found in essential oils, such as citral and geraniol, contain no rings in their structure.

A whole new branch of organic chemistry was opened by Wallach's fundamental discoveries, and other chemists moved forward with the synthesis of the true terpenes and other terpene-like alicyclic compounds. Wallach's work also had a great impact on the development of the essential-oil industry in Germany, enabling it to quadruple its output between 1880 and 1895, while the total chemical industry only doubled its production. In addition, the industry was no longer entirely dependent upon foreign supply sources, since terpene synthesis was now possible if circumstances required.

Wallach ended his discussion by pointing to an unexplored area of investigation: the chemical processes in the plant organism that cause the formation of such an infinite variety of essential oils. The search for the answer to this question has occupied chemists and biochemists for much of the twentieth century.

Critical reception

At the time Otto Wallach received the Nobel Prize in Chemistry, many academic and scientific institutions were recognizing his accomplishments with special honors. These awards, in several countries, continued for several years. He was elected an Honorary Fellow of the British Chemical Society in 1908, and a year later he received an honorary doctor of science degree from the University of Manchester. In 1909, he also received an honorary doctor of medicine degree from the University of Leipzig and an honorary doctor of engineering degree from the Technological Institute of Braunschweig. In 1912, he was nominated to honorary membership in the Verein Deutscher Chemiker and the Société Chimique de Belgique and was elected president of the Deutsche Chemische Gesellschaft. He also received the Kaiserlicher Allerorden III. Klasse (Imperial Order of the Eagle) in 1911, the Davy Medal in Gold and Silver in 1912, and the Königlicher Kronorden II. Klasse (Royal Order of the Crown) in 1915. These honors, especially those awarded after 1910, indicate that the academic and scientific institutions honoring Wallach during those years probably supported the decision to award him the Nobel Prize.

Although Wallach had many American students, there appeared to be very little public comment in the United States when he was awarded the Nobel Prize. For example, *The New York Times* of November 14, 1910, stated only that "the Nobel Prize for chemistry has been awarded to Professor Otto Wallach of the University of Göttingen." *Outlook* for December 3, 1910, commented on the Nobel Prize in Literature but did not mention the other prizes for that year. *The American Review of Reviews* for late 1910 and early 1911 reported in separate items the recipients of the 1910 Nobel Prizes in Physiology or Medicine, Physics, and Literature, but for some reason failed to report that Wallach had been awarded the Chemistry prize. An editorial in *The Independent* for December 15, 1910, noted that the Nobel Prizes had been "worthily awarded," but without regard to Nobel's will that the prizes be given for the most important work done during the previous year. Pointing out that Wallach was a brilliant youth who gained his doctorate at the age of twenty-two, the editorial commented that, at that time, a prize of $40,000 would have been most welcome if the Nobel Foundation had been in existence. The editor observed that since Wallach did not receive such a boost, he had to work his way up the academic ladder round by round. Although the editorial was correct in observing that Wallach was honored for work done several years earlier, it incorrectly gave the impression that Wallach was being honored for his Ph.D. research.

Otto Wallach was not a controversial individual in his professional or private life, and public reaction generated by his Nobel award, although surprisingly limited, was either neutral or favorable.

Biography

Otto Wallach, the son of Gerhard and Otillie Thoma Wallach, was born in Königsberg, Prussia (now Kaliningrad, in the Soviet Union) on March 27, 1847. His father was a government official. Otto's early school years were in Potsdam, where he developed a strong interest in chemistry and a fondness for art and its history.

When he was twenty, Wallach decided to study chemistry at Göttingen, but after one semester there, he left for personal reasons to study in Berlin. There he attended lectures by August Wilhelm von Hofmann. He soon returned to Göttingen, however, where he obtained his doctorate under Hans Hübner in 1869. After a brief period in Berlin as assistant to Hans Wichelhaus, he became assistant to August Kekulé at Bonn in the spring of 1870. Before the year ended, he had again left Bonn for a brief period of military service (in the Franco-Prussian War), followed by employment in Berlin as the chemist for Aktien-Gesellschaft für Anilin-Fabrikation (Agfa), but the noxious factory vapors there adversely affected his health. He resigned in 1872 and returned to Bonn as an assistant in the organic laboratory, later becoming *Privatdozent*. In 1876, he was appointed *Extraordinarius*, and in 1879, he took over the instruction in pharmacy, an area relatively unfamiliar to him.

Wallach returned to Göttingen in 1889, this time as Victor Meyer's successor in Wöhler's chair. He also served as director of the Chemical Institute there until he retired in 1915.

A bachelor throughout his life, Wallach died in Göttingen on February 26, 1931.

Scientific Career

Otto Wallach experienced success in his investigation of the terpenes and other alicyclic compounds because he was a careful, methodical, and patient experimentalist. His highest ideal was the carefully and reliably performed experiment, rather than the brilliant theoretical speculation.

Wallach conducted his earliest experiments when he was a youth in Potsdam. His apparatus was crude and homemade, and his experimental procedures sometimes produced offensive odors. Since he came from a family of lawyers with little interest in the natural sciences, he did not find much sympathy for his chemical interests among relatives and friends.

As a student at Göttingen and Berlin and in his early days at Bonn, Wallach worked on problems in general organic chemistry. His work with Wichelhaus in 1868 was concerned with the nitration (reaction with nitric acid) of beta-naphthol, and his Ph.D. thesis dealt with position isomers in the toluene series. Position isomers are compounds that are identical in their molecular formulas and functional groups (groups of atoms that undergo change in a reaction) but differ in the location of the functional group in the molecule. During this early period, Wallach discovered the class of compounds known as imino chlorides, and he also observed that concentrated sulfuric acid causes the nitrogen-containing compound azoxybenzene to change into p-hydroxyazobenzene, a compound with the same molecular formula but a different structure. The azoxybenzene reaction later became known as the Wallach rearrangement.

When Wallach assumed the responsibility for the instruction in pharmacy at Bonn in 1879, he entered an area that was relatively foreign to him. This change of direction had a profound effect on his scientific career, leading him—as he prepared his lectures in pharmacy—to an interest in the chemistry of the volatile oils.

In 1884, August Kekulé granted Wallach's request for permission to investigate the ethereal oils contained in several flasks that had been stored in a cupboard in Kekulé's private laboratory. Kekulé had obtained these samples for research purposes, but the flasks had remained unopened for many years.

Wallach began his investigations at a time when the study of essential oils and terpenes was in a state of complete confusion. The so-called ethereal oils from many different plants had been isolated, and the constituents of these oils had been named according to their origin. Many of these constituents had the same molecular composition, but because of the presence of impurities, they often differed in their physical properties, especially with respect to their optical properties. Since they had different physical properties and had been obtained from different sources, they were thought to be different substances, but they had not been examined experimentally to determine whether they really did have different structures. So many substances with the same composition had been described that it seemed unlikely they could all be different. For example, one terpene, subsequently identified as pinene, had been referred to in the chemical literature by at least twenty names.

As he began the seemingly impossible task of bringing order to this confused area, Wallach recognized the need to determine definite, reliable distinguishing characteristics for the different terpenes. Once these characteristics had been determined, they would have to provide consistent explanations of the behavior and interrelationships of the various terpenes. Only after these conditions had been met would it be possible to determine the constitution (molecular structure) of the individual compounds.

Wallach began by carefully distilling the essential oils in order to separate and purify the constituents. He then examined the behavior of the separate fractions with a series of relatively simple chemical reagents, trying to find reactions that formed crystalline products. He was able to show by his approach that many terpenes, believed at the time to be different, formed the same products when treated under the same conditions. He also improved the reaction conditions in many cases by modifying the solvents and reagents that had been previously used. In addition, his experiments provided greater understanding of terpene behavior, particularly in cases where a reagent and a terpene combine to form a so-called addition product.

After three years of busy experimentation, Wallach had identified eight terpenes that were obviously different from one another. Each of these was unambiguously characterized in such a way that anyone who followed Wallach's procedures could easily duplicate his results. This list of eight was subsequently modified during later investigations by Wallach and others.

The second phase of Wallach's program not only revealed his instinct for choosing the most significant line of research but also provided the body of fundamental knowledge which opened the field of alicyclic chemistry to many other investigators. His efforts during this phase were directed at establishing the behavior and mutual relationships of the individual terpenes, an objective which he felt had a higher priority than that of determining their molecular structure.

Others who had investigated the terpenes before Wallach observed that many reactions involved a change in the structure of the starting terpene without any change in molecular formula—a process known as isomerization. They concluded that these and related reactions involved a rearrangement of the carbon-atom framework (the carbon skeleton) of the molecule. These conclusions, however, were based on conjecture rather than on experimentation. Wallach investigated as many cases as possible to determine the conditions and the causes, as well as the direction of the isomerizations. He found that the influence of strong acids or high temperatures caused these isomerizations, whereas alkalies generally had no effect, at least among the hydrocarbon compounds. In 1891, Wallach published a chart showing the relationships that existed among pinene and eleven other terpenes. Eighteen years later, his book *Die Terpene und Campher* (1909; terpenes and camphor) included fourteen pages of tables showing such relationships.

An outstanding example of the value of Wallach's experimental methods in establishing these relationships was observed when, in 1895, the structural formula for alpha-terpineol was published simultaneously in different articles by Wallach and Ferdinand Tiemann and F. Wilhelm Semmler. Using this structure and the alpha-terpineol relationships previously established by Wallach, the structure of an entire series of terpenes was established in a single stroke.

Previous work had demonstrated that the naturally occurring $C_{10}H_{16}$ terpene hydrocarbons were related to the $C_{10}H_{14}$ benzene-type hydrocarbon called p-cymene (1-isopropyl-4-methylbenzene). In particular, certain chemical reactions changed limonene, phellandrene, and other compounds into p-cymene or one of its derivatives. The difference of two hydrogen atoms in the molecular formulas indicated that the $C_{10}H_{16}$ compound had one carbon-carbon double bond fewer than the $C_{10}H_{14}$ compound. Carbon-carbon double bonds exist when two adjacent carbon atoms have three substituents each rather than the maximum number of four. This relationship explained why terpenes isomerize so readily: One of the carbon-carbon double bonds could become "saturated" (four substituents on each carbon) by adding a simple compound, such as water or an acid, and these added components could, under certain conditions, be split off to form a double bond again, but this time in a new direction. The terpene carbon skeleton required by the relationship to p-cymene was also consistent with the possibility considered by Wallach in 1887 that the terpenes might be formed from isoprene molecules. Isoprene has its five carbon atoms arranged in such a way that if two molecules of isoprene were to combine, the carbon skeleton for the terpenes could easily be formed.

The suggestion that the difference between a terpene hydrocarbon and p-cymene is one double bond, however, failed to account for the structure of a number of terpenes, including camphor and pinene, a widely used terpene that had been known for a longer time than many of the others. In 1893, Julius Bredt established the correct structure for camphor after more than thirty incorrect structures had been proposed by earlier workers. A year later, Gustav Wagner proposed a structure formula for pinene analogous to the Bredt camphor structure; however, it was Wallach's previous observations on terpene relationships that led Wagner to his proposal. Terpenes that differ from p-cymene by one double bond contain one ring of six carbon atoms, as does p-cymene, but compounds such as camphor and pinene are bicyclic (that is, they contain two rings, and the rings share one or more common sides). Camphor contains two five-atom rings with two shared sides, and pinene contains a four-atom ring and a six-atom ring with two shared sides.

During his career, Wallach published 126 papers on the terpenes. His pioneering role in terpene chemistry began to wane about 1895, but he continued to work in this area. In these later years, he turned his attention to simple analogs of the terpenes as model compounds for the more complicated terpene structures. In particular, he used simple alicyclic five- and six-membered rings to study isomerizations in which a carbon-carbon double bond shifted or a ring rearranged.

He also began research on the oxygen-containing terpene compounds thujone and fenchone. Wallach had isolated fenchone in 1891. Both compounds are bicyclic molecules; fenchone is similar to camphor, containing two five-atom rings, while thujone combines a three-atom ring with a five-atom ring. Wallach also continued to work on his old researches until his final years, partly because of his belief that more information was needed to justify fully the old structural formulas.

Wallach's contributions to terpene chemistry and organic chemistry in general can be assessed by picturing the large gap that would exist if his work were missing. His contributions include not only the results of his investigations of terpenes but also his method of attack. Through his meticulous experimentation and perseverance, he brought organic analysis to a high degree of perfection. His investigations laid the foundation for research on the synthesis of aromatic chemicals, which later found application in the manufacture of drugs, perfumes, and spices. His work on the terpenes also led to later studies revealing their relationship to various vitamins and to the sex hormones, and it made possible the use of ethereal oils in industry, resulting in significant economic advances, especially in Germany. Wallach's work found wide recognition in scientific circles, and he received numerous special honors in Germany and other countries.

Bibliography

Primary
CHEMISTRY: "On the Action of Concentrated Sulfuric Acid on Azoxybenzene," *Berichte der deutschen chemischen Gesellschaft*, vol. 13, 1880 (with L. Belli); 126 research papers on terpenes published in *Justus Liebigs Annalen der Chemie*, from vol. 215, 1884, to vol. 418, 1919; "Zur Kentniss der Terpene und ätherischen Oele. IV.," *Justus Liebigs Annalen der Chemie*, vol. 238, 1887; summary of terpene research, *Berichte der deutschen chemischen Gesellschaft*, vol. 24, 1891; "Zur Constitutionsbestimmung des Terpineols," *Berichte der deutschen chemischen Gesellschaft*, vol. 28, 1895; *Die Terpene und Campher*, 1909.

Secondary
Asimov, Isaac. *Asimov's Biographical Encyclopedia of Science and Technology.* Garden City, N.Y.: Doubleday, 1964. This biographical sketch is very brief, but it gives the main details concerning Wallach's professional career. The very brief

discussion of his research contributions is nontechnical and easily understandable. The account also refers to other biographical sketches in the same book dealing with a few of Wallach's associates.

Leicester, Henry M. "Otto Wallach." In *Dictionary of Scientific Biography*, vol. 14, edited by Charles Coulston Gillispie. New York: Charles Scribner's Sons, 1976. Wallach is one of the scientists listed in this valuable reference work. The article includes details about his life and a discussion of his work and its significance. Includes a brief primary and secondary bibliography.

Partington, James Riddick. *A History of Chemistry*. 4 vols. New York: St. Martin's Press, 1961. This four-volume work is a scholarly treatment of the history of chemistry and includes biographical material. There is one page devoted to Wallach's career and his work. Although brief, the section on Wallach includes selected references to his original publications.

Partridge, William S., and Ernest R. Schierz. "Otto Wallach: The First Organizer of the Terpenes." *Journal of Chemical Education* 24 (1947): 106-108. This biographical sketch was written to commemorate the one-hundredth anniversary of Wallach's birth. It includes information about Wallach's life and career, and it gives a brief, nontechnical account of his important research contributions. In discussing Wallach's Nobel Prize, this article repeats an earlier error in the same journal (volume 7, 1930) that attributes the award to his work on azoxybenzene.

Ružička, Leopold. "Otto Wallach." In *Great Chemists*, edited by Eduard Farber. New York: Interscience, 1961. This biographical article is a reprint of a memorial lecture that Ružička wrote about a year after Wallach's death. It includes a portrait, information about his life and career, insights into his personality, and a discussion of his scientific contributions.

Richard B. Bennett

1911

Chemistry
Marie Curie, Poland and France

Physics
Wilhelm Wien, Germany

Physiology or Medicine
Alvar Gullstrand, Sweden

Literature
Maurice Maeterlinck, Belgium

Peace
Tobias Asser, The Netherlands
Alfred Fried, Austria

MARIE CURIE
1911

Born: Warsaw, Poland; November 7, 1867
Died: Sallanches, France; July 4, 1934
Nationality: Polish; after 1895, French
Area of concentration: Radioactivity

Curie discovered two new radioactive elements, radium and polonium. She purified radium and contributed much to an understanding of the properties of these substances

The Award

Presentation

On December 10, 1911, in the Hall of the Academy of Music, Stockholm, the King of Sweden gave Marie Skłodowska Curie the Nobel Prize in Chemistry. Prior to the presentation, Dr. E. W. Dahlgren, Head Librarian of the National Library and President of the Royal Swedish Academy of Sciences, explained why the Academy had taken the unprecedented step of honoring a Nobel laureate with a second award. Dahlgren noted that after the discovery of radioactivity in uranium and thorium it became clear that a compound's radioactivity varied directly with the amount of these elements present. Yet pitchblende became more radioactive after the uranium was removed.

Marie and Pierre Curie concluded that other matter, more highly radioactive than uranium, must be present. After purifying tons of pitchblende, the Curies found small quantities of radium and polonium compounds. Then, in 1910, Marie Curie isolated pure radium, thereby removing all doubt as to its status as a true element.

For chemists, the discovery of radium was significant because its behavior proved that one element can transform itself into another, thereby dispelling the notion that atoms are unchanging. The Curies' discovery also stimulated a productive search for other radioactive substances that increased scientists' understanding of the very nature of matter and gave rise to an entirely new area of study, radiology. Radium affected other branches of science, especially medicine, where it showed promise in treating cancer and lupus.

Dahlgren ended his speech by turning to Curie and addressing her directly, noting that in 1903 she and her husband had shared the Nobel Prize for the discovery of radioactivity. Now Marie Curie was receiving the award herself for discovering the elements radium and polonium, for purifying radium, and for investigating its compounds. Dahlgren concluded that such work merited the additional recognition bestowed upon it by the Swedish Academy.

Nobel lecture

On December 11, 1911, Marie Curie delivered her Nobel lecture, "Radium and the

New Concepts in Chemistry." It was at once a tribute to her dead husband (to whom she gave credit for many of the recent developments in the study of radioactivity), a recognition of the contribution to the science made by her close friend Ernest Rutherford, and an assertion of how much she alone had done to isolate radium and examine its properties. She began by noting that barely fifteen years earlier Henri Becquerel had discovered that uranium is radioactive—the term is Marie Curie's— and that in 1898 she and her husband had identified two new radioactive substances, polonium and radium. Marie Curie was certain that these were true elements, but the former was isolated with bismuth, the latter with barium, and initially the new elements were chemically indistinguishable from these nonradioactive materials.

Purifying radium was tedious: A ton of pitchblende contains only a few tenths of a gram of the element. Curie explained the process, which required "several thousands of crystallizations." The first proof that radium is an element came from spectrum analysis (in which each substance produces a unique pattern, like a fingerprint). The purer the sample, the less visible the barium spectrum became, and the more obvious that of radium. Finally, in 1907, she was able to isolate a sample of radium compound pure enough to determine an accurate atomic weight— 226.45—and so assign it a place in the periodic table (arranged then by atomic weight rather than by atomic number). Three years later, together with André Debierne, she succeeded in isolating radium itself and found its melting point to be about 700 degrees Celsius. She noted with regret that similar efforts to purify polonium had not yet succeeded because even less polonium than radium is present in pitchblende—five thousand times less—and polonium disintegrates much more rapidly, having a half-life of 140 days, compared to radium's two thousand years. Yet she recently had obtained a sample of sufficient quality to produce its own spectrum and so provide evidence that it is indeed an element.

Having discussed the chemical nature of her work, Curie briefly explained radioactivity. As she observed, Ernest Rutherford and Frederick Soddy had provided the theoretical groundwork and experimental evidence to explain this phenomenon, but she repeatedly asserted her claim to being the first who recognized it as an atomic property. Her summary of the disintegration theory, which maintains that radioactive elements spontaneously give off particles and energy, not only paid homage to Rutherford but also further demonstrated the importance of her own work in understanding radioactivity. Because helium is present in all radioactive materials, some had suggested that these were merely compounds of helium. Rutherford had shown that the alpha particles emitted by radioactive substances are charged helium atoms, but perhaps this finding showed only that helium compounds were returning to their elemental state. By proving that radium is an element, Curie removed all possible objections to Rutherford's theory of atomic transmutation.

Although Curie had not yet separated polonium from its salts, she had prepared enough polonium compounds to collect large numbers of alpha particles emitted from this highly radioactive material. Alpha particles being helium atoms without electrons, the number of one equals that of the other. Thus, Curie's work provided an accurate way to determine Avogadro's number. In 1811, Amedeo Avogadro had stated that all gases, at the same pressure and temperature, will have the same number of molecules in any given volume, but actually finding that number had been difficult. Since alpha particles could be measured electrometrically or photographically, so could the number of helium atoms.

In her conclusion, Curie noted how chemistry had changed since the discovery of radioactivity. Previously, researchers had worked with materials they could see and weigh; now scientists were conducting experiments on invisible substances, detecting the presence of a billionth of a gram of radium that no scale was sensitive enough to measure. Here was a new world of science, almost metaphysical, which Curie labeled "the chemistry of the imponderable."

Critical reception

On January 23, 1911, the French Académie des Sciences had voted to admit Édouard Branly rather than Marie Curie, even though she was the only one of the six candidates who was listed in the first rank. The year ended with even greater unpleasantness. Physically ill, she was further debilitated by the revelation in November of her liaison with a married man five years her junior, the physicist Paul Langevin. Four duels were fought over the affair, including one between her lover and Gustave Théry, editor of *L'Œuvre*. Some newspapers, especially Théry's, urged Curie to return to Poland and, claiming she was Jewish, tried to rouse anti-Semitic feelings against her.

The popular press devoted almost equal attention to the Nobel Prize, the first to be awarded to a previous winner, and the sex scandal. *The New York Times* for December 11, 1911, in its discussion of the presentation of the prizes the previous day, mentioned Curie's involvement in the divorce suit filed by Langevin's wife, and six days later it ran a biographical piece that included portraits of Curie and Langevin. The account was more amused than censorious, and it contained high praise for the Nobel laureate: "Her appearance gives little indication of her remarkable faculties, and she is entirely unspoiled by her success." *Scientific American* (November 25, 1911) was more discreet in reporting the award, confining its laudatory sketch to a discussion of Curie's scientific work.

Most scientists were pleased with the Swedish Academy's choice, if only because the prize served as compensation for the behavior of the Académie des Sciences and the French press. Many believed that she deserved this second award. Rutherford wrote to American scientist Bertram Boltwood that he was glad of the decision, and to Curie herself he said, "My heartfelt congratulations on this recognition of your scientific work. Only a few days ago, I mentioned to Langevin that I thought you should be awarded the prize." Svante Arrhenius, who had received the Nobel Prize in Chemistry in 1903, called the discovery of radium "the most important during the last century of chemical research"; yet, as the Swedish Academy observed, it had not been specifically honored with an award, the Curies' 1903 prize having been for work on radioactivity. Some, however, saw this distinction as overly fine. Robert

Reid, one of Curie's biographers, felt the second award undeserved, and Boltwood acerbically replied to Rutherford's expression of joy, "Mme Curie is just what I have always thought she was, a plain darn fool, and you will find it out for certain before long."

Boltwood's lifelong hostility to Curie is difficult to understand. Reid's objection is more comprehensible, but only because radioactivity, thanks to the work of the Curies and Rutherford, is no longer a mystery, and no one doubts that radium is an element. At the beginning of the twentieth century these issues were by no means clear. Chemists in particular were loath to abandon the notion of inert, immutable atoms. Until Marie Curie, by isolating a pure sample of radium, proved that it was not a compound of helium and lead (as Lord Kelvin, the leading British chemist of his day, had maintained), it remained possible to believe that radioactivity involved a straightforward chemical reaction in which molecules separated into their constituent elements, like water returning to hydrogen and oxygen. Hence she did not exaggerate in claiming that "the task of isolating radium is the corner-stone of the edifice of the science of radioactivity" and thus was worthy of the recognition it received.

Biography

Marie Skłodowska Curie was born in Warsaw, Poland, on November 7, 1867. Her father, Wladyslaw Skłodowska, taught mathematics and physics in a secondary school, while to supplement the family's income her mother, Bronislawa Boguska Skłodowska, who had also taught, operated a boardinghouse. An outstanding student, Marie was graduated from high school with highest honors in 1883. Able to read French, German, Russian, and Polish, she began tutoring in 1884 while participating in the underground, or "floating," university, so named because it frequently had to vary the site of classes to avoid detection by the Russian authorities ruling Poland.

In 1886, she accepted the post of governess for the Zorawski family in Szczuki, some sixty miles north of Warsaw, sending her earnings to her older sister Bronia to support her medical studies in Paris. For seven hours a day Marie tutored her employer's two daughters; she then gave lessons to the peasants, who had no other source of education. As a researcher, she would reveal this same indefatigable spirit. Kazimierz Zorawski, the family's eldest son, fell in love with Marie but yielded to his parents' opposition to the match. Disappointed, Marie nevertheless remained with the Zorawskis until Easter, 1889, when she returned to Warsaw. There she continued to work as a governess and began some rudimentary studies in chemistry under Napoléon Mercier.

At Bronia's invitation Curie went to Paris in 1891, enrolling at the Sorbonne. Two years later (in July, 1893) she took a degree in physics, finishing first in her class; the following year, supported by a scholarship from her native Poland, she took a degree in mathematics, this time graduating second. In 1894 she also met Pierre Curie, whom she married on July 26, 1895. Together they discovered radium and explored its properties; following Pierre's death in April, 1906, she continued her work on radioactivity. After directing the Radiological Service of the French Red Cross during World War I, she presided over the Institut du Radium, which attracted researchers from around the world. Much honored by scientific institutions and universities in the United States and Europe, Curie died on July 4, 1934, and was buried in the same grave as her husband at Sceaux, France.

Scientific Career

A fellow Pole introduced Marie Skłodowska to Pierre Curie because she was studying the magnetic properties of steel, on which Pierre was an authority. In 1897 she published a comprehensive article on the subject. By this time she, like so many other researchers around the world, had become fascinated with Wilhelm Röntgen's discovery of the X ray (on November 8, 1895) and Henri Becquerel's observation that uranium compounds spontaneously give off something similar that is capable of exposing photographic film in the dark (February 28, 1896). Searching for a topic for her doctoral work—at a time when no woman in Europe had received a Ph.D.—she decided to investigate the source of this radioactivity and to look for other materials that exhibited the same mysterious behavior as uranium. Since uranium ionizes gases, making them into conductors of electricity, she used Pierre's sensitive electrometer, which he had developed for his work on crystals and magnetism, and she soon observed that thorium, too, can ionize gases.

More important, she found that regardless of form (powdered or solid), temperature, wetness, or the presence of other substances, uranium's activity remained constant. She therefore concluded that the unusual behavior of uranium could not be the consequence of molecular interaction but rather must be a property of the atom itself. This theory was as revolutionary in the late 1890's as Galileo's had been some three hundred years earlier, for scientific orthodoxy maintained that the atom is inert and immutable. The Curies themselves hesitated to reject other possibilities; even after Rutherford set forth his disintegration theory in 1903, they refused to rule out the possibility that radioactive materials might somehow draw energy from outside sources and retransmit it, though by the time she published her treatise on radioactivity in 1910, Marie had become converted to Rutherford's view.

Working with pitchblende and chalcolite, the ores of uranium and thorium respectively, she observed higher levels of radioactivity than predicted solely on the basis of the amounts of these two known radioactive elements present. Other substances in the ores must therefore be emitting radiation, too. In April, 1898, Pierre joined his wife in the search for these materials; three months later they published their first joint paper, reporting the discovery of the element polonium (on July 18, 1898), and on December 26, 1898, they announced that they had found a second new radioactive element, which they named radium.

The discovery of two new radioactive elements was exciting in itself, and it suggested that this property was much more common in nature than had been supposed. In her 1911 Nobel lecture, Marie Curie predicted the discovery of some thirty radioactive elements. If one includes isotopes, a concept not then known, her figure underestimates the prevalence of such material. From a purely scientific viewpoint, the Curies' identification of radium was most important for providing a tool that allowed an understanding of radioactivity. For example, when Rutherford distinguished between alpha and beta particles, he was unable to deflect the former with an electric charge, so that for some years researchers believed that alpha particles were neutral. Only after the Curies had provided a sufficiently active source of alpha particles was he able to determine that they were in fact affected by a current.

As Marie Curie noted in her Nobel lecture, she and her husband had recognized two new elements, more radioactive than uranium and thorium; the task was to prove the existence of these substances. While Pierre focused on the physical properties of radium (easier to isolate than polonium), Marie diligently prepared increasingly pure samples by boiling tons of pitchblende in a shed or in the open air. Despite the lack of help, of adequate facilities, and of money, Marie later referred to this time as "the best and happiest years of our life" because the couple was "entirely consecrated to work." After four years she was able to crystallize one-tenth of a gram of radium chloride, and on March 26, 1902, she recorded an atomic weight of 225.93 for the element, very close to the accepted figure. During this period the Curies published thirty-two papers discussing many of radium's properties, such as its ability to induce radioactivity in nearby substances. They also noted that radium kills cancer cells more rapidly than healthy ones, and in 1903 they found that radium gives off large quantities of heat, seemingly forever. While they had not, as the popular press suggested, discovered perpetual motion, they had made an important observation that helped Rutherford understand what was occurring inside the atom.

On June 25, 1903, Marie Curie presented her dissertation, *Recherches sur les substances radioactives* (1903; *Radioactive Substances*, 1903), which summarized her discoveries. In that year, too, the Royal Society (England) presented the Curies with the Davy Medal, and together they shared half the Nobel Prize in Physics, with Antoine-Henri Becquerel receiving the other half. The following year she and Édouard Branly received the Osiris Prize, but she remained largely in the shadow of her husband. It was Pierre who delivered the Nobel lecture for the couple, and when the Sorbonne belatedly recognized the Curies' work by creating a special professorship in physics, Pierre received the teaching post, while Marie was appointed his laboratory supervisor. After a visit to the Curies' laboratory, the chemist George Jaffe said that Pierre provided the ideas, Marie the "powerful temperament and persistence that maintained their momentum." Sir William Ramsay expressed a common sentiment when he remarked that "all the eminent women scientists have achieved their best work when collaborating with a male colleague."

The tragedy of Pierre Curie's death revealed Marie Curie's talents. Within two weeks of her husband's funeral, she was back at work, using research to combat sorrow. When the French government offered her a pension, she declined, so on

May 1, 1906, she was given Pierre's post at the Sorbonne, the first woman to hold such a position. She delivered her inaugural lecture to a packed audience; making no reference to her personal loss, she began her address with the last sentence Pierre had spoken in that same room as she reviewed a century of thought on the structure of matter. In that same month Andrew Carnegie donated $50,000 to provide salaries for Curie's laboratory assistants. For the next four years she and her staff worked to isolate a sample of pure radium; her success was rewarded with a second Nobel Prize. At the urging of the Solvay Conference she also prepared the international standard of radium, the unit of radiation bearing her name, the curie.

In 1912, the Pasteur Institute and the Sorbonne agreed to create a Radium Institute. One part, devoted to research, would be directed by Curie, while Dr. Claude Regaud would supervise the medical division. The building, in the rue Pierre Curie, was finished on July 31, 1914, but Curie would have to wait until the end of World War I to use it for further study of radioactivity.

When the war broke out, France had only one gram of radium. Placing this sample within a forty-five-pound lead case, Curie moved it to Bordeaux in September, depositing it in a vault for safekeeping. She then dedicated herself to using her knowledge of radiology to help the wounded. On November 1, 1914, she and her daughter Irène drove the first of what would eventually be a fleet of radiological cars—called "petites curies"—to the front lines to examine thirty soldiers. To operate the equipment, she and Irène trained 150 technicians, who by war's end had X-rayed more than one million casualties.

With the coming of peace Curie returned to her laboratory, but it was ill-equipped to rival the Cavendish Laboratory in England or the research facilities in the United States. When an American journalist, Marie Mattingley Melony, interviewing Curie for *The Delineator*, asked what she most wanted, Curie replied, "A gram of radium," then worth about $100,000. The energetic reporter launched a campaign to grant Curie her wish, and in 1921 President Warren G. Harding presented her with a mahogany and lead casket containing the radium she wanted. She returned to France with much-needed equipment, money, and a quantity of mesothorium as well.

Her own scientific work produced no dramatic results in these years, but, as she observed, a person can discover radium only once. She did continue to promote research in many ways: Only she could have elicited the generosity that Marie Melony had tapped in 1921 and that would bring Curie to America again in 1929 for a second gram of radium, this one for the Marie-Skłodowska-Curie Institute in Warsaw. As vice president of the League of Nations' International Committee on Intellectual Cooperation, she urged countries to reward their scientists who were aiding mankind, though she herself refused to profit from her discoveries. As director of the Radium Institute, she attracted talented researchers such as Margaret Perey, who discovered francium there, and Frédéric Joliot, who, together with Irène Curie, produced the first man-made radioactive element and so earned the Nobel Prize in Chemistry in 1935. Four years earlier they had misinterpreted the results of their experiments with beryllium and so had missed the opportunity of discovering the neutron, but it was their work that allowed James Chadwick to identify this sub-atomic particle. Curie herself worked on purifying actinium in order to study its alpha particles.

A lifetime of exposure to intense radioactivity took its toll. She underwent repeated operations for cataracts, and she suffered recurring bouts of radiation sickness. On July 4, 1934, Marie Curie, whose discoveries had done so much to aid cancer patients, died of leukemia.

Bibliography

Primary
PHYSICS: *Recherches sur les substances radioactives,* 1903 (*Radioactive Substances,* 1903); *Les Théories modernes relatives à l'électricité et à la matière,* 1906; *Traité de radioactivité,* 1910 (2 vols.); *L'Isotopie et les éleménts isotopes,* 1922-1923; *Radioactivité,* 1935 (2 vols.).
BIOGRAPHY: *Pierre Curie,* 1924 (English translation, 1923).
OTHER NONFICTION: *La Radiologie et la guerre,* 1921.
EDITED TEXT: *Œuvres de Pierre Curie,* 1908.

Secondary
Curie, Ève. *Madame Curie: A Biography.* Garden City, N.Y.: Doubleday, Doran, 1938. A firsthand account of the Curies' domestic and scientific life by their older daughter. A flattering, well-informed narrative, ably translated from the French by Vincent Sheean.
Giroud, Françoise. *Marie Curie: A Life.* Translated by Lydia Davis. New York: Holmes & Meier, 1986. A personal interpretation of Curie's life, weighted toward the domestic side but with a good overview of the science. Most of the bibliographic references are to French works.
Ogilvie, Marilyn Bailey. *Women in Science: Antiquity Through the Nineteenth Century.* Cambridge, Mass.: MIT Press, 1986. A survey of the life, followed by a balanced assessment of the role Marie Curie played in research she undertook with her husband. Concludes that her most productive period came before 1906, but that Marie provided ideas as well as labor. Includes bibliographical references.
Opfell, Olga S. "Pale Glimmer of Radium: Marie Curie." In *The Lady Laureates: Women Who Have Won the Nobel Prize.* Metuchen, N.J.: Scarecrow Press, 1986. Concentrates on biography, with little discussion of Curie's work or its significance. Offers suggestions for further reading.
Raven, Susan. "First Great Woman Scientist—and Much More." *The New York Times Magazine,* December 3, 1967. Celebrates the one hundredth anniversary of Curie's birth. A good introduction to the life and work, with a number of fascinating photographs.
Reid, Robert. *Marie Curie.* New York: Saturday Review Press, 1974. The first full-

length biography of Curie to appear in almost forty years, it reinterpreted Curie's life in many ways and sought to dispel various myths that had accumulated, such as that concerning the severe poverty of her college years. Reid drew on unpublished materials and newspaper accounts of the period to provide a scientific and cultural context for the Curies' work and so emphasize the importance of their contribution. Contains a selected but well-chosen bibliography.

Rutherford, Ernest. "Marie Curie." *Nature* 134 (July 21, 1934): 90-91. In this obituary Rutherford pays tribute to a fellow scientist and friend of more than three decades. Provides a short biographical sketch, notes the significance of Curie's discoveries, and praises her medical work during World War I.

Joseph Rosenblum

1912

Chemistry
Victor Grignard, France
Paul Sabatier, France

Physics
Nils Gustaf Dalén, Sweden

Physiology or Medicine
Alexis Carrel, France

Literature
Gerhart Hauptmann, Germany

Peace
Elihu Root, United States

VICTOR GRIGNARD
1912

Born: Cherbourg, France; May 6, 1871
Died: Lyons, France; December 13, 1935
Nationality: French
Area of concentration: Organomagnesium reagents

Grignard discovered and developed the Grignard reagent, which involves the reaction of an alkyl halide with magnesium metal in anhydrous ether. This reagent opened the field of organometallics in the synthesis of various functional groups

The Award
Presentation

Professor Henrik Gustaf Söderbaum, President of the Royal Swedish Academy of Sciences, presented the Nobel Prize in Chemistry to both Victor Grignard and Paul Sabatier, the cowinners of the 1912 award. He opened his address on December 10, 1912, by defining the aim of a scientist in extending the limits of human knowledge and pointing out the necessity of the new technical devices and methods that contribute to resolving complicated problems of contemporary science. He stressed the importance of the Grignard reagent and of Sabatier's new metal-catalyzed hydrogenation methods in organic synthesis, a relatively new field at the time. He mentioned Friedrich Wöhler's cornerstone synthesis in 1828 and its significance in the application of chemistry in everyday life. As a result, he said, branches of industry have created a livelihood for millions of people.

Grignard's method was then briefly described, and its virtues—the simplicity of the procedure, the low cost, and the enormous variation of new carbon-carbon bond formations—were pointed out. Söderbaum further declared that, because of its wide application, no known method of organic synthesis is superior to Grignard's. Finally, Söderbaum expressed the confidence that the reagent would be essential in the future organic preparation of alkaloids and vegetable organic bases.

Nobel lecture

On December 11, 1912, Grignard delivered his Nobel lecture, entitled "The Use of Organomagnesium Compounds in Preparative Organic Chemistry." He opened his talk by acknowledging the contribution of other chemists who worked before him and concurrently with him in the field. He then proceeded to define organometallics and classify them as either very reactive and unstable (such as sodium and potassium compounds) or rather inert and stable (as mercury compounds are). Organozinc compounds, first discovered by Sir Edward Frankland in 1849, were the only stable and also reactive organometallics known to scientists at the end of the nineteenth century. Some disadvantages, the most important being high flammability, convinced Philippe Antoine Barbier, professor at the University of

Lyons and Grignard's mentor, to switch from zinc to magnesium. After several tries and adjustments, Grignard discovered that the absence of atmospheric oxygen and the presence of anhydrous ether as solvent speeded up the reaction of alkyl halides with the magnesium to yield a clear solution that was reactive toward many reagents. Among others, these included water, oxygen, carbon dioxide, and all carbonyl compounds.

Grignard discussed the nature of the species (which he called mixed organic magnesium compound) and suggested the possibility of ether complexation—that is, of ether participation during its formation. After describing the general procedure, he made a comparison between organozinc and organomagnesium compounds. He stressed the possibility that a wide variety of organic halides would react with many organic functional groups when magnesium is used and gave a summary of the various reactions and products. The lecture ended with an astounding question: Is magnesium, Grignard wondered, "playing a very active part in the natural syntheses of organized matter?" He based his point on Richard Willstätter's discovery that several chlorophyll compounds contain a considerable amount of magnesium, and he questioned the possibility of two transformation cycles in living matter: synthesis via magnesium and oxidation via iron. He thus declared the biological role of magnesium as the problem for the future.

Critical reception

The Nobel Prize Committee found great difficulties in deciding the early winners of the award. Many reports on given candidates constituted "decision proposals" by individual members of the committee who actually nominated those same scientists. As a result, the voting would begin with three or even four proposals that had to be narrowed down in successive rounds to a choice that had to be voted upon.

Grignard's name first appeared in the 1910 voting; it was suggested by Oskar Widman, who, on his own initiative, gave a written report. Although the members were not opposed in principle to awarding Grignard the prize, a dispute over the priority to his work had arisen between him and his mentor Barbier. Thus, as Hammarsten pointed out to the section, "this was not a good time for Grignard." The addition of A. G. Ekstrand to the committee gave a diligent and accommodating personality to the group which helped the planning of future winners. The award was given two years later to Grignard and was shared by Paul Sabatier, who discovered and expanded the field of catalytic hydrogenation using fine metals. The justification given was that both scientists developed methods of great utility in the synthesis of organic compounds, and if only one were rewarded, several years would go by before the committee could recommend the other, since both fields and nationalities were the same. Grignard himself was not happy with the decision. He believed that Sabatier should have shared the prize with his collaborator and co-author Jean-Baptiste Senderens and that subsequently a prize should have been divided between himself and Barbier. He expressed this feeling at a large gathering held in his honor on February 8, 1913, in the Great Amphitheatre of the Faculty of

Sciences in Nancy. Senderens later bitterly expressed the opinion that he was deprived of his just share of the prize, since he was neither Sabatier's assistant nor his student, but worked as "co-equal collaborator." On the other hand, although the organomagnesium reaction had been earlier known as the Barbier-Grignard reaction, Barbier insisted that credit for its development should go to Grignard, even though he himself had been the one to prepare the first reagent. No hard feelings, therefore, were created between Grignard and his mentor, in contrast with Sabatier and Senderens, whose destroyed scientific association erupted in the literature in the form of polemic articles in *Berichte*.

French scientists were elated with the outcome of the 1912 Nobel chemistry awards. The results were declared to be a triumph over the thesis that "chemistry was a predominantly German science" (*Le Temps*, November 28, 1912). Grignard's discovery had already been highly appreciated, as evidenced by the unusual decision of the editors of one chemistry journal to publish a "very full abstract" of the thesis. Since university publications were rarely given this distinction, it "indicated the importance which the editors attached to this work."

Winning the award had a great propaganda effect on the institutions with which Grignard and Sabatier were affiliated and which they (especially Sabatier) had, at times, partially financed. Funds from various sources, such as the state, the municipality, and private industry, started pouring in; government efforts to improve research facilities in the provincial universities (Toulouse for Sabatier, Nancy for Grignard) were justified. This was stressed by C. Bayet, the Director of Higher Education in the Ministry of Public Instruction of France, in interviews with *Le Temps*; the opinion was also expressed in *L'Illustration* (November 30, 1912). As a result, Söderbaum's suggestion, expressed in his presentation speech, that more industrial jobs were being created for people working on synthetic procedures such as Grignard's seemed to be accurate.

The effects of Grignard's accomplishments in chemistry were clearly summarized in Söderbaum's words; he hailed Grignard for "push[ing] back appreciably the frontiers of our knowledge, of our ability to observe" and for "opening up prospects of new conquests for our science." F. G. Mann was quoted as saying that Grignard's "own output of original work was not large, but no other man has initiated the means whereby so vast a field of synthetic chemistry has subsequently been developed."

Because of the abundance of great scientists during the early years of the Nobel Prizes and the limited number of prizes that could be awarded, many complaints were heard. One of the main arguments was against the preference of the committees to reward fundamental science rather than accede to Nobel's explicit inclusion of "inventions" and "improvements" within the purview of the prizes. Thus, scientists who worked in a specialty early in its development had a better chance than those who entered the field later and did work of comparable (or even superior) quality. In fact, a laureate in chemistry remarked about his own work that "there's no denying it. At a certain stage in the development of a field, Nobel awards start being given out . . . then after a while they stop giving awards in that field, and work that is just as good doesn't get prizes." This is probably the reason that the Nobel Prize in Chemistry for 1950 to Otto Diels and Kurt Alder was the only other award ever given to synthetic organic chemists who established a unique reaction. Nevertheless, Karl Ziegler and Giulio Natta were awarded the Nobel Prize in 1963 for "discoveries in the chemistry and technology of the high polymers." As a specialist in the field of organometallics, Ziegler developed the organolithium and organoaluminum compounds—in many respects, a modification of the Grignard reagents.

Biography

François Auguste Victor Grignard, the son of Théophile Henri and Marie Hébert Grignard, was born in Cherbourg, France, on May 6, 1871. He attended local schools, and in 1889 he won a scholarship to the École Normale Spéciale at Cluny. After two years, the school, which was intended to produce teachers for modern secondary schools, was closed; Grignard then joined the faculty of sciences, University of Lyons, but failed his licentiate examination in mathematics (1892). He left to fulfill his compulsory military service and later returned to the university to earn degrees in mathematics and physics. He accepted a junior post in the Faculty of Sciences and began his prizewinning work with a study of the alkylzinc compounds developed earlier by Sir Edward Frankland, under professor Philippe Antoine Barbier, with whom Grignard published his first paper, in 1898. He earned his doctorate in 1901 and was later appointed *maître de conférences* at the University of Besançon (1905-1906) and the University of Lyons (1906-1908), adjunct professor of general chemistry at the University of Lyons (1908), professor of organic chemistry at the University of Nancy (1909-1919), professor of general chemistry at the University of Lyons (1919), director of the School of Industrial Chemistry at the University of Lyons (1921), and finally dean of the Faculty of Sciences at the same institution.

His initial association with Barbier led to the discovery and development of organomagnesium reagents in the so-called "Grignard reaction," which yields a wide variety of organic functional groups. He also worked extensively on the synthesis of fulvenes, quantitative ozonization, condensation of aldehydes and ketones, and catalytic hydrogenation. He was the author of some 170 publications and was working on his *Traité de chimie organique* when he died. This work was eventually finished by his son Roger and his student Jean Cologne.

Grignard married Augustine Marie Boulant in 1910 and had a daughter and a son, Roger, who followed in the academic footsteps of his father. Grignard died on December 13, 1935, in Lyons, France.

Scientific Career

The intellectual superiority that Victor Grignard displayed in school seemed at first to destine him to be a secondary school teacher. He was therefore introduced by several of his teachers to concepts of higher algebra and physics, and efforts were made to have him continue his education at a higher level. His father, a sailmaker and later a foreman in the local marine arsenal, would never have suspected the eventual accomplishments of his son, nor would he have had the funds to send him to the École Normale Supérieure, the cradle of French higher education. An unexpected turn of events, however, saved the day for organic synthesis. Grignard failed the licentiate exams that would have made him a teacher in 1892, then joined the army to fulfill his military service. After his discharge, he was convinced by his friend Louis Bouveault to "try" chemistry, a field he considered inferior—purely empirical, incoherent, and consisting mainly of a collection of facts to memorize. Chemical experimentation with Bouveault, his first immediate supervisor, gradually impressed him while he was studying at the University of Lyons. Credit should also be given to his mentor, Philippe Antoine Barbier, the head of the department, a demanding supervisor who required the utmost of his assistants and coworkers. Grignard earned the trust and respect of Barbier and continued his association with him for fourteen years.

Barbier had just begun investigating the possibility of attaching two organic radicals (carbon-containing groups that remain unchanged during the course of reaction) using a metal. Organometallic compounds (compounds resulting from the union of an organic radical with a metal) were known for years, but their reactivity was either high (organosodium or potassium) or low (organomercury). Sir Edward Frankland and James Wanklyn's use of zinc gave good results, but the variety of compounds that could be prepared was limited, and the spontaneous ignition at ordinary temperatures made these species a real hazard in the laboratory. The contributions of Alexander Butlerow and Alexander Saytzeff did not change the overall picture of those reactions. Barbier thought of mixing the two reactants in the presence of magnesium, but the results were inconsistent. He quickly abandoned the idea, but he suggested it to Grignard as a project for his doctoral thesis. Grignard first prepared the organomagnesium compound in the presence of anhydrous ether and then reacted it with the second reactant. The process, an instant success, was first communicated by Henri Moissan to the Academy of Sciences in May, 1900, and was published a few months later in *Comptes rendus*. As a result, Grignard was awarded the doctorate (with honorable distinction) the next year and dedicated his thesis to the university where the discovery had been made. The reaction, which was given his name, became the focus of his career and was extensively adopted by many chemists in the synthesis of numerous compounds.

During the first years, French chemists explored the reaction, and they were followed soon by scientists from other countries, such as Germany, Russia, England, Italy, Switzerland, and the United States. The ease of the process and the variety of reactions the reagent undergoes allow unlimited combinations, and it may be said that no branch of organic chemistry is beyond its reach. Thus, by the end of 1905 (five years after the initial communication by Moissan), the number of publications using this reaction mounted to two hundred; 332 more were added by August, 1908. By the end of Grignard's life, the literature contained about six thousand references dealing with his reaction. Despite his instant success, Grignard had to wait four more years until he was awarded the post of *maître de conférences* and another five years until he received the title of professor and a laboratory of his own.

Grignard continued his association with Barbier at Lyons for several years, interrupted by a one-year (1905-1906) appointment at the University of Besançon, where the facilities were very limited. The chemists at Besançon were more interested in teaching than in research, despite the fact that the chairman of the department, Léon Boutroux, was one of Louis Pasteur's students. Grignard himself passed over this period in silence in his autobiographical notes. In 1909 he joined the University of Nancy, and the next year he was given the rank of professor, thus becoming the head of one of the best-equipped laboratories in the provincial universities. It was there that he learned of his Nobel Prize. In a celebration on February 8, 1913, in the Great Amphitheatre of the Faculty of Sciences at the university, he was given a bronze ornament by his colleagues and a cross set with brilliants by the Association of Alumni of the Chemistry Institute of the University of Nancy.

Grignard remained at Nancy until 1919, with intermittent duties in the French army during World War I, in which, as a corporal, he was assigned to investigate methods for the synthesis of toluene, an explosive solvent, from the cracking of heavy oils. He was also responsible for the analytical control of war gases. With numerous collaborators, such as Edward Urbain, Grignard investigated acute problems of the chemical warfare industry. On a trip to the United States in 1917, he lectured at the Mellon Institute (now the Carnegie Mellon Institute) on the collaboration of science and industry in France and the United States. After the end of the war, he returned to Lyons to succeed his retiring former mentor Barbier. While trying to polish and optimize the conditions of his reaction, Grignard also dealt with other synthetic problems, including the condensation of aldehydes and ketones, hydrocarbon cracking, ketone splitting of tertiary alcohols, quantitative ozonization, catalytic hydrogenation, and dehydrogenation.

During the later stages of his academic career, Grignard was involved with administrative duties that eventually slowed down his research. From 1921, he was given the additional post of director of the School of Industrial Chemistry at the University of Lyons and became the vice president of the University Council. The final ceremony in which a public ovation was given to him was held on May 12, 1933, in the Festival Hall of the University. This occasion coincided with Grignard's nomination as Commander of the Legion of Honor and the forty-fifth anniversary of his entrance into higher education. During the ceremony he was addressed by several officials of the French government, the School of Chemistry, alumni, collaborators, and other scientists and was given a plaque by the Lyons sculptor L. Bertola. In response, Grignard gave a moving speech in which "the modesty of a real scholar" was clearly evident.

The last years of Grignard's life were devoted to the writing of a handbook of organic chemistry. Two volumes appeared during his lifetime, two were left to the editors, and two more were almost at the editorial stage at the time of his death. The publication of this work, for which there was no precedent in the French anguage, was originally planned to involve fifteen volumes, but the death of the original publisher, Charles Moureu, in 1929 and the almost unexpected death of Grignard left the work to be completed posthumously. Forty years of his life were dedicated to research; 170 pages were published during his lifetime. More important, though, for him, was the universal acknowledgment of his reaction and the enormous impact it had on organic synthesis.

Apart from his Nobel Prize, Grignard's awards included the Cahours Prize, the Berthelot Medal, the Prix Jecker, the Lavoisier Medal, and the title of Commander of the Legion of Honor. He was an honorary member of the chemical societies of America, England, Belgium, France, Romania, and Poland as well as of the Society of Industrial Chemistry of France, the Technological Society of Delft, and the International Faculty of Sciences, London. He was a member of the Royal Society of Uppsala and the Academies of Sciences of France, Romania, Poland, and Belgium.

Grignard was an exceptional research worker, but he was also a devoted teacher. Thirty-three years of his life were devoted to instruction, and he is credited with the development of the universities he served and the competent successors he left. His very well-known, logically constructed organic chemistry lecture was published after his death by his son (and student) Roger Grignard and Jean Cologne in 1937 and had several editions.

Bibliography

Primary

CHEMISTRY: "Sur Quelques Nouvelles Combinaisons organometalliques du magnésium et leur application à des synthèses d'alcohols et d'hydrocarbures," *Comptes rendus de l'Académie des sciences*, vol. 126, 1898; "Sur les combinaisons organomagnésiennes mixtes et leur application à des synthèses d'acides, d'alcohols, et d'hydrocarbures," *Annales de l'Université de Lyons*, vol. 6, 1901; "Le Magnésium en chimie organique," *Bulletin de la Société chimique de France*, vol. 13, 1913; *Traité de chimie organique*, 1935-1939.

Secondary

Baker, Albert A., Jr. "François Auguste Victor Grignard." In *Dictionary of Scientific Biography*, vol. 5, edited by Charles Coulston Gillispie. New York: Charles Scribner's Sons, 1972. This is a short biography of Grignard with a brief description of his scientific work. It also includes a good bibliography of original works and secondary literature.

Crawford, Elisabeth T. *The Beginnings of the Nobel Institution: The Science Prizes, 1901-1915*. New York: Cambridge University Press, 1984. This book uses many contemporary references to outline the early difficulties the Nobel Prize Committee faced in choosing the award recipients. It gives detailed accounts of the several close votings and the justification of each member's choice. The book also describes how the Committee finally worked as one member in planning the lineup of the award winners in the future.

Farber, Eduard. *Nobel Prize Winners in Chemistry, 1901-1961*. Rev. ed. New York: Abelard-Schuman, 1963. This book gives a biographical sketch and a description of the prizewinning work of all Nobel Prize winners in Chemistry from the beginning until 1961. It includes a translation of the procedure that Grignard himself published in 1913. A one-page description of the consequences in theory and practice is also given.

Nobelstiftelsen. *Nobel Lectures: Chemistry, 1901-1921*. New York; Elsevier, 1966. This book is a compilation of all Nobel Prize award presentation speeches and acknowledgment lectures. It also includes short biographies with dates and important highlights of the recipients' lives.

_____. *Nobel: The Man and His Prizes*. 3d ed. New York: Elsevier, 1972. This book gives an account of Alfred Nobel's life and his decision to institute the Nobel Prize awards. It also includes a brief description of the scientific accomplishments of the chemistry prize winners in simple terms.

Wasson, Tyler, ed. *Nobel Prize Winners*. New York: H. W. Wilson, 1987. This book gives a brief but detailed account of the lives of all Nobel Prize winners. The text avoids scientific terms and gives only a few references and selected works of every individual recipient.

Paris Svoronos

1912

Chemistry
Victor Grignard, France
Paul Sabatier, France

Physics
Nils Gustaf Dalén, Sweden

Physiology or Medicine
Alexis Carrel, France

Literature
Gerhart Hauptmann, Germany

Peace
Elihu Root, United States

PAUL SABATIER
1912

Born: Carcassonne, France; November 5, 1854
Died: Toulouse, France; August 14, 1941
Nationality: French
Areas of concentration: Catalysis and applied chemistry

Sabatier developed an efficient method of hydrogenating unsaturated hydrocarbons through the use of finely divided metals as catalysts. Because many commercial substances can be prepared from saturated fats, his discovery had a significant practical application

The Award

Presentation

Henrik Gustav Söderbaum, President of the Royal Swedish Academy of Sciences, presented Paul Sabatier with the Nobel Prize in Chemistry on December 10, 1912. In his address, Söderbaum defined the role of the scientist: to expand the boundaries of knowledge. He noted that among the various ways this may be accomplished is the invention of new methods and devices. No longer could a solitary researcher working with inferior equipment make miraculous discoveries; twentieth century science is far too sophisticated and the old methods too limited. Therefore, the Nobel Prize in Chemistry in 1912 was awarded to two Frenchmen, each of whom invented a new method. Sabatier's award was for his work in synthesizing organic compounds through the use of finely divided metals as catalysts to achieve hydrogenation.

Söderbaum briefly surveyed this relatively new field of chemistry, beginning with the work of Jöns Jakob Berzelius' follower Friedrich Wöhler in 1828. He went on to emphasize the practical applications of the work done by the 1912 recipients, whose discoveries, he said, had "provided a livelihood for millions of men" and generated tremendous wealth. The Sabatier method involved the reduction of organic compounds through the use of such powdered metals as platinum, cobalt, and nickel. It opened up many new fields of scientific research because, among other things, it was simple, had a high yield, and was wholly safe.

Söderbaum concluded by quoting one of Sabatier's own principles: "In the study of the phenomena of the physical world, no matter what these phenomena may be, the basis of any system must be observation, precise, strict, and free from all preconceptions." The award was presented for the recipient's adherence to his own principles, which produced such outstanding results as the new hydrogenation method.

Nobel lecture

Sabatier presented his Nobel lecture, "The Method of Direct Hydrogenation by Catalysis," on December 11, 1912. He not only presented his method but also revealed a teacher's knowledge of the history of science. He began by noting his collaborator, Jean-Baptiste Senderens, and two of his students, Alphonse Mailhe and Marcel Murat, all of whom made significant contributions to the discovery.

In the past, hydrogenation consisted of nascent hydrogen being released from a substance along with heat, which could then transform substances through the transmittal of some of this released hydrogen. Marcelin Berthelot had used a concentrated solution of hydroiodic acid, which, when heated to a high temperature, releases hydrogen to organic compounds. This method, however, was extremely dangerous. Other researchers had induced some transformations with platinum, but the applications were limited. That is where the situation remained when Sabatier approached it in the early 1890's.

The success of Ludwig Mond and others in isolating nickel carbonyl by the action of carbon dioxide on powdered nickel suggested to Sabatier that one might successfully add metals to incomplete gaseous molecules. By 1894, he and Senderens had produced nitro metals by making nitrogen oxide react with copper, cobalt, and nickel. At about this time, Henri Moissan's inconclusive experiments with acetylene suggested great possibilities. Sabatier based his approach on the theory that the cause of the catalytic activity was not simple condensation but a true chemical combining of the gas with the surface of the metal.

Sabatier and Senderens performed a similar experiment using ethylene. When ethylene is directed toward hot nickel, cobalt, or iron, it burns brilliantly, deposits carbon, and releases ethane gas instead of hydrogen. This suggested that the metal brought about the hydrogenation of the ethylene. Further experiments achieved similar results with acetylene. Sabatier then applied the same principle to the hydrogenation of benzene. In 1901, he was sufficiently convinced of the correctness of his process to state that "vapour of the substance together with an excess of hydrogen is directed on to freshly reduced nickel held at a suitable temperature (generally between 150 and 200 degrees C.)." The result of this simple—and completely safe—principle was "the transformation of unsaturated ethylenic or acetylenic hydrocarbons into saturated hydrocarbons, and the transformation of nitro derivatives into amines." Another advantage of the method was that it yielded only the desired product and thus gave very high yields.

Sabatier summarized his and others' subsequent experiments with his method, then turned to some of the more interesting results of his experiments, which had led him to a general theory of the production of mineral oils in the earth. Among a number of interesting discoveries, he found that liquid fatty acids can be transformed into solid acids by hydrogenation (the basis of the oleomargarine industry) and that hydrogenation provides an almost infinite number of potential syntheses, including perfumes.

Sabatier ended his lecture with an attempt to explain hydrogenation by catalysis. He theorized that hydrogen reacts very rapidly on the metal and produces a compound on its surface. He concluded by noting that many of his conjectures had proved correct and may have many industrial applications.

Critical reception

The growth in the significance and reputation of the Nobel Prize as the twentieth century progressed is nowhere more obvious than in the meager American and British reaction to Paul Sabatier's award for chemistry in 1912. Neither the venerable British publication *Nature* nor *The New York Times* devoted more than a sentence or two to the announcement that the chemistry prize had been awarded to two French chemists. Had the winners been British or American citizens, there undoubtedly would have been a greater reaction, but up until 1912 it was Germany and France that had most recognized and exploited the significance of the prizes with enthusiastic nationalism.

On the continent, and especially in France, therefore, the announcement of the awards was greeted by the scientific establishment with immediate attention and not a little controversy. In fact, the chemistry awards of 1912 both provoked the greatest dissension of the first fifteen years of the Nobel Prizes and produced the most questionable moment in Sabatier's otherwise exemplary career.

A number of issues concerning these awards contributed to the controversy. For the first time ever, the chemistry prize had been awarded jointly (although the physics prize had been so awarded several times). Also, cowinner Victor Grignard questioned the division of the prize between himself and Sabatier, since he would have preferred to see the award for 1912 be given jointly to Sabatier and his collaborator Senderens. That way, at some time in the future, Grignard could have shared it with his teacher, Philippe Antoine Barbier. The most damaging action as far as Sabatier was concerned, however, came in regard to his collaborator, Senderens.

For the only time in the first fifteen years of the Nobel Prizes, there was an actual protest to the academy: a letter from Senderens himself, summarizing his long collaboration and including an observation that Sabatier demonstrated a rather pronounced tendency to pretend that he was the sole creator of the methods in question. Sabatier had contributed to the problem a year earlier when, in a speech to the British Chemical Union, he had referred to Senderens as his "student," without clarifying his partner's position as an independent researcher. (During their collaboration, Senderens, an abbot, taught chemistry at the Institut Catholique and finished his doctoral research in Sabatier's laboratory after his own director died. He was himself the director of several laboratories and, after leaving Sabatier in 1905, went on to a distinguished career in industrial chemistry.) Although Sabatier continually gave Senderens credit in his Nobel Prize address, the damage had been done.

Despite this controversy, however, there was no apparent objection in the scientific community to the choice of Sabatier. In fact, both Sabatier and Senderens had been nominated as early as 1907 and several times thereafter. Sabatier incorrectly attributed his award to the German scientific community, when in fact his only nomination by a German had come in 1911. In his winning year, he was nominated by the secretary of the French Academy of Sciences and a Swedish member of the

Nobel Committee. Only the omission of Senderens marred an otherwise popular and acceptable choice.

Sabatier's career was enhanced in several immediate ways by the honor. Because both he and Grignard were from provincial universities, their shared award stimulated a substantial increase in funding and other support for scientific research in the provinces. Another immediate result was the creation of a new section of the Academy of Sciences for members who did not live in Paris—Sabatier was admitted immediately, Grignard in 1926.

Biography

One of the most important figures of the French scientific milieu of the early twentieth century, Paul Sabatier was born on November 5, 1854, in Carcassonne in southern France, the son of Pauline (née Guilham) and Alexis Sabatier. He was the youngest of seven children in a family of limited means but genteel heritage. Sabatier followed his brother Théodore to the *lycée* in their home city, where they pursued an interest in mathematics and science under the direction of an uncle who was a professor there. When their uncle moved to the *lycée* at Toulouse, Sabatier followed him and was further encouraged to pursue a scientific career by the public lectures on physics and chemistry. Deciding that he wanted to become a professor, he spent three years as a boarding student at the Collège Ste.-Marie. In 1874, he placed high in his entrance exams and was admitted to both the École Polytechnique and the École Normale Supérieure. He was graduated first in his class from the latter college in 1877.

Sabatier spent a year teaching secondary school physics, then entered the Collège de France as a graduate assistant to the renowned chemist Marcelin Berthelot. After earning his doctorate with a thesis on the thermochemistry of sulfur compounds, he began teaching physics at the University of Bordeaux. When a position opened at the University of Toulouse, he moved there and held the chemistry chair for nearly fifty years.

In 1884, Sabatier married Germaine Herail, the daughter of a judge. They had four daughters; Sabatier's life was shattered by his wife's death in 1898. He did not remarry but devoted himself to his children, his research, and his university. In 1905, he became dean of the science faculty at Toulouse, a position he held until his formal retirement in 1929.

In a life filled with honors and awards, the Nobel Prize was the crowning achievement, but he also accomplished much for the University of Toulouse and the advancement of science in the French provinces. After his retirement, he continued to be involved in the university community until shortly before his death on August 14, 1941.

Scientific Career

From his early days as an honor student at the *lycée* in Carcassonne, Sabatier showed both great intellectual curiosity and the capacity to work hardest on the subjects that were the most challenging. Though he took little monetary interest in the applications of his work, he nevertheless stressed in his own research and that of his students that work which was useful to society was as important as pure theoretical work. In his decision to reject the lure of Paris, then the center of the French scientific establishment, and his successful efforts to turn Toulouse into a major research institution, he demonstrated a loyalty and a vision that made him one of the central figures in the decentralization of French science.

Following his transfer to the *lycée* at Toulouse in 1868, he was exposed to the public lectures on chemistry and physics that stimulated his desire both to teach and to pursue research in the sciences. He spent the next three years at the Collège Ste.-Marie in Toulouse and then moved to Paris, where he spent two more years in preparation for the university. In 1874, he placed sufficiently high in the qualifying examinations to be admitted to both the École Polytechnique and the École Normale Supérieure. He chose the latter institution, perhaps because he was fourth on the list there, and was graduated first in his class in 1877. He spent the school year of 1877-1878 teaching physics at the *lycée* at Nîmes. When the eminent chemist Marcelin Berthelot asked the director of the École Normale to recommend a graduate assistant, Sabatier was the choice. He accepted the position with the knowledge that if he did not show promise as a research chemist he would be returned to secondary teaching. Sabatier, however, demonstrated his capacity to work long and hard and, following his mentor's lead in thermochemical studies in inorganic chemistry, earned his doctorate in 1880 with a dissertation on the thermic qualities of metal, alkali, and alkali-earth sulfides and polysulfides.

The years in Paris, both as undergraduate and graduate student, were not easy ones for the young prodigy from the provinces. Sabatier was a devout Roman Catholic in a scientific milieu dominated by a secular, anticlerical scientism. His master, Berthelot, was one of the most outspoken of the freethinking liberals, and young Sabatier despaired of his chances at ever gaining a position in Paris. In addition, he was outspoken in his attraction to the new atomistic theory of Dmitry Mendeleyev and Lothar Meyer, which was in opposition to Berthelot's preference for the traditional notation of chemical equivalents. Despite his misgivings, Sabatier dedicated his thesis to Berthelot and was awarded his degree.

With doctorate in hand, Sabatier began his professorial career teaching physics at the University of Bordeaux—his other choices having been Lyons and Algiers—and only a year later, apparently with a strong recommendation from Berthelot, received an appointment at the University of Toulouse, where he was to spend the rest of his career. Two years later, at the minimum required age of thirty, he was offered the chair in chemistry, a position he retained until his retirement. During the 1880's, he continued his investigations in inorganic chemistry. He developed a technique for isolating hydrogen sulfide using vacuum distillation; he achieved the isolation of boron and silicon selenides; he identified the cupric salts containing four atoms of copper; he prepared nitrosodisulfonic acid and argentocupric salts. By studying the spectrophotometric change of color in chromates and dichromates, he identified the partition of a base separating two acids. He made an analysis of the speed of transformation in metaphosphoric acid. Before he ever began the study that would bring him the Nobel Prize, he had published more than ninety articles detailing the results of his research. For these efforts he was recognized by the Academy of Sciences with the 1897 Prix La Caxe.

In the early 1890's, Sabatier became interested in the synthesis of metals by reducing them from their oxides through the addition of hydrogen. When he learned of Ludwig Mond's success in 1890 in preparing nickel carbonyl by adding carbon monoxide to finely divided (powdered) nickel, his interest shifted to organic chemistry, particularly to the question of how unsaturated compounds (those able to combine chemically) become saturated (reluctant to combine). With his collaborator, Jean-Baptiste Senderens, he decided to investigate whether other unsaturated gases, such as nitrogen peroxide, would affect metals in a similar way and, in 1896, succeeded with iron, nickel, copper, and cobalt.

At this point, Sabatier learned that Henri Moissan and Charles Moureu had failed to achieve results with acetylene, and he became interested in pursuing a similar experiment. Ever the professional, he discreetly ascertained that Moissan and Moureu had no further interest in the matter and made a parallel attempt with a less active compound, passing ethylene gas over slivered nickel oxide at a temperature of 300 degrees Celsius. The result was a bright incandescence, carbon deposits in the test tube, and the release of gas. Instead of this gas being hydrogen, as Moissan and Moureu had assumed, Sabatier and Senderens found it to be largely ethane, which had resulted from the hydrogenation of the ethylene. Perhaps most important in the long run was Sabatier's revolutionary conclusion that the process was a chemical one rather than mere physical absorption.

Until this time, hydrogenation (the addition of hydrogen to a molecule) had been accomplished through the use of catalytic agents of the platinum family, which were far too expensive to be practical in large-scale industrial applications. Sabatier's success with the much cheaper nickel stimulated him to pursue further researches in the area, which he did for most of the next thirty years.

Just as Sabatier's work was progressing rapidly, he suffered the great tragedy of his life. In 1898, his wife died. After an interruption of many months, Sabatier returned to the laboratory, where, in 1899, he and Senderens successfully hydrogenated acetylene into ethane, again using nickel as the catalytic agent. They then repeated the experiments using reduced cobalt, platinum, iron, and copper, though these elements proved to be less vigorous catalysts than nickel.

With these successes behind them, Sabatier and Senderens turned to the major challenge of benzene, which had resisted attempts at hydrogenation by Berthelot, among others. By the end of 1900, Sabatier and Senderens had demonstrated that benzene can be wholly transformed into cyclohexane through contact with nickel at a temperature of 180 degrees Celsius—a moment that Sabatier recalled as "one of the greatest joys of my life." Following this success, Sabatier became completely convinced of the efficacy, simplicity, and safety of the technique and began expanding its application—particularly to the transformation of unsaturated hydrocarbons into saturated hydrocarbons. From 1901 to 1905, Sabatier and Senderens continued the generalizing of the process, demonstrating that nickel as a catalyst could hydrogenate nitriles into amines, aldehydes and acetones into alcohols, and both carbon dioxide and carbon monoxide into methane, as well as causing many other transformations.

In 1905, seeking a new challenge, Senderens returned to his own laboratory at the Institut Catholique. Sabatier's blossoming reputation led to his appointment as dean of the Faculty of Sciences at Toulouse, a position he had been denied twenty years earlier. This was followed two years later with a watershed in Sabatier's career. He was offered both the chair of chemistry at the Sorbonne, which had been held by Moissan, and the chair formerly held by Berthelot at the Collège de France, certainly two of the most prestigious academic positions in the country. To the amazement of most of the French scientific community, he chose to remain at Toulouse— all the more surprising a decision because Sabatier was aware of the Academy of Sciences' rule that all prospective members had to reside in Paris (the 1912 Nobel Prizes were to change that). Why he refused these offers is a matter of conjecture, but several things probably contributed. First, Sabatier was the newly installed dean of a faculty undergoing a major transition. Second, increased funding from several sources was flowing into the provincial laboratory, and he had to recognize that in Paris he would have neither equivalent facilities nor the significant personal autonomy he enjoyed at Toulouse. Third, Sabatier was rather a maverick in the French scientific community. He believed in teaching applied science; he was a conservative Catholic; and he was outspoken in his rejection of notation by chemical equivalents in favor of the periodic table. Finally, Toulouse was his home and he clearly felt comfortable there.

Although Sabatier had, from his earliest days at Toulouse, been a dedicated teacher involved in the affairs of the university, his appointment as dean and his burgeoning reputation involved him more and more in the administrative—and political—activities of the university. He continued his laboratory work, by this time being assisted by his students Alphonse Mailhe and Marcel Murat. After 1907, he and Mailhe established that some metallic oxides functioned as catalysts not only for hydrogenation and dehydrogenation but also for hydration and dehydration. With Murat, he achieved a method for the efficient hydrogenation of benzoic acid and its esters.

Following his receipt of the Nobel Prize, Sabatier, in 1913, published his major work, *La Catalyse en chimie organique*, translated into English in 1923 as *Catalysis in Organic Chemistry*. In this book, he not only presented the results of much of his research but also advanced a theory of catalysis which disagreed with the assumptions of such notable earlier chemists as Jöns Jakob Berzelius and Wilhelm Ostwald. Before Sabatier's theory, it was accepted that such catalyzed reactions as platinum on the combustion of oxygen and hydrogen were caused by the absorption of the gases into the porous metal. Sabatier, however, believed that a short-lived, unstable intermediary substance forms on the surface of the catalyst. This intermediary agent, produced by a reaction between the catalytic agent and one of the reactants, then combines with the second reactant to regenerate the catalyst. Where his predecessors identified the physical nature of the catalyst as accelerating a reaction, Sabatier argued that the catalyst actually induces the reaction through the chemical affinity (attraction) of the catalyst for another substance.

After 1912, though he continued his research, more of his energies were directed to the metamorphosis of Toulouse into a major research institution. Between 1906 and 1909, Sabatier founded the Institut de Chimie (institute of chemistry), the Institut Électrotechnique (electrical technology), and the Institut Agricole (agriculture). Money became more plentiful after his Nobel Prize, and Sabatier donated much of it to the Institute of Chemistry. The success of these technical schools in producing engineers changed Toulouse from a university with 64 percent of its enrollment in law to one where 40 percent of the enrollment was in science (and another 25 percent in pharmacy and medicine). From his youth, Sabatier had expressed as a goal the decentralization of the Ministry of Education. At first there were placement problems, since the development of French industry lagged behind the rest of Europe. Then there were financial crises, especially following World War I, but Sabatier's vision did not falter. He managed to keep his programs healthy, even though he offended some members of the faculty and administration in doing so.

In addition to the French Academy, Sabatier was a foreign member of many learned groups, including the academies of Britain, Spain, the Netherlands, and Belgium, and the American and British Chemical Societies. Among his many awards were the French Jecker Prize (with Senderens in 1905), the Davy Medal (1915) and the Royal Medal (1918) of the Royal Society, and the Franklin Medal (1935) of the Franklin Institute in the United States.

Considering the incredible advances of modern science, it is easy to overlook the contributions of Paul Sabatier. He did not make the kind of discovery that made Marie Curie a household name, and his methods and techniques have been largely superseded by more modern processes. If his achievements seem to lack glamour, however, it is necessary to remember that many of the prosaic but practical products that typify the twentieth century had their origins in his laboratory. Three characteristics stand out in a survey of Sabatier's career: his conviction that, whatever the problem, talent and hard work will prevail; his support of science that has a practical application; and his commitment to the provincial university where he spent forty-seven years as a faculty member, twenty-two of them as dean of the faculty of science.

Bibliography

Primary
CHEMISTRY: *Recherches thermiques sur les sulfures*, 1880; *Leçons élémentaires de chimie agricole*, 1890; *La Catalyse en chimie organique*, 1913 (*Catalysis in*

Organic Chemistry, 1923); "How I Have Been Led to the Direct Hydrogenation Method by Metallic Catalysts," *Industrial and Engineering Chemistry*, vol. 18, 1926.

Secondary

Crawford, Elisabeth T. *The Beginnings of the Nobel Institution: The Science Prizes, 1901-1915*. New York: Cambridge University Press, 1984. In this account of the science prizes awarded between 1901 and 1915, Crawford details the legal and political maneuvering that went into the establishment of the awards following Nobel's death and the nature of the committees that awarded the early science prizes. She provides much information about the decision to award Sabatier and Grignard the prize jointly, which was the first and only time, until 1929, that the chemistry prize had been divided.

Dupuy, Charles H., and Kenneth L. Rinehart, Jr. *Introduction to Organic Chemistry and Related Processes*. New York: John Wiley & Sons, 1967. This is one of the most clearly written of the many introductory textbooks in organic chemistry, with a good discussion of saturated hydrocarbons.

Farber, Eduard. *Nobel Prize Winners in Chemistry, 1901-1961*. Rev. ed. New York: Abelard-Schuman, 1963. Farber's book contains not only a brief biographical sketch of each winner but also a description of the prizewinning work and, most important, a comment on the applications of the work in the years since the award.

Noller, Carl. *Textbook of Organic Chemistry*. Philadelphia, Pa.: W. B. Saunders, 1966. Another good introductory textbook, which includes a brief discussion of Sabatier and Senderens and an elaborate discussion of hydrogenation and related matters.

Nye, Mary Jo. *Science in the Provinces: Scientific Communities and Provincial Leadership in France, 1860-1930*. Berkeley: University of California Press, 1986. Without a doubt, this provides the best single study of Sabatier's career at Toulouse and his role in decentralizing leadership in the French sciences. An entire chapter is devoted to Sabatier by Nye, who actually began the work as a study of Sabatier.

Partington, James Riddick. "Paul Sabatier." *Nature* 174 (1954): 859-860. This notice pays tribute to Sabatier's development of his system of catalysis on the one-hundredth anniversary of his birth.

Paul, Harry W. *From Knowledge to Power: The Rise of the Scientific Empire in France, 1860-1939*. Cambridge, England: Cambridge University Press, 1985. This book covers Sabatier's entire scientific career. While he is only one of hundreds of scientists discussed, the book provides a superb background to the French science of the period. It also provides some insights into Sabatier's career as a university administrator.

Sabatier, Paul, and Paul H. Emmett. *Catalysis Then and Now*. Translated by E. Emmet Reid. Englewood Cliffs, N.J.: Franklin Publishing Co., 1965. This is a revised translation of Sabatier's 1913 book, expanded to include much of his later work; it serves as a good introduction to the development of Sabatier's methods.

Daniel J. Fuller

1913

Chemistry
Alfred Werner, France and Switzerland

Physics
Heike Kamerlingh Onnes, The Netherlands

Physiology or Medicine
Charles Richet, France

Literature
Rabindranath Tagore, India

Peace
Henri Lafontaine, Belgium

ALFRED WERNER
1913

Born: Mulhouse, France; December 12, 1866
Died: Zurich, Switzerland; November 15, 1919
Nationality: French; after 1894, Swiss
Areas of concentration: Coordination chemistry and chemical bonding

Werner broadened existing ideas of chemical bonding to include compounds which are today known as coordination compounds. He studied their properties and originated many basic experimental methods for investigating them. These studies led to an understanding of the arrangement of the atoms in space—the stereo-chemistry of coordination compounds

The Award

Presentation

Former Councillor Theodor Nordström, President of the Royal Swedish Academy of Sciences, presented the 1913 Nobel Prize in Chemistry to Alfred Werner. He began his address by discussing the concept of valence—the combining power of an atom. Valences were traditionally thought to come in two varieties: positive and negative. An atom with a valence of (+2) could combine with one other atom of (−2) valence or with two other atoms of (−1) valence each. Any combination of atoms would be possible if it allowed even matching of (+) and (−) valences. A limitation of this primitive valence theory was its inability to deal with so-called "complex" or "molecular" compounds. Werner was able to achieve an understanding of this group of compounds by expanding the idea of valence to include secondary valences. Some atoms have four such valences, some have six, as Werner and others had demonstrated experimentally. The entities bonded to an atom by these secondary valences take up certain orientations in space.

Werner was able to show that when six secondary valences are used (giving a "coordination number" of six), the bonded entities are able to spread out evenly in space to produce an octahedral arrangement. This "octahedron theory" has been substantiated by extensive experimental work involving the preparation, purification, and characterization of hundreds of compounds. In some cases, compounds have been found to exist in two forms differing only in a subtle way, as revealed by the rotation of the plane of polarized light. This optical isomerism, previously known for tetrahedral carbon compounds, was shown by Werner to occur in octahedral metal coordination compounds as well. This stereochemical finding has been called the most important discovery in chemistry in recent times, Nordström concluded, and it makes Werner the founder of inorganic stereochemistry.

Nobel lecture

On December 11, 1913, Alfred Werner delivered his Nobel lecture, entitled "On the Constitution and Configuration of Higher-Order Compounds." After paying tribute to his teacher, Arthur Hantzsch, Werner discussed the contributions made by several Scandinavian chemists to the field of molecular compounds. C. W. Blomstrand and P. T. Cleve had tried to understand the properties of cobalt-ammonia complexes in terms of paired chains of ammonia molecules bonded at one end to the cobalt atom. In some formulations, a double cobalt atom was assumed. Later work by S. M. Jörgensen resulted in modification of the Blomstrand theory to permit single ammonia molecules to be bonded between the metal atom and the acid radicals (such as chloride or nitrite) that were present.

Starting from these ideas, Werner was led by his experiments to the view that no chains of ammonia molecules existed, but that all the ammonia molecules bonded directly to the metal. When acid radicals bonded directly to the metal, it was found that they became unavailable for the conduction of electricity in water solution. Thus it became possible to define the number of entities directly bonded to the metal—the "coordination number," as Werner called it. Metals such as platinum or cobalt have a maximum coordination number of six. Hence a metal compound with fewer than six groups bonded to the metal atom can be expected to be able to react with additional molecules or groups until the total reaches six. This insight in turn makes it possible to build a structural theory that clarifies the changes that occur when complexes are subjected to heat or when they interact with water to give acidic or basic solutions.

In the final half of his lecture, Werner concentrated on compounds in which the metal atom bonds to six groups. It was of interest to explore the arrangement in space, or stereochemistry, of the six groups. Werner considered three possibilities: a hexagonal planar structure in which the six groups occupied positions equidistant from one another and from the metal atom, and existed in the same plane; a prismatic structure with two superimposed equilateral triangles of groups sandwiching a metal atom; and an octahedral structure similar to the prismatic structure but with one triangle twisted by 60 degrees relative to the other. Using diagrams of these possible structural types, it is possible to predict the number of ways of arranging the bonded groups when they are of more than one kind—if, for example, cobalt were to bond to four ammonia molecules and two chlorides. The hexagonal model leads to a prediction of three arrangements of ammonia molecules and chlorides around cobalt: Chlorides could occupy adjacent, alternate, or diametrically opposite positions relative to one another. A chemist attempting to verify the hexagonal model would be trying to prepare and identify three different compounds (isomers) with the same composition: one cobalt, two chlorides, and four ammonias. The prismatic model would similarly predict three isomers, but the octahedral model predicts only two: The chlorides may occupy either adjacent positions or diametrically opposed positions at the corners of the octahedron centered on the metal atom.

Critical reception
Werner was at the peak of his productivity as a scientist when, in the second

week of November, 1913, he received word that he had been awarded the Nobel Prize in Chemistry—the first Swiss chemist to be a recipient. Public reaction was immediate and enthusiastic, particularly in Werner's own city of Zurich and in the rest of Switzerland. A torchlight parade took place near the University in Zurich, and Werner received a wreath of honor from the assembled students. A few months after the Nobel Prize ceremony, the Swiss Chemical Society held a special conclave to honor Werner, and a fund was established to provide a Werner Prize each year to a young and deserving member of the society.

Newspapers in Zurich carried notices of the Nobel Prize award to Werner, and *The New York Times* carried a small item on the prizes, noting that "Professor Werner" had received from the hand of the King of Sweden a prize worth $40,000.

S. M. Jörgensen, the Danish chemist who had attacked Werner's coordination theory, lay on his deathbed as Werner and his wife passed through Copenhagen on their way to Stockholm in December, 1913. It is possible, though not certain, that Werner may have visited his old rival and made peace with him.

Biography

Alfred Werner was born on December 12, 1866, in Mulhouse, the fourth child of a French ironworker Jean-Adam Werner and his second wife, Salome Jeanette (née Tesche). Mulhouse is a city in Alsace, a region that fell under German rule in 1871. The Werner family, although basically French, stayed in Mulhouse, and Alfred was subject to both French and German influences while growing up. His elementary education took place in a Catholic parochial school.

After graduation from the equivalent of high school at age nineteen, he combined a year of compulsory military service in the German army with some coursework in chemistry in Karlsruhe, Germany. Werner then attended the Polytechnic University in Zurich, Switzerland, obtaining his first degree in the field of chemistry in 1889. By now he was deeply interested in chemical research, and he continued his studies under the direction of Arthur Hantzsch, a chemistry professor at the Zurich Polytechnic; he was awarded the doctorate in 1890. As his work became known through his publications, Werner was able to move to a position at the University of Zurich, where he held a professorship. In 1894, he married Emma Giesker, a pastor's adopted daughter, and shortly afterward became a Swiss citizen. The Werners had two children: Alfred, born in 1897, and Charlotte, born in 1902. Werner's fame attracted many graduate students and coworkers, and a steady volume of research reports emanated from the laboratory at Zurich. Other universities, such as those of Berne, Basel, Vienna, and Wurzburg, made offers to Werner, but he declined them all. He was promoted to the highest academic rank, Ordinarius Professor, in 1895, and began to receive honorary memberships and degrees in recognition of his work. He also became involved in administrative work at his university and devoted much time to planning the construction of a new building for the chemical institute. The building was completed and dedicated in 1909.

As is sometimes the case with individuals of strong motivation and dedication to scientific achievement, Werner had personal habits which eventually ruined his health. He worked long hours, often in a poorly ventilated laboratory, and smoked cigars frequently. He enjoyed late hours playing cards or chess, and social drinking. Although he also devoted himself to hiking and other outdoor activities, the net effect of his life-style was to produce periodic exhaustion, headaches, and, on one occasion, a severe bout of pneumonia. A year or two after he received the Nobel Prize he began to have trouble lecturing. He spent time in various health resorts in an attempt to find rest and relaxation, but to little avail. Symptoms of progressive degenerative disease—probably arteriosclerosis—appeared and grew worse. He resigned from the university in 1919 and died shortly afterward in a Zurich hospital, about a month before his fifty-third birthday.

Scientific Career

Werner's early ideas on chemical bonding and valence, as expressed in his thesis "Beitrage zur Theorie der Affinitat und Valenz" (1891; "Contributions to the Theory of Affinity and Valence," 1967), provided the starting point for most of his future endeavors. He regarded the existing ideas of valence, embodied in the work of August Kekulé, as too rigid. He preferred to think of chemical affinity as a force which radiated out equally in all directions from an atom's central core. Two years later, from these preliminary ideas, grew Werner's coordination theory, with its concepts of primary and secondary valence, coordination number, and coordination sphere stereochemistry. The 1891 publication was a milestone in Werner's academic career, since he was able to use it as part of his credentials in applying for a post at the University of Zurich.

Although Werner's most enduring fame rests on his work with inorganic complex compounds, he started his scientific career as an organic chemist. In 1890, Werner's name appears as coauthor (with Arthur Hantzsch) of a paper entitled "On the Spatial Arrangement of the Atoms in Nitrogen-Containing Molecules." The paper was excerpted from Werner's doctoral dissertation and contains a theory of nitrogen stereochemistry based on the concept of a tetrahedral nitrogen atom. Using this concept, it was possible to account for the puzzling existence of isomeric forms of organic nitrogen compounds such as oximes, which contain carbon-nitrogen double bonds. The new theory provided a clear structural basis for organic nitrogen compounds and motivated the extensive experimental work, much of it carried out by Hantzsch and his students, that led to its eventual acceptance.

Werner also contributed to the understanding of organic salts such as organic ammonium salts and oxonium salts. With regard to the former, he showed that a tetrahedral nitrogen atom could serve as the core of a structural model that predicted optical isomerism for certain salts. In this work, Werner was using the same idea that served so well with inorganic coordination compounds: that an atom (nitrogen in this case, but metal atoms such as cobalt and platinum in later cases) could exhibit two levels of valence in the same compound. An ammonium salt containing four organic groups and an acid radical such as chloride need not have all five parts bonded the same way to nitrogen, but could have four bonded one way to make a tetrahedral arrangement, with the chloride held differently (ionically).

A turning point in Werner's scientific career occurred in the events leading up to his important paper "Contribution to the Constitution of Inorganic Compounds," published in 1893. Werner awoke suddenly at 2:00 A.M. with a new idea that may have come to him in a dream. He went to his desk and began to write the paper, which he completed more than twelve hours later. The paper is remarkable for the way in which Werner brings together hundreds of experimental details from the literature and systematizes them. He demonstrates the intellectual power and comprehensive knowledge that impressed colleagues and competitors alike. This paper contained the basic ideas of the coordination theory that would be his major scientific interest for the rest of his life. It also marked the beginning of a time when Werner began more and more to think of himself as an inorganic chemist.

For him, there were two sorts of valence, or chemical binding power, available to an atom of any particular element. The traditional sort, which chemists had long recognized, Werner called the *Hauptvalenz* (principal valence). An element such as cobalt or iron could exhibit a principal valence of three, for example. This meant that an atom of iron or cobalt could combine with three singly charged negative ions, such as chloride ions, or with one triply charged negative ion, such as a phosphate ion, to form a neutral salt. In addition, Werner postulated a secondary valence (*Nebenvalenz*) for each atom. The secondary valence of a metal atom could be satisfied not only by binding negative ions ("acid radicals," as Werner called them) but also by binding neutral molecules such as water or ammonia. In this way it became possible to account for the existence of addition compounds and salt hydrates which had not been adequately explained by existing ideas of valence.

Werner began systematic investigation of the coordination compounds of cobalt, chromium, and platinum with the aim of confirming his theoretical ideas. His views came under vigorous attack from some chemists, such as S. M. Jörgensen in Copenhagen. Critics charged that Werner had broken with tradition without adequate evidence. Instead of building little by little to a theory, he had jumped ahead by a leap of intuition, and this was felt to be unscientific by some members of the older generation.

Assisted by his friend and frequent collaborator Arturo Miolati, Werner produced studies of the electrical conductivity of solutions of cobalt complexes and platinum complexes that supported his idea of primary and secondary valences. In particular, the Werner theory differed from the Jörgensen theory in relation to complexes in which cobalt bonds to three neutral ammonia molecules and to three acid radicals such as nitrite. Werner and Miolati showed that the conductivity of such compounds was indeed very small, just as the new coordination theory would predict, but in contrast to the prediction of the Jörgensen theory. These studies tended to confirm the idea of a coordination number of six for cobalt in these complexes. Similar studies confirmed a coordination number of four for the platinum complexes.

It was much more difficult for Werner to satisfy his critics in the matter of the octahedral geometry he had postulated for the six-coordinate cobalt complexes. Modern methods of structure determination leave no doubt that Werner was right, but methods such as X-ray diffraction were not available in a sufficient state of perfection during Werner's lifetime to be of use. Instead, chemical methods were used, in which the attempt was made to isolate all the possible isomers corresponding to a given elemental composition. The great limitation of chemical methods lies in the fact that only negative evidence is obtained—it is impossible to determine whether a possible isomer has been overlooked.

A variation of the isomer-counting chemical method of structure proof involves the resolution of optically active compounds. The experimental evidence for tetrahedral carbon consisted mainly of the ability of chemists to separate compounds such as tartaric acid into optically active isomeric forms. This kind of experiment had been done by Louis Pasteur and had become a standard method in organic chemistry for detecting asymmetric carbon atoms—those bearing four different substituents. Werner sought to apply an extension of this method to prove the octahedral structure for cobalt atoms in complexes.

The search for resolvable cobalt complexes proved to be a long and difficult one. With the wisdom of hindsight, one can say that Werner and his coworkers, such as the indefatigable American chemist Victor King, may not have used the most promising methods for quick solution of the problem. They resorted to long sequences of fractional crystallizations to obtain the first successful resolution, which was only achieved in 1911. Ultimate success was probably attributable to their decision to use a resolving agent, which produced much better results than the previous technique. Ironically, it was later shown that some of the compounds that Werner had in his laboratory are capable of spontaneous resolution, requiring only that the experimenter allow sufficient time for crystallization to occur and recognize that resolution has occurred. Apparently Werner and King were unaware of this potentially simplifying factor. After years of effort, other resolutions were accomplished, including that of a compound with an optically active anion (negative ion) and another compound containing only cobalt, ammonia, hydroxide, and bromide— with no organic carbon. Even the most skeptical critics of the concept of asymmetric octahedral cobalt atoms were now convinced.

Werner was a rare individual who possessed the power of intellect and singleminded love of chemistry that made it possible for him to draw together a mass of experimental facts into a coherent whole. His coordination theory, confirmed by his own experiments and by those of countless successors, is the basis upon which rest all structural ideas in modern coordination chemistry. Werner was a chemist, a university professor, and an administrator who worked for better laboratory facilities at his institution and for the establishment of inorganic chemistry as a recognized and respected area of chemistry. He adhered to the highest intellectual standards himself and expected the same of others. He is considered to have been the founder of coordination chemistry, which has become a rapidly expanding and fruitful area of chemical endeavor, both in academia and in industry.

Bibliography

Primary

CHEMISTRY: "Beitrage zur Theorie der Affinitat und Valenz," *Vierteljahrsschrift der Zürcher Naturforschenden Gesellschaft*, vol. 36, 1891 ("Contributions to the Theory of Affinity and Valence," *Chymia*, vol. 12, 1967); *Lehrbuch der Stereochemie*, 1904; *Neuere Anschauungen auf dem Gebiete der anorganischen Chemie*, 1905 (*New Ideas on Inorganic Chemistry*, 1911).

Secondary

Karrer, Paul. "Fasciculus Extraordinarius: Alfred Werner (1866-1919)." *Helvetica Chimica Acta* 3 (1967): 196-224. This centennial tribute contains articles by Paul Karrer (winner of the Nobel Prize in Chemistry in 1937), who studied with Werner, and by G. Schwartzenbach, who developed uses for coordination compounds in chemical analysis. Various memorabilia such as letters and photographs are included. Research papers make up the remainder of the volume.

Kauffman, George B. "Alfred Werner." In *Dictionary of Scientific Biography*, vol. 14, edited by Charles Coulston Gillispie. New York: Charles Scribner's Sons, 1976. A short biography is provided, as well as an excellent account of Werner's achievements in coordination chemistry. This reference is more widely available in general libraries than the author's full-length biography of Werner.

—————. *Alfred Werner: Founder of Coordination Chemistry*. New York: Springer-Verlag, 1966. Kauffman's biography, published in the centennial year of Werner's birth, is the best available source for information on Werner's life, and it also serves as a key to the author's many other writings on Werner. Kauffman was able to use original letters written by Werner and interviewed Werner's daughter and other people who knew Werner. Contains a complete list of Werner's own writings, lectures, memberships, and honors, together with references to reviews of his works and to other biographical material.

—————. *Classics in Coordination Chemistry*. Part 1, *The Selected Papers of Alfred Werner*. Mineola, N.Y.: Dover, 1968. English translations are given for six of Werner's original scientific papers from the period between 1893 and 1914. All the original experimental details are included, permitting the reader to see the methods that Werner worked out for studying complex compounds. There are photographs of Werner and his collaborators and of some of their equipment and samples. Annotations place the papers in historical context.

—————. "General Historical Survey to 1930." In *Comprehensive Coordination Chemistry*, vol. 1, edited by Geoffrey Wilkinson. Oxford: Pergamon Press, 1987. The earliest discovered coordination compound may have been the dye alizarin, mentioned in historical writings dating from 450 B.C. Kauffman traces the experimental work on coordination compounds from the eighteenth to early twentieth centuries, including references to the work of Leopold Gmelin, F. A. Genth, and O. W. Gibbs. Werner's coordination theory is discussed, as are earlier theories by Thomas Graham, Jöns Jakob Berzelius, and several others. Post-

Werner developments such as early X-ray diffraction results are included. An extensive list of references is provided.

Kauffman, George B., ed. *Werner Centennial*. Washington, D.C.: American Chemical Society, 1967. Much of this volume is devoted to technical research papers only indirectly related to Werner; nevertheless, it contains several chapters of historical materials, including personal recollections by one of Werner's coworkers, details of the Werner-Jörgensen controversy, and discussions of Werner's researches on organic nitrogen compounds and dyes. Extensive references are given, and photographs of Werner, his laboratory, and some of his original correspondence appear.

Nobelstiftelsen. *Nobel Lectures: Chemistry, 1901-1921*. New York: Elsevier, 1966. A complete translation of Werner's Nobel lecture (originally presented in German) is found in this reference.

Wheland, G. W. *Advanced Organic Chemistry*. 2d ed. New York: John Wiley & Sons, 1949. Wheland discusses Werner's theory of racemization of optically active carbon compounds and the work of Werner and Hantzsch on syn- and anti-isomerism in oximes. The author cites more recent work in these areas, showing how the original ideas have been extended.

John R. Phillips

1914

Chemistry
Theodore William Richards, United States

Physics
Max von Laue, Germany

Physiology or Medicine
Robert Bárány, Austria

Literature
no award

Peace
no award

THEODORE WILLIAM RICHARDS
1914

Born: Germantown, Pennsylvania; January 31, 1868
Died: Cambridge, Massachusetts; April 2, 1928
Nationality: American
Area of concentration: Atomic weights

Richards developed procedures for the accurate determination of the atomic weights of thirty different elements. His precise work in the identification and removal of sources of error in previous experimenters' work distinguished him as an innovator in chemical methods

The Award

Presentation

The 1914 Nobel Prize ceremonies were postponed because of the international tensions leading to World War I. The Nobel Committee decided to announce the 1914 awards the following year, however, shortly before announcing the 1915 winners; the ceremonies themselves were postponed until after the war. Professor Henrik Gustav Söderbaum, an analytical chemist and a member of the Nobel Committee for Chemistry, prepared the address for the presentation of the Nobel Prize in Chemistry for 1914 to Theodore William Richards. Söderbaum surveyed the early history of atomic weight determination and described the important contributions that Richards had made to this field. Söderbaum first noted the quantitative scope of Richards' work. Twenty-one atomic weights were determined by Richards himself or by those under his direct supervision; nine other weights were obtained by those trained by him.

Richards' work was also important because he determined the weights of those elements which were considered fundamental—that is, they were used to calculate the atomic weights of other elements.

In the beginning of his work, Richards was understandably hesitant to question the values for the atomic weights of elements that had been obtained by the respected chemist Jean-Servais Stas. These had been accepted as valid for more than thirty years. In 1904, however, after many years of careful work, Richards demonstrated that Stas's atomic weight for sodium was too high and that his value for chlorine was too low. Many of the other elements determined by Stas were then redetermined.

Richards not only demonstrated the incorrectness of the previous results but also determined the causes of the mistakes and pointed out ways to avoid them in the future. For example, he showed that working with smaller amounts of material in very dilute solutions helped to prevent impurities precipitating with solids. He also developed special apparatus for the exclusion of moisture; he was cited as a "reformer of chemical methods and practices."

Nobel lecture

Originally because of World War I and later because of a family illness, Richards was unable to attend the Nobel ceremonies. His lecture, dated December 6, 1919, was simply entitled "Atomic Weights." He began the lecture by acknowledging his debt to the scientists who studied atomic weights before him—especially Jöns Jakob Berzelius, Charles de Marignac, and Jean-Servais Stas. He spoke of his desires to know more about the fundamental nature of matter and to help man better control his living circumstances as motivating his study.

Richards chose to study atomic weights because "these unique numbers seemed to be the most definite and unchanging of all the properties of material." He saw atomic weights as hieroglyphics that tell the story of the beginning of the universe. Accuracy in determining atomic weights is a first step in understanding their meaning, in providing insight into the mysteries of chemistry.

In the laboratory, Richards determined the amount of one element needed to combine with a given amount of another element. His first study of atomic weights was performed in graduate school at Harvard University under the guidance of Professor Josiah Parsons Cooke. They came to the conclusion that the ratio of oxygen to hydrogen was 16.000 to 1.008, considerably less than the 16 to 1 ratio previously thought.

Next Richards studied samples of copper from Germany and America and found them to have the same atomic weight, a weight higher than previously reported. The new atomic weight for copper was confirmed by electrochemical studies. These results led Richards to question the accuracy of earlier published work concerning atomic weights. He began with barium and extended his study to other alkaline earth metals.

The most crucial set of experiments undertaken by Richards were those in which he revised the procedure used by Stas to determine the atomic weights of sodium and chlorine. He found that Stas had an "unsuspected impurity" in his silver that had caused him to recover less silver chloride than should have been produced. This in turn caused a low value for the atomic weight of chlorine and a high one for sodium. Additional problems were also the result of impurities in the precipitate. Richards was able to find the reasons for Stas's errors and to eliminate them. He also realized that smaller amounts of material would lead to smaller errors. These new weights for sodium and chlorine led to the redetermination of a number of other alkali metals, sulfur, and nitrogen; lithium, iron, calcium, and carbon were also determined.

Comparisons of samples of radioactive and common lead showed a significantly lower atomic weight for the radioactive samples. Richards was fascinated with the existence of two kinds of atoms of lead; he mused that "no one knows how many other elements may also possess so-called isotopic forms of this kind." He recognized that a substance might have several atomic weights "according to the circumstances of its life history." He understood that his contributions in accurately determining atomic weights would be crucial to the study of this phenomenon.

The *Christian Science Monitor* presented its readers with an excellent account of the practical use of Richards' work in the assaying of ores. The newly calculated weight of copper was two-fifths of one percent more than the previous one; this small difference meant an increase of six thousand dollars on a million dollars worth of copper ore. Similar differences in the atomic weights of other elements would affect the market value of their ores. Atomic weight studies had practical value.

In its announcement, *The New York Times* provided a brief biographical sketch of Richards and his accomplishments. Surprisingly, the fact that he was the first American to be awarded the Nobel Prize in Chemistry was not noted. *The Times* of London (November 13) announced Richards' selection in a single sentence. The short article was more concerned that a German, Max von Laue, had received the physics prize for 1914, England being at war with Germany at the time.

The *Literary Digest* rejoiced in "Three Nobel Prizes for America." It erroneously reported that the physics prize for 1914 was shared by Thomas Alva Edison and Nikola Tesla. Edison was supposedly being honored for his work on the perfection of the incandescent lamp and Tesla for the invention of the induction motor, alternating current, and for his work in power transmission. This rumor had been circulating for some time. Since the work of these researchers was already well known to its readership, the magazine devoted more than half of its article to Richards' work. It included an extensive quotation from *The Christian Science Monitor* article noted above and provided a picture. The accuracy of Richards' work was repeatedly stressed: A series on a particular element might consist of "25 or even 50 determinations."

At the time of the Nobel award, Richards was not well known to the American people. Certainly, he was not anywhere near as familar as Edison. Writing in *The Nation*, Arthur G. Webster saw this as a problem of the American educational and value systems. He noted that the Stockholm Academy of Sciences does not make awards based on newspaper polls and popularity contests—Americans had never heard of Albert Michelson before he was awarded the 1907 physics prize. He called attention to the greater interest of Europeans in the "conversation of educated men."

Biography

Theodore William Richards, the first American to receive the Nobel Prize in Chemistry, was born in the Germantown section of the present city of Philadelphia, Pennsylvania, on January 31, 1868. He was the son of talented parents—his father, William Trost Richards, was a landscape and marine painter of some prominence; his mother, Anna Matlock Richards, was a poet.

Richards was educated at home by his mother until the age of fourteen, when he entered Haverford College as a sophomore. His initial interest in science was stimulated by family friend and Harvard professor Josiah Parsons Cooke, Jr. Cooke, for example, showed Richards Saturn through a telescope when the boy was six.

After being graduated from Haverford College in 1885, Richards moved to Harvard to study chemistry under Cooke. He received an A.B. with highest honors in 1886 and a Ph.D. in 1888. His doctoral work was an introduction to atomic weight studies; he determined the relative weights of hydrogen and oxygen.

In the year after receiving his doctorate, Richards studied in Europe on a Parker Fellowship. He then returned to Harvard, to which he was connected for the rest of his career. He began as an assistant in analytical chemistry in 1889, was promoted to instructor in 1891, to assistant professor in 1894, and to full professor in 1901. Richards married Miriam Stuart Thayer in 1896; they would have three children, a girl and two boys. In 1912, Richards was appointed to the Erving Professorship in Chemistry and became director of the Wolcott Gibbs Memorial Laboratory, positions he held until his death.

During Richards' career as a faculty member, Harvard became an important training center for physical and analytical chemists. Gilbert N. Lewis, Farrington Daniels, James B. Conant, and Otto Honigschmid were all his students.

Theodore William Richards died at Cambridge, Massachusetts, on April 2, 1928.

Scientific Career

Richards' principal area of scientific research involved the determination of atomic weights. This study began when he went to Harvard as an undergraduate in 1885. Under the tutelage of an old family friend, Josiah Parsons Cooke, Jr., Richards studied the relative weights of oxygen and hydrogen. It had long been thought, and indeed seemed reasonable, that the ratio of these weights should be whole numbers. It was thought that oxygen weighed exactly sixteen times more than hydrogen, a ratio of 16:1. Richards, under Cooke's direction, found this not to be the case: He found a value of 15.869 for oxygen compared to a unit value for hydrogen. This was the subject of his doctoral thesis in 1888.

As a result of the quality of his graduate research, Richards was awarded a Parker Fellowship for a year of study in Europe. He spent the first part of his year in Göttingen, Germany, where he studied analytical chemistry and worked with two prominent chemists, Paul E. Jannasch and Victor Meyer. His projects involved determination of sulfate in the presence of iron and vapor density determinations. In the spring semester, he went to several European laboratories and spent time discussing research problems and techniques.

Upon returning to the United States in the fall of 1889, Richards accepted a position at Harvard and began the next phase of his atomic weight studies. His work with hydrogen had led him to be suspicious of the accepted value for the atomic weight of copper. Richards investigated copper from Lake Superior and from Germany and found that they had the same atomic weight. The values that he obtained, however, were one-half of a percentage point higher than had been previously reported. He repeated the classical procedures and found problems with each of them, including the difficulty of avoiding impurities in precipitates and gases and of avoiding water in products. He confirmed his results with eleven experiments and set about examining other metals.

In the course of the copper work, Richards had analyzed barium sulfate and found that the reported value of barium was also incorrect. This was redetermined, as were other metals of its group: strontium, zinc, magnesium, and calcium. During the strontium work, Richards encountered two experimental problems that tested his ingenuity. Strontium bromide readily took up water as it was transferred to a weighing bottle. To prevent this, Richards invented a bottling apparatus which permitted the transfer of material and the stoppering of the bottle in the absence of air; this new tool was used in his reactions thereafter.

The second instrument developed at this time was a nephelometer. Most of the metals were determined by displacing the silver in a silver nitrate solution: A small, known amount of pure strontium bromide was added to a silver nitrate solution of known concentration. Silver bromide precipitated; it was collected, and the amount of strontium was determined with respect to the weight of silver. The problem was that silver bromide was not 100 percent insoluble. The nephelometer allowed the determination of the amount of silver halide which remained in solution by comparing its turbidity with standards.

In 1895, Cooke died, and Harvard needed someone to take his place as a physical chemist. The college sent Richards to study in Germany for a year with Wilhelm Ostwald in Leipzig and Walther Nernst in Göttingen. This was an important move in Richards' life, as Sir Harold Hartley reported in the "Theodore William Richards Memorial Lecture" (1919). His outlook was changed; he was no longer an old-fashioned investigator but a modern physical chemist bringing to his problems the resources of a new theory.

Upon returning to Harvard in 1897, Richards determined the atomic weights of cobalt and nickel by preparing pure bromides. These were of interest because their weights were close, and scientists were wondering whether two elements could have the same weight. With great experimental care, Richards found cobalt to be slightly heavier. He also worked on a redetermination of the atomic weight of iron.

There was great interest in uranium at the beginning of the twentieth century because Marie Curie had discovered radioactivity in uranium ore samples and because uranium was the heaviest of the known elements. Richards' atomic weight studies of uranium took four years. He determined a new value which was 1.5 units lighter than previous work had suggested.

In 1903, Richards began one of his most important sets of atomic weight determinations—those of sodium and chlorine. He had prepared very pure salt crystals of sodium chlorine for some temperature studies that he was doing. Upon analysis, he found the atomic weight of sodium was 0.2 percent lower than expected from the work of Stas. At first, Richards suspected an error in his own work; however, it gradually became clear that the error was in Stas's experimental design. Richards found problems with precipitated silver chloride having some sodium chloride hidden within it. He also found that errors were introduced in the preparation of the sodium chloride. It was made in contact with platinum and hence had some of that metal as contaminant. Richards and his colleague, Roger Clark Wells, published a seventy-page paper in the *Journal of the American Chemical Society* (May, 1905), in which they show how they eliminated Stas's errors and ultimately arrived at new atomic weights for sodium and chlorine. The value for silver was also corrected in these experiments. This work was of great significance, because silver, sodium, or chlorine had been involved in the determination of virtually all other atomic weights: Changes in the values of these elements necessitated recalculation of all atomic weights.

One of Richards' most important analyses was the comparison of the atomic weights of radioactive and common lead. Sir Frederick Soddy had introduced the idea of isotopes, that is, that two materials could have the same chemical behavior and yet differ in their weights. Dr. Kasimir Fajans of Karlsruhe sent one of his pupils, Max E. Lambert, to Harvard to study the weights of lead with Richards. For ordinary lead, an atomic weight of 207.2 was determined, but radioactive lead weighed as low as 206.08. Two different varieties of lead did indeed exist. This type of atomic weight determination was the only conclusive evidence of the validity of the isotope theory until the mass spectrometer was designed in 1919.

Although Theodore Richards was most famous for determination of the atomic weights of a large number of chemical elements, almost one-half of his three hundred scientific papers are in other areas of physical chemistry. His work can be considered under the topics thermochemistry, electrochemistry, and compressibility of atoms.

Richards wrote more than sixty papers on thermochemistry, the relationship of chemistry and heat. One of his interests was in preparing standards for the calibration of thermometers. Very pure salts change from the solid to liquid state within a sharp temperature range; these transitions can serve as points on the thermometer.

Richards improved an instrument called an adiabatic calorimeter. Many chemical reactions give off heat, which is measured in the form of calories. (One calorie is the amount of heat required to increase the temperature of one gram of water by one degree Celsius.) When measuring the heat from a reaction, an experimenter had to determine how much heat was transferred to the jacket of the container. Richards redesigned the apparatus so that the outside of the system was heated at the same rate as the calorimeter. He used this device to measure the heat changes in many chemical and physical reactions.

There are three important laws, the laws of thermodynamics, that explain the behavior of heat in systems. Through his observations, Richards came very close to formulating the third law several years before Walther Nernst did so.

In his electrochemical work in determining the weights of copper and silver, Richards confirmed that a given quantity of electricity will liberate amounts of elements in proportion to their atomic weights. He thus showed that Michael Faraday's law holds with great exactness. Gilbert Newton Lewis, the great physical chemist, was Richards' first graduate student; they carried out electrochemical studies on amalgams (mixtures of metals with mercury).

For more than twenty-five years, Richards was also concerned with the compressibility of elements. He developed a method to subject elements to great pressures and determine their new volumes. With extensive graphs, he demonstrated that compressibility is related to atomic weight in a periodic way. He hoped to demonstrate other properties related to an atom's compressibility but was not very successful. In all of his chemical studies, Theodore William Richards exerted the greatest care and exactness. The son of an artist, he often explained his work using a quote from Plato: "If from any art, you take away that which concerns weighing, measuring, and arithmetic, how little is left of that art."

Bibliography

Primary
CHEMISTRY: "The Relative Values of the Atomic Weights of Hydrogen and Oxygen," *Proceedings of the American Academy of Arts and Sciences*, vol. 23, 1887 (with J. P. Cooke); "Some Electrochemical and Thermochemical Relations of Zinc and Cadmium Amalgams," *Proceedings of the American Academy of Arts and Sciences*, vol. 34, 1898 (with G. N. Lewis); "The Use of the Transition Temperatures of Complex Systems as Fixed Points in Thermometry," *Proceedings of the American Academy of Arts and Sciences*, vol. 34, 1899 (with J. B. Churchill); "A Revision of the Atomic Weights of Sodium and Chlorine," *Journal of the American Chemical Society*, vol. 27, 1905 (with R. G. Wells); "Fundamental Properties of the Elements," *Science*, vol. 34, 1911; "The Atomic Weight of Lead of Radioactive Origin," *Journal of the American Chemical Society*, vol. 36, 1914 (with Max E. Lambert); "Ideals of Chemical Investigation," *Science*, n.s. vol. 44, 1916; "Atomic Weights and Isotopes," *Chemistry Reviews*, vol. 1, 1924.

Secondary
Baxter, Gregory P. "Theodore William Richards." *Science* 68 (1928): 333-339. This obituary written by a pupil, colleague, and friend provides an overview of Richards' contributions to various fields of chemistry. It stresses the great care and exactness with which Richards approached each new problem. It provides the nonscientist with an appreciation of Richards' work.
Forbes, George Shannon. "Investigations of Atomic Weights by Theodore William Richards." *Journal of Chemical Education* 9 (1932): 452-458. Forbes wrote an excellent biographical and scientific sketch of his mentor, Richards. This article provides the general reader with personal insights into Richards' philosophy and his high ethical standards. Although atomic weight studies are the principal topic of this paper, Forbes does allude to the importance of the physical chemistry studies of Richards. There is no bibliographic material.
Harrow, Benjamin. *Eminent Chemists of Our Time*. 2d ed. New York: Van Nostrand, 1927. As the title suggests, this book provides biographical summaries of the important chemists of the early part of the twentieth century; an essay on Richards is included. Highlights Richards' career but contains personal informa-

tion such as his office furnishings, family, and finances.

Hartley, Harold. "Theodore William Richards Memorial Lecture." *Journal of the Chemical Society*, 1930: 1930-1968. This is a rather detailed account of the major accomplishments of Richards' scientific career. It provides a clear account of the various chemical procedures that finally led Richards to propose an atomic weight for silver that differed from that determined by Stas. The article also provides diagrams and explanations of the bottling device and the nephelometer, instruments that Richards developed. This is a somewhat technical paper but very clearly written.

Ihde, Aaron J. *The Development of Modern Chemistry*. New York: Harper & Row, 1964. This book provides the general reader with the historical background necessary to understand Richards' contributions to chemistry. Chapter 11 on the growth of the specialization of analytical chemistry is especially helpful for the work on atomic weights. The areas of radiochemistry and chemical thermodynamics, to which Richards contributed, are also discussed in ways understandable to the nonspecialist.

——————. "Theodore William Richards and the Atomic Weight Problem." *Science* 164 (1969): 647-651. This article provides the general reader with an overview of Richards' scientific contributions in the context of the work that had previously been performed in determining the atomic weights of atoms. The article includes listings of biographical sketches of Richards and of some of his more general addresses.

Kopperl, Sheldon Jerome. *The Scientific Work of Theodore William Richards*. Madison: University of Wisconsin Press, 1970. This dissertation of more than four hundred pages provides a definitive study of Richards. It includes a comprehensive listing of all Richards' works as well as an analysis of his contributions to the areas of atomic weight determination, thermochemistry, electrochemistry, and compressibility of gases. It also gives personal biographical material.

Helen M. Burke

1915

Chemistry
Richard Willstätter, Germany

Physics
Sir William Henry Bragg, Great Britain
Sir Lawrence Bragg, Great Britain

Physiology or Medicine
no award

Literature
Romain Rolland, France

Peace
no award

RICHARD WILLSTÄTTER
1915

Born: Karlsruhe, Germany; August 13, 1872
Died: Locarno, Switzerland; August 3, 1942
Nationality: German
Areas of concentration: Enzymes and plant pigments

Willstätter developed methods for extracting plant pigments and used these techniques to establish that there are only two types of chlorophyll responsible for the photosynthetic ability of plants. He also researched carotenoids and anthocyanins, the two other groups of molecules responsible for color in plants

The Award

Presentation
The presentation address was given by Professor Olof Hammarsten, Chairman of the Nobel Committee for Chemistry of the Royal Swedish Academy of Sciences, on December 10, 1915. Hammarsten was a physiological chemist whose research went back to the time before Richard Willstätter's birth, and he stressed the seminal nature of Willstätter's contributions. Not only was his work itself highly important, but also it laid the scientific foundations for future work unraveling the complexities of the photosynthetic process.

Earlier work on chlorophylls, the green plant pigments, had accumulated information about the chemical nature of these materials, but it suffered from a common difficulty. The processes used to remove the pigments from the rest of the plant caused changes in the pigments so that their original form could not be known. Willstätter developed extractive methods that did not suffer from this weakness and was able to "elucidate in all its essential parts the question of the chemical nature of chlorophyll."

Although the emphasis of the address and of the award was on the chlorophyll work, Hammarsten also pointed to Willstätter's work establishing the chemical nature of the carotenoids, the yellow plant pigments, and the anthocyanins, the blue and red plant pigments. World War I prevented Willstätter from attending the award presentation in 1915, and it was not until 1920 that he received the tangible award.

Nobel lecture
World War I delayed Willstätter's acceptance of the 1915 award until June 3, 1920, at which time he delivered his Nobel lecture, "On Plant Pigments." Willstätter used the delay to advantage, however, and presented a retrospective view of his work in a way that most laureates cannot. He began by stating that the intention of his work was "to establish the constitutional characteristics of the most widely distributed plant pigments, of chlorophyll in particular, and to gain some criteria with regard to its chemical function." He then proceeded to show how well his results matched his intention.

Willstätter recalled the work of Jöns Jakob Berzelius, done in the 1830's, in which acid and base extractions were used to investigate plant pigments, saying it formed the basis for his own work. These treatments cause reactions in various parts of the chlorophyll molecule. By careful analysis of the products from such treatments, Willstätter developed an understanding of these changes and reconstructed the nature of the original molecules. The information gathered was used to develop a successful method for isolating the intact chlorophyll molecule.

Prior to Willstätter's work, it had been suggested that there were a large number of pigments responsible for the shades of green in any one plant and an unimaginable number responsible for the shades seen in the whole plant world. Applying his extracting and derivational methods to more than two hundred plants, Willstätter showed that the truth was much simpler. Chlorophyll from all plants is the same and exists in two forms: blue-green chlorophyll a and yellow-green chlorophyll b. Further, these have nearly identical chemical structures, differing only by being in different oxidation states.

An outstanding result of Berzelius' early work was the recognition of a relationship between the structure of the molecules in the pigments in blood and those in leaves. Willstätter established that in both cases there was a common transformation product, phylloporphyrin. Although unable to provide the details about the chemical nature of this substance, Willstätter did show that the metal (magnesium in plant pigment and iron in blood pigment) was bound in an electrically nondissociable form to four nitrogen atoms.

Willstätter recalled briefly some results of his researches on the structure of the carotenoids and the anthocyanins, work largely unfinished because of the pressures of World War I. In these remarks, he offered insight into the effects that the war had on his research, and by inference on research in general, by relating that the flower beds that had been carefully nurtured to provide the raw materials for his program were abandoned and the flowers carried by the basketful to wounded soldiers in the local hospitals.

In closing, Willstätter expressed his hope that the methods of research that he had developed would continue to bring solutions to the problems of biochemistry, and he commended the scientists at Stockholm University who were working to understand enzymes.

Critical reception

Richard Willstätter's winning of the Nobel Prize passed almost unnoticed both at the time of the award, in the fall of 1915, and four and a half years later, when he accepted it in the summer of 1920. The primary reason for this lack of attention was the disruption of international contacts caused by World War I.

The Times of London announced the granting of the chemistry and physics awards in an article of less than two column inches on November 15, 1915. The remainder of the page was taken up with articles whose headlines spoke about heroes of the air, German U-boats, the czar's tour of the Northern Front, and the death of Booker T. Washington. *The New York Times'* announcement was equally brief and buried by the war news. Clearly, the press and the public had their minds on other things. This is further evidenced by the fact that the Nobel Committee made no chemistry awards at all in 1916, 1917, or 1919. The 1918 prize was awarded to Fritz Haber.

Willstätter makes only short reference to the award in his biography, commenting that, while at work on some war research, he received a telephone call from a Berlin newspaper telling him of the action of the Royal Swedish Academy. Included in the biography is a short, two-sentence note of congratulations from Willstätter's mentor, Adolf von Baeyer. The note is somewhat curious, as it is dated October 15, 1915—a month prior to the public announcement of the award.

When the time came to accept the award in 1920, Willstätter was part of a group of scientists, predominantly German, whose awards had been delayed and who accepted the awards together. The war was still on people's minds, and the award to Fritz Haber in 1918 received their major attention. Haber had been deeply involved with Germany's chemical weapons research, and many angry voices were raised in objection to his award. Willstätter, on the other hand, had developed a gas mask, ultimately used by both warring sides as a means of protection from chemical weapons, and did not receive public criticism. His own reaction to the awards lecture, as presented in his biography, was that it did not seem important, probably because the work for which the award had been made was far behind him. He mostly enjoyed the opportunity to be removed from the pressures of war-torn Germany and to be in the company of other fine minds.

Willstätter's death in 1942 finally brought the public acclaim that, in better times, might have come at the time of the award. *The New York Times* called him the "Einstein of Chemistry," a reference both to his being Jewish and to the quality and importance of his work; it editorialized about his "extraordinary technical proficiency and rare insight." *Chemical and Engineering News*, the *Journal of the American Chemical Society*, and the *Proceedings of the Indian Academy of Science* all carried obituary articles with similar statements of praise for Willstätter and his contribution to biological chemistry.

Biography

Richard Martin Willstätter was born in Karlsruhe, Baden, Germany, to Max and Sophie (née Ulmann) Willstätter on August 13, 1872. His early education was in Karlsruhe and Nuremberg. At the *Realgymnasium* in Nuremberg, Willstätter's academic performance earned a nomination to the prestigious royal Maximilianeum, but he was refused admission because he was Jewish. Willstätter stayed in Nuremberg, graduating in 1890, and then enrolled in the Munich Technical University. He stayed one year, then transferred to the University of Munich to do research under Alfred Einhorn and study with Adolf von Baeyer. Willstätter received his Ph.D. in 1894 and remained at the university, becoming an associate professor in 1902. In 1903, he married Sophie Lesen, with whom he had two children before her death in

1908. In 1905, Willstätter became professor of chemistry at the Federal Institute of Technology in Zurich. Ten years later, he moved to the Kaiser Wilhelm Institute in Berlin and, in 1916, returned to the University of Munich as professor of chemistry, succeeding Baeyer.

In 1924, Willstätter, at the age of fifty-eight, entered retirement, resigning his position to protest the treatment of Jews in the hiring practices of the university. No longer on the faculty, Willstätter nevertheless continued research there. Fifteen years later, the Nazi purge of Jews forced him to flee Germany under threat of arrest. He fled to Locarno, Switzerland, in 1939, where he remained until his death on August 3, 1942.

Scientific Career

Richard M. Willstätter's major scientific contributions can be placed in four chronological and subject-matter periods. He started his researches as a doctoral candidate in 1890 working under Alfred Einhorn—but with Adolf von Baeyer as his chief mentor. During this period, Willstätter learned and practiced the available techniques of chemical structure characterization by working on various alkaloids. He continued working in this area for some time following the granting of his Ph.D. in 1894. At the conclusion of that work, he entered a time during which he published a series of papers on quinones and quinone imines (at one time called "Willstätter imines"), which are chemicals that form the basis of many dyes. In 1906, while at the Federal Institute of Technology in Zurich, Willstätter inaugurated a new period by shifting his research effort into the realm of photosynthesis. This included his Nobel Prize-winning work on chlorophyll and other plant pigments and related work dealing with hemoglobin and with the photosynthetic process of plants. Following World War I, and with his appointment in 1916 to succeed Baeyer at the University of Munich, Willstätter again changed directions and began a study of the function of enzymes. This work was slowed when Willstätter resigned his position in 1924 to protest anti-Semitism in the university. He was still able to do some research through some of his students at the university, although even that came to the point where it could only be done over the telephone. With the rise of Nazism, life for Jews in Germany became increasingly difficult, but Willstätter declined several offers of university and industrial positions outside Germany because of his love for his homeland. When the Nazis issued their edict against Jews, Willstätter was one of the first victims, and his scientific work ended in 1938.

Any one of these periods of his career contained a quality and quantity of work that would have assured Willstätter an acclaimed position as a chemist. Equally impressive is that all of his work was done with great verve. In his acceptance of the 1933 Josiah Willard Gibbs Medal of the American Chemical Society, he described his love of research: "To delve into nature's secrets is something beautiful beyond description; it is an enviable privilege of the scientist to conquer obstacles, when all known devices were deemed inadequate for their circumvention, and to penetrate far enough to lift nature's veil a little more and more from her hidden treasures."

The common threads that run through Willstätter's work are structure and function and their relationship. His doctoral dissertation dealt with the investigation of a cleavage product of cocaine that had been discovered by Einhorn. Einhorn had determined this product to be based on a six-membered ring and turned the task of further elucidation of its structure over to Willstätter. Willstätter's thesis added much to the understanding of the molecule but did not solve the structural problem. In fact, the solution came four years later when he proved that the compound was actually based on a seven-member ring. Working on that problem (and others that were interpolated into his time as a student) gave Willstätter a sound basis in structure determination and a high respect for the necessity of careful, high-quality, reproducible work.

Upon Willstätter's graduation, Einhorn extracted a promise from the young researcher that he would not enter cocaine research. Willstätter honored the promise by initiating a study of atropine, a very similar substance. In so doing, he earned the lasting enmity of Einhorn. Willstätter was able to show, by using the chemical techniques available at that time, that atropine was composed of one seven-member carbon ring and a second ring containing five carbons and a nitrogen. As final proof of his suggested structure, Willstätter carried out the complete synthesis of atropine, pointing the way to the synthesis of cocaine.

During the time that German chemistry was almost synonymous with analine dye chemistry, Willstätter was right in the midst of this work, doing research on the preparation, structure, and properties of quinonoid substances. Most notable in this area of work were his experiments dealing with aniline black, an industrial dye material, and the controversy that was generated by his results. Willstätter and coworkers, using carefully controlled laboratory methods, prepared and characterized what they considered to be pure aniline black in the form of a nigraniline, a triquinonoid substance. Arguments were brought against this suggestion by chemists working in the dye industry who favored an azine structure; they claimed that Willstätter's work was faulty and his materials impure. This controversy, actively debated for more than three years, was evidently quite painful to Willstätter and was still not resolved at the time of his death.

Early in his student years with Baeyer, Willstätter had expressed the ambition of solving the chemical problems associated with plant pigments and their place in the assimilation of carbon dioxide by plants. With his move to Zurich in 1905, he had the opportunity and the facilities to begin this work. The first of twenty-four papers with chlorophyll as their subject was published in 1906, and the work continued until the disruption caused by World War I. This area of research can be divided into four sections: chlorophyll, hemoglobin, photosynthesis, and anthocyanins and carotenoids. Before any of this could start, however, the first need was to develop methods of producing large enough quantities of the pigments in pure form. Willstätter satisfied that need by using extractions with immissible solvents (a technique that had been recently suggested by G. G. Stokes) that were followed by a series of reactions depending on the acid and base characteristics of the separated materials.

Two questions concerning chlorophyll were soon answered. Chlorophyll was not a class of substances with a large number of members, different ones for different plants, as had been suggested. It was rather a single substance occurring in two modifications, together, in all plants. The magnesium known to be associated with chlorophyll was not an impurity but was an integral part of the molecule. In further refining these answers, Willstätter showed that chlorophyll a and chlorophyll b exist in a constant ratio to each other in all plants and that chlorophyll b is an oxidized form of chlorophyll a. The magnesium ion is chemically bound with the four nitrogen-containing groups within the organic part of the molecule. Later work developed the three-dimensional structure of chlorophyll, but the proximate structure determined by Willstätter stands as true.

Almost as a sideline, Willstätter researched the colored component of blood, because it was recognized as being similar to chlorophyll. He applied the same degradation techniques to hemoglobin that he had to chlorophyll and produced the same parent organic compound from each—a molecule containing thirty-one carbon atoms. The difference between them lay in the replacement of chlorophyll's magnesium by iron in hemoglobin. Fifteen years later Hans Fischer showed that, in this case, Willstätter had erred and that the two pigments had foundation compounds that differed by one carbon atom, with the hemoglobin molecule being the larger.

When Willstätter dropped his efforts on chlorophyll itself, he remained keenly interested in the process of photosynthesis. His interest led him to perform experiments dealing with measuring the ratio of absorbed carbon dioxide to evolved oxygen; the process as it occurs in the dark; the relation between chlorophyll content and rate of photosynthesis; and the variation of chlorophyll content during the process of photosynthesis. There were no great successes in this work, but new knowledge was gained, and the development of new knowledge was something of which Willstätter was always proud.

Moving to the nongreen parts of plants, Willstätter looked into the chemistry of the groups of substances known as the anthocyanins and carotenoids, which are responsible, in large measure, for the bright and varied colors of flowers and fruits. He again utilized his insight into chemical separations to isolate the various molecules present. As with chlorophyll, there proved to be a relatively small group of compounds present. These few compounds, in various combinations and acid or base modifications, were responsible for the vast number of hues evident in flowers and fruits. Willstätter again applied his experience with degradation analysis to propose structures for many of these materials. At this point, however, most of his coworkers were drafted into military serivce. Although Willstätter was deferred from service because of an earlier mountain-climbing injury, the research work was halted. The Nobel award certificate that Willstätter carried with him when he escaped from Germany was decorated around its border with green leaves, blue cornflowers, scarlet geranium blossoms, and cherry-red berries in recognition of this section of his work.

The move to the University of Munich brought Willstätter to the last phase of his researches—the structure and function of enzymes. It was this area to which he referred at the close of his Nobel address as the "most important future problem of physiological chemistry." Utilizing his belief that good experimentation required materials of high purity, Willstätter first applied his talents and insight to the purification of individual enzymes from the mixtures that were, at that time, used for research purposes. His separation method was fractionation based on selective adsorption of the colloidal enzymes on a variety of solid adsorbents, followed by finer separation based on the chemical properties of the individuals. In this manner he was able to obtain samples of pure enzymes for further structure and function characterization. Undertaken with a large group of collaborators, Willstätter's work included studies of enzymes in the classes of glucosidases, lipases, proteinases, peptidases, and peroxidases. He was, however, working under the conception that enzymes were not pure substances but rather were chemical systems, so he never attempted to crystallize an enzyme. He made significant contributions in terms of enzyme specificity, activation, and inhibition, as well as investigating the effect of pH and temperature on the enzyme's activity. By this work, Willstätter prepared the ground for later discoveries, some made by his young collaborators.

There are several indications of Willstätter's place of importance in the development of chemistry; one is the treatment accorded him by his peers. Willstätter was elected a member of the Prussian Academy of Sciences and of most of the academies in Europe as well as the American Academy. The British Chemical Society named him an honorary fellow in 1927. He was awarded the Davy Medal by the Royal Society of London in 1932 and the Josiah Willard Gibbs Medal by the American Chemical Society in 1933; he had previously been elected as a foreign member of both these societies. Several universities conferred honorary degrees upon Willstätter, including the University of Paris, University of Oxford, and Manchester University. Clearly, his work was seen as being of high quality by those who were involved in doing chemical research.

Another indication is the work that was accomplished by others following the trails that Willstätter opened. He is generally recognized as a great pioneer in organic chemistry, breaking new ground and establishing new methods for the solution of the problems uncovered there. Several other Nobel Prizes have been awarded for research in the areas of structural chemistry, chlorophyll, photosynthesis, and enzyme studies. All of those studies reach back to contributions made by Willstätter. It is unclear whether Willstätter's greater contribution was in the answers that he found in his own research or in the questions that his research opened for others to attempt to answer.

Bibliography

Primary

CHEMISTRY: *Investigations on Chlorophyll: Methods and Results*, 1913 (with Arthur Stoll); *Investigations on the Assimilation of Carbon Dioxide*, 1918 (with Stoll);

"Leaf Pigments," in Emil Abderhalden, ed., *Handbook of Biological Methods*, 1924; "Alkalimetric Determination of Amino Acids and Peptides," in *Handbook of Biological Methods*, 1925; *Problems and Methods in Enzyme Research*, 1927; *Investigations on Enzymes*, 1928 (with Wolfgang Grasmann, Heinrich Krant, Richard Kuhn, Ernst Waldschmidt-Leitz, and O. Ambros); "A Chemist's Retrospects and Perspectives," *Science*, vol. 78, 1933; "Chlorophyllase," in *Handbook of Biological Methods*, 1936.

Secondary

Armstrong, Henry E. "Scientific Worthies: XLV. Richard Willstätter." *Nature* 120 (1927): 1-5. A somewhat philosophical review of Willstätter's life and early work, this short article considers the way Willstätter attacked problems and led others in solving them. Also included is a summary of the pigment research.

Huisgen, Rolf. "Richard Willstätter." *Journal of Chemical Education* 38 (1961): 10-15. This relatively short article, written by a German organic chemist, reviews Willstätter's chemical contributions in the context of more modern knowledge and also weaves in biographical information about Willstätter's progress through the European university system.

Robinson, Robert. "Willstätter Memorial Lecture." *Journal of the Chemical Society*, 1953: 999-1026. This lecture was delivered to the members of the Chemical Society and consists of a very thorough summary of Willstätter's life and work. It provides great insight into the scientist and the man and is the best short English-language source to be found.

Stieglitz, Julius. "Richard Willstätter, Leader in Organic Chemistry." *The Chemical Bulletin* 20 (1933): 173-177. This article is a review of Willstätter's chemistry and life written to acquaint members of the American Chemical Society with him prior to his visit to Chicago to receive the Gibbs Medal.

Willstätter, Richard. *From My Life: The Memoirs of Richard Willstätter*. Translated by Lilli S. Hornig. New York: W. A. Benjamin, 1965. Willstätter's biography was prepared by Arthur Stoll, posthumously, from a partly completed manuscript written by Willstätter in exile. The original manuscript was prepared without reference to original source material and is written in blocks of time rather than in strict chronology. The book treats all facets of Willstätter's life. Willstätter's years in Switzerland are written about by Stoll in an epilogue.

Kenneth H. Brown

1918

Chemistry
Fritz Haber, Germany

Physics
Max Planck, Germany

Physiology or Medicine
no award

Literature
no award

Peace
no award

FRITZ HABER
1918

Born: Breslau, Germany (modern Wrocław, Poland); December 9, 1868
Died: Basel, Switzerland; January 29, 1934
Nationality: German
Areas of concentration: Electrochemistry and nitrogen fixation

Artificial nitrogen-bearing fertilizers are of great importance in agriculture; Haber developed the first successful industrial method for combining atmospheric nitrogen with elementary hydrogen to form ammonia, a compound that is now used in agriculture around the world

The Award

Presentation

Dr. A. G. Ekstrand, President of the Royal Swedish Academy of Sciences, made the presentation address for the 1918 Nobel Prize in Chemistry. Because of international events of the time—the ending of World War I—the prize ceremony was postponed until 1920.

Ekstrand opened his address with an account of the importance of nitrogen-bearing fertilizers in crop production. Natural fertilizers, such as Chilean nitrates, were diminishing in supply so rapidly that artificial nitrogen fertilizers were being manufactured in ever-increasing amounts. The annual consumption of Chilean saltpeter was about one-half million tons, he said, and experts were of the opinion that the Chilean deposits would be exhausted within the foreseeable future. In the first decade of the twentieth century, several methods had been developed for fixing the nitrogen of the atmosphere into a usable form, but few methods survived the trial stage.

In 1904, Fritz Haber and coworkers began working at temperatures around 500 degrees Celsius and pressures of 150-200 atmospheres. Aided by catalysts such as iron, uranium, and osmium, they were able to produce more than one-fourth of a kilogram of ammonia per hour from each liter of gas used, measured at the high pressure. Heat was given off in the reaction, so the high temperature was self-sustaining. In 1910, a large factory was built at Oppau, near Frankfurt-am-Main, using the Haber ammonia process, with an annual capacity which now reached thirty thousand tons of ammonia.

The cost of producing calcium nitrate fertilizer from ammonia made by the Haber process was about the same as for that made by hydroelectric methods and was cheaper than that made by the Frank-Caro cyanamide process. In addition, Haber's process was the only method capable of operating without the use of cheap hydroelectric power. It could produce ammonia much more cheaply than any other process. Haber factories now supplied the great majority of all nitrogenous fertilizers used in Germany, Ekstrand concluded, and the method had been applied extensively in the United States.

Nobel lecture

Fritz Haber gave his Nobel lecture, "The Synthesis of Ammonia from Its Elements," on June 2, 1920, to the Royal Swedish Academy of Sciences. He said that the chemical combination of gaseous nitrogen with gaseous hydrogen to form gaseous ammonia had been known for more than a century, but it was not until the twentieth century that production of ammonia from its elements had been carried out on a substantial scale. In order to do this, a combination of successful experiments with the proper thermodynamic conditions of pressure and temperature was necessary.

Haber saw that such a synthesis of ammonia would perhaps be the most useful way of satisfying the needs of Germany, and human needs in general, for the artificial production of ammonia on an industrial scale. He said that he shared fully the conviction of Johann Gottlieb Fichte, the German philosopher, that the immediate object of science lies in its own development and in directing its influence upon the world. Therefore he had concentrated on the problem of artificial manufacture of ammonia from the nitrogen which makes up 80 percent of the air.

When chemists began to distill coal in the nineteenth century, they found ammonia among the distillation products. In 1870, ammonia was nothing but an unneeded by-product of this distillation. By 1900, however, its usefulness in agriculture had been discovered. With an average of only 1 percent nitrogen in coal, it was obvious that distillation of coal could not supply the necessary amounts of nitrogen in fertilizer form. The need for fixed nitrogen was in the range of millions of tons per year by the beginning of the twentieth century. A demand of this magnitude could be met from only one source: the almost unlimited nitrogen supply in the atmosphere.

The combination of nitrogen with hydrogen had been accomplished with the aid of electric discharge, but this method required the use of electrical energy in alarming amounts, which could be supplied cheaply enough only by hydroelectric generating plants. When he began working on the problem of the synthesis of ammonia in 1904, spontaneous combination of nitrogen and hydrogen to form ammonia was unknown; it was even held to be impossible. Various chemists and chemical engineers had worked on this problem, and Haber particularly cited Robert Wilhelm Bunsen, who had worked with Lyon Playfair in 1860 to produce small samples of ammonia by direct combination of its constituent elements. He also mentioned the cyanamide process of Adolf Frank and Heinrich Caro, which could make calcium cyanamide from nitrogen and calcium carbide. Calcium cyanamide reacts with water to form ammonia, and this latter process can take place in the soil. The only raw materials required in the Frank-Caro process are lime, coal, and nitrogen.

Haber had investigated the synthesis of nitric oxide by electrical discharge and concluded that nitrogen fixation on a large scale by this method was not feasible. In 1905, he also concluded that synthesis of ammonia from nitrogen and hydrogen was impossible. Then, in 1906, it seemed necessary to make a new study of the equilibrium in the ammonia process. Walther Nernst, as well as Haber and Robert LeRossignol, began such studies. These led Haber and LeRossignol in 1908 to take up ammonia synthesis once again, this time using catalysts to speed up the reaction. They found metallic osmium to be the most suitable catalyst. Badische Anilin-und-Soda-Fabrik aided them by undertaking the synthesis of ammonia under industrial conditions. The company substituted electrolytic (very pure) hydrogen for water-gas (impure) hydrogen, and this resulted in a successful synthesis of ammonia on a large scale for the first time.

Haber said that his method was important because very high temperatures are not necessary, nor is coal consumption required, and it promises to relieve the world of its worries about future exhaustion of supplies of saltpeter. This method may not be the final solution, but it brings new nutritive riches to mankind and aids the farmer in "changing stones into bread."

Critical reception

"Ill-advised and undiplomatic," not to mention untimely, were probably some of the kinder terms which greeted the announcement that the Nobel Prize in Chemistry for 1918 was to be awarded to Fritz Haber, the man most people regarded as chiefly responsible for the use of poison gas weapons by the German army in the just-concluded World War I. Feelings against Germany were very strong well into the 1920's among its former enemies, and giving any kind of recognition to Haber at that particular time was considered by many to be unpardonable.

When the announcement was made, there was an immediate outcry, particularly from the French scientists and scholars, attacking the Swedish Academy vehemently for "awarding the Nobel Prize for chemistry to the German who invented and developed asphyxiating gas for the German Army" in World War I. *The New York Times* for January 26, 1920, reported that Haber "was attached to the Great General Headquarters of the German Army throughout the war, in charge of poison gas and flame throwers." Other prizewinners, in economics and medicine, were French, and they declined to receive the prizes because of Haber's selection in chemistry. One headline read: "Nobel Prizes Go Begging." Dr. Francis Helme, a leading French scholar, "bitterly attacked the Swedish for honoring a German who invented, perfected, and worked out the use of deadly chlorine gas and other deathly fumes." Helme also accused the Swedes of manufacturing gas masks for the German army during the war.

An editorial in *The New York Times* the next day discussed the fact that the two French scholars, in advance of the formal announcement, had both refused to accept the honors, because of the award to Haber. The paper said that, although Haber undoubtedly had many scientific achievements to his credit besides his work on poison gas, "general sympathy will be felt with the Frenchmen who did not care to be honored in such company." This was possibly the lowest point in the entire history of the Nobel Prizes.

The New York Times for January 28, 1920, printed a letter to the editor from the

Swedish legation in Washington defending the award to Haber. Haber's method of producing ammonia, the letter stated, had been invented and published several years before the war, had proved to be of the greatest value to the world at large, and was available to all nations to the same extent. The letter also stated that no gas masks were ever made in Sweden and that during the war there was in Sweden a prohibition on the export of any kind of war material. American chemist Jerome Alexander, in a letter to *The New York Times* on February 13, 1920, defended the award to Haber, but not without offering critical remarks of his own about the defense by the Swedish legation. He said that Haber's ammonia process made Germany independent of imported nitrates which could be used for agriculture but could also be used for manufacture of "chemicals, dyes, and above all, explosives." He went on to say that the statement by the Swedish legation that "Haber plants in Germany were erected with a view to producing agricultural fertilizers" was a half-truth, since Germany did have a vital need for nitrates for explosives: "[W]ithout the Haber process it is doubtful if Germany would have started the war," Alexander said.

The remarks of the first secretary of the Swedish legation in Washington, correcting "certain remarks in the daily press" concerning the propriety of awarding the Nobel Prize in Chemistry to Haber, were published in full in *Science*, on February 27, 1920.

The full reply of Jerome Alexander to the Swedish legation was also published in *Science*, on April 2, 1920. He said that the reply of the Swedish legation "contains some erroneous conclusions and some half-truths which should not be allowed to pass unchallenged." He went on to say that whereas the Haber process "will ultimately be of great vaue to the world at large, the patents, secrets, experience, and profits were all Germany's (until after the war)." He then concluded that "the pro-German activities of certain Swedes and Swedish-Americans, and especially the abuse of Swedish diplomatic privilege by such Germans as Count Luxberg . . . have naturally created an atmosphere of suspicion against Sweden; so that . . . it is easy to understand how many believe that the award of the Nobel Prize to him was, *at this time*, ill-advised and undiplomatic."

Biography

Fritz Haber was the son of Siegfried Haber, a prosperous chemical merchant; he was born in Breslau, Germany, now Wrocław in Polish Silesia, on December 9, 1868.

Haber was a student of the aging Robert Wilhelm Bunsen at Heidelberg, who, as Haber reported in his Nobel lecture, had worked on the synthesis of ammonia from its elements but had only succeeded on a very limited scale. Under Bunsen, Haber learned analysis but little else in chemistry. Haber also studied with August Wilhelm von Hofmann, professor of chemistry at Berlin from 1865 to 1892, who discovered a method for reducing amides to amines and developed several coal tar dyes, and with Carl Theodore Liebermann, who first synthesized alizarin in 1869— leading to the German coal tar dye industry. Haber's first research in chemistry was under Liebermann and concerned derivatives of piperonal and indigo.

In 1894, Haber accepted an assistantship, under Hans Bunte, in chemical and fuel technology at the Technische Hochschule Karlsruhe, where, in 1906, he became professor of physical chemistry and electrochemistry and director of the institute. In 1898, he published his highly original book on electrochemistry, *Foundations of Technical Electrochemistry on a Theoretical Basis*, which made him famous enough that the German Bunsen Society sent him as their delegate to the meeting of the American Electrochemical Society in 1902. In 1911, Haber moved to Berlin as director of the Institute for Physical Chemistry and Electrochemistry. He remained there until 1933, when he felt constrained to resign because of the Nazi government's anti-Semitic policies and moved to Cambridge, England. He died less than a year later, on January 29, 1934, in Basel, Switzerland, where he had gone for convalescence, broken in spirit by his rejection by the Germany he had served with such loyalty and fervor. Thus, although he suffered castigation for his efforts on behalf of Germany in World War I, Germany sent him away; ironically, he was rejected in the end by the country he loved so well.

Scientific Career

Although he also wrote an outstanding book on thermodynamics, *Thermodynamics of Technical Gas Reactions* (1905; English translation, 1908), the work for which he received the Nobel Prize was in industrial chemistry—the development of a large-scale method for synthesizing ammonia. Upon being graduated from Charlottenburg, and after spending a few months in the chemical industry at his father's encouragement, he studied chemical engineering for one semester under Georg Lunge at Zurich, spent another half year in his father's chemical business, and then returned to academic life with Ludwig Knorr at Jena. There he conducted an investigation of diacetosuccinic ester.

Although his early training was mostly in organic chemistry, Haber chafed at the routine nature of the work and sought to return to chemical engineering. In 1893, he obtained an assistantship with Hans Hugo Christian Bunte, professor of chemical technology at Karlsruhe. At Bunte's suggestion, he began to study the pyrolysis (breaking apart by heat) of hydrocarbons. As a result of these studies, he proposed Haber's rule, which holds that the carbon-to-carbon bond is stronger than the carbon-to-hydrogen bond in aromatic hydrocarbons, whereas the reverse is true for aliphatic hydrocarbon compounds.

Upon attaining the rank of *Privatdozent*, his interest turned to electrochemistry. He had been working on electrochemical reduction of nitrobenzene and had also studied gas electrodes in general. He was made Professor Extraordinarius at Karlsruhe in 1898 and a full professor in 1906. He worked with electrode determinations of acidity, developing the theory of the quinhydrone electrode, which was used to measure acidity in solution. In 1909, he helped to develop the glass electrode, which is still the most widely used electrode for measuring acidity.

In his 1905 *Thermodynamics of Technical Gas Reactions*, he showed that the indeterminant constant quantity that came out of the free energy equation in gas reactions (an integration constant related to the change in entropy) would disappear at the absolute zero of temperature. This idea was more completely worked out by Walther Nernst in his heat theory (1906), now commonly known as the third law of thermodynamics. J. E. Coates, in his Haber memorial lecture (1937), said that "in the history of this problem [Nernst's heat theorem] Haber must be accorded an honorable place."

Haber began his work that led to the synthesis of ammonia in 1904, when he was still working in electrochemistry. In his first paper on the subject, in 1905, he noted: "Drs. O. and R. Margulies (Vienna) opened up the question as to whether it might be possible to look for a metal which could be used, along with the exchange properties of nitrides and hydrides, for the preparation of ammonia from nitrogen and hydrogen." In his Nobel lecture, Haber stated that for a long time the idea of combining nitrogen with hydrogen to form ammonia had occupied science: "Combination with hydrogen directly from the elements had been induced by various forms of electrical discharge. . . . Indirect combination, on the other hand, had been developed with remarkable technical results." By indirect combination, Haber was referring to the cyanamide process wherein nitrogen combined with carbide to form calcium cyanamide, which in turn reacted with water to form ammonia. He continued that "the spontaneous association of the elements was unknown in 1904 when I began to occupy myself with the subject; it was held to be impossible."

Methods for causing nitrogen to combine with oxygen had been considered by chemists before Haber's time, but no more than sixteen grams of nitric acid could be produced per kilowatt-hour of electrical energy by this method; Haber calculated that a complete conversion of electrical energy into chemical energy ought to have produced thirty times as much. Thus, this method had not achieved the hoped-for efficiency in nitrogen fixation.

Haber turned his research efforts toward developing a method for direct conversion of nitrogen and hydrogen into ammonia. The fact that this reaction produced heat energy led Haber to believe that the reaction might be able to maintain itself without the addition of energy and thus be economically very attractive. He began to study the equilibrium conditions in the reaction for the formation of ammonia from its elements, nitrogen and hydrogen, and the effects of various metal catalysts on this equilibrium. His results were discouraging. Neither high temperature nor high pressure would increase the ammonia yield. In fact, if catalysts were to produce practical results, he concluded at this time, at normal pressures the temperature could not exceed 300 degrees Celsius.

A year later, however, Nernst used his new heat theorem to make some new predictions about the ammonia equilibrium, predictions that were different from what Haber had found by experiment. It appeared that a new series of experiments was necessary; as a result of these new studies, Haber was encouraged, in 1908, to take up again the problem of ammonia synthesis that he had abandoned three years before as hopeless.

He now found that by using metallic osmium as a catalyst he could make several grams of ammonia per hour in a small chamber at high pressure; the reaction itself produced enough heat to maintain the proper temperature. He therefore decided to enlarge his operation and built a small industrial plant. He had success enough to attract a large company, Badische Anilin-und-Soda-Fabrik, to bring its considerable resources to his process and to develop further the modern industrial process for ammonia production. Haber openly acknowledged his indebtedness to his collaborator, LeRossignol. The high-pressure system required for Haber's process had been developed by LeRossignol, whose abilities in this regard were widely known and respected.

Haber's book *Thermodynamics of Technical Gas Reactions* was another of his important fundamental contributions to chemistry. G. N. Lewis and Merle Randall, in their classic book *Thermodynamics* (1923), state that Haber's book was "the first systematic study of all the thermodynamic data necessary for the calculation of the free energy changes in a group of important reactions. . . . This book is a model of accuracy and critical insight." That Haber was already thinking about methods for nitrogen fixation is shown by his reference in the book to the "inertness of nitrogen": "This peculiar inertness of nitrogen will always place a serious handicap on the cheap technical preparation of ammonia."

With the onset of World War I, Haber became a consultant to Germany's Ministry of War. He was later given his own department, which developed techniques for gas warfare. The department eventually employed more than one hundred university personnel and some two thousand assistants. In a lecture given sometime after the war, Haber stated that he himself had "never been concerned with the admissibility of gas weapons by international law." He said that Germany's war minister "would never have sanctioned poisoning of food or water supplies, or have permitted weapons . . . which caused needless suffering." He maintained that "even one real opposing opinion" would have kept him from participating in gas warfare development.

Haber spent eight years after the war, from 1920 to 1928, attempting to extract gold from seawater in an attempt to help Germany pay the enormous reparations demanded by its former enemies for the destruction caused by the war. The attempt proved futile, and this failure was one of the great disappointments of Haber's life. Managing to be philosophical about the failure, however, he stated: "If there is no gold, there will at least be a fine book."

The reorganization of the Institute for Physical Chemistry and Electrochemistry also occupied Haber's energies after the war. He tirelessly enlisted scientists to do research there, and he worked to reestablish ties between German scientists and the international scientific community. The institute hosted numerous scientific gatherings and produced an ever-increasing number of publications. Haber himself became involved with work being done at the institute on the theory of spectra. His last work, performed in 1933, was concerned with hydrogen peroxide catalysis. The Nazi regime, by this time, was instituting racial policies that made the free pursuit of research increasingly difficult. Haber resigned from the institute in May, 1933, rather than continue to work under the anti-Semitic policies of the Nazis.

Bibliography

Primary

CHEMISTRY: *Foundations of Technical Electrochemistry on a Theoretical Basis*, 1898; *The Thermodynamics of Technical Gas Reactions: Seven Lectures*, 1905; "Concerning the Ammonia Equilibrium," *Berichte der deutschen chemischen Gesellschaft*, vol. 40, 1907; *Chemistry in War*, 1922; *Five Lectures*, 1924; "Inequality and Radical Chains in Reaction Mechanisms for Organic and Enzymatic Processes," *Berichte der deutschen chemischen Gesellschaft*, vol. 64, 1931.

GENERAL: *Life and Vocation*, 1927.

Secondary

Berl, Ernst. "Fritz Haber." *Journal of Chemical Education* 19 (May, 1937): 203-207. Writing from his personal acquaintance with Haber, Berl gives a brief but authoritative account of Haber's scientific work, including some material not found elsewhere.

Coates, J. E. "The Haber Memorial Lecture." *Journal of the Chemical Society*, November, 1939: 1642-1672. This is probably the best and most extensive account in English of Haber's scientific accomplishments. Coates's lecture, delivered before the (British) Chemical Society on April 29, 1937, three years after Haber's death, is comprehensive, is scientifically knowledgeable, and, while sympathetic, is not uncritical. He discusses Haber's responsibility for German gas warfare frankly, for example, but he also quotes Haber's own defense of his actions.

Jaenicke, Johannes. "The Gold Episode." *Die Naturwissenschaften* 23 (1935): 57. Contains an account of Haber's frustrating attempt to extract gold from seawater after World War I in order to help Germany pay the heavy reparations demanded by its former enemies.

Reinmuth, Otto. "Editor's Outlook." *Journal of Chemical Education* 8 (January, 1931): 1-3. Haber's life is briefly sketched, including an account of his scientific career. His work in organic chemistry and ammonia synthesis, his war work on gas weapons, and his attempt to extract gold from seawater are all discussed.

_____. "Reversing the Nitrogen Debit." *Journal of Chemical Education* 5 (November, 1928): 1464-1472. Contains an account of the nitrogen cycle in nature, with a graphic representation of the cycle. The article emphasizes the importance of Haber's work on nitrogen fixation. Reinmuth also includes illustrations of industrial installations for preparing and testing catalysts for use in ammonia synthesis.

Joseph Albert Schufle

1920

Chemistry
Walther Hermann Nernst, Germany

Physics
Charles-Édouard Guillaume, Switzerland

Physiology or Medicine
August Krogh, Denmark

Literature
Knut Hamsun, Norway

Peace
León Bourgeois, France

WALTHER HERMANN NERNST
1920

Born: Briesen, West Prussia (modern Wąbrzeźno, Poland); June 25, 1864
Died: Bad Muskau, near Berlin, Germany; November 18, 1941
Nationality: German
Areas of concentration: Electrochemistry and thermodynamics

Nernst did research on electrochemical reactions in solution and developed an equation that relates electrode potential to ion concentration. He then turned to the thermodynamics of chemical reactions and created his heat theorem, which became known as the third law of thermodynamics

The Award

Presentation

Professor Gerard de Geer, President of the Royal Swedish Academy of Sciences, presented Walther Nernst for the 1920 Nobel Prize in Chemistry. He provided a concise appraisal of the situation that Nernst faced in his research activities. For almost a hundred years, chemists had been making thermochemical measurements in an attempt to gain knowledge of the connection between chemical affinity (attraction) and the attendant temperature changes in their calorimeters. He called attention to the importance of the first law of thermodynamics in this endeavor and referred to the equation of Jacobus Henricus van't Hoff that allowed chemists to calculate the point of equilibrium at some particular temperature if the point of equilibrium at another temperature were known.

Professor de Geer emphasized that in order to measure the chemical affinity of a given reaction and hence to calculate the point of equilibrium, the chemist needed to know what happened to the specific heats of substances as the absolute zero of temperature is approached. He noted that Nernst had discovered that the heat released and chemical affinity both become independent of temperature as the absolute zero of temperature is approached. This allowed the evaluations of specific heats to proceed, and hence made possible the calculation of the point of equilibrium.

Professor de Geer also pointed out the practical benefits of Nernst's discovery. With the knowledge of the point of equilibrium in a reaction and its relation to temperature, the products can be maximized, enabling the effective application of a reaction to commercial production.

Nobel lecture

Nernst delivered his Nobel lecture, entitled "Studies in Chemical Thermodynamics," on December 12, 1921. He used the galvanic cell (Daniell cell) as the focal point of his discussion on chemical thermodynamics, because of the adaptability of the cell to an explanation of his work. Nernst acknowledged the background of the previous investigators to whom he referred in deriving the equation that successfully predicts the potential of a galvanic cell.

Next, he called attention to a law previously stated by Marcelin Berthelot: Chemical affinity (free energy) can be equated with the heat evolved by a chemical reaction. This law provides a good approximation when large amounts of heat are released, but it does not hold true when more precise measurements are made. Nernst then explained his strategy for dealing with this challenge. He realized that a detailed knowledge of the specific heats of condensed substances was essential in order to determine the nature of entropy near the absolute zero of temperature. He realized, during a lecture one day, that the chemical affinity and total energy changes in a chemical reaction would approach the same value as the temperature approached absolute zero because of the fact that the specific heats of these condensed phases would also approach zero.

Therefore, the entropy change in a chemical or physical process would approach and in theory become zero at the absolute zero of temperature. This is the essence of his heat theorem, and it means that entropies of substances at room temperature have finite values. These values can be used to determine the entropy change for a chemical reaction. Nernst called attention to the large number of measurements of the specific heats of solids and liquids, including liquid hydrogen, at the lowest temperatures possible. Extrapolations of the curves showing the relationship of the specific heats to temperature led to the assumption that they would be zero at absolute zero. In the statement of the second law of thermodynamics by Rudolf Clausius, Hermann Helmholtz, and Josiah Gibbs, an acknowledgment is made that heat evolved in a chemical reaction is not equal to the free energy change. Free energy is the maximum external work capability of a chemical system. This is why Nernst referred to the Daniell cell in his Nobel lecture. The external work performed by the chemical reaction is the cell's capability to turn an attached electric motor. The heat evolved, however, is measured by running the same reaction in a calorimeter.

Nernst also stated that vitreous fluids would experience a drop in the value of the specific heat to zero as the absolute zero of temperature is approached. He expressed a strong belief that evidence would subsequently show that gases would subscribe to the same relationship of temperature and specific heat. Nernst believed that his heat theorem was a universal law and that the newly developed quantum theory would supply a firm basis for his ideas.

Critical reception

The reaction to the announcement that the 1920 Nobel Prize in Chemistry was being awarded to Walther Nernst was decidedly mixed. While Nernst was well respected in the scientific community, his name was also linked to Germany's development of poison-gas warfare in World War I, concluded only two years before. Moreover, the last Nobel chemistry award to have been announced, the 1919 prize, announced in 1920, had gone to a German scientist, Fritz Haber, who had also been involved in the German gas warfare effort. Although the award to Nernst appeared to be significantly less protested than that to Haber (Haber had been in a more powerful position in the German war department), many nevertheless found the award unsettling.

The New York Times ran an article bluntly headlined "Nobel Prize Winner Made German Gas." The article quoted American scientists on Nernst's work. Lee H. Backeland of Columbia University called Nernst "one of the best-known physical chemists in Germany," citing his invention of the Nernst lamp and stating that his work was "mostly along theoretical lines." He noted that Nernst's work was in some ways a development of the earlier work of American chemist Josiah Willard Gibbs of Yale University. Backeland asserted that "during the war [Nernst] took a leading part in the chemical gas warfare."

A. W. C. Menzies, a Princeton University chemistry professor, noted that Nernst was "known especially as the discoverer of the third law of thermodynamics." *The New York Times* article also included the reaction of an unnamed American scientist who claimed that the "proximity of Sweden to Germany and German influence" played a large part in the Nobel Prize decisions. Germans, he complained, received a "larger share of Nobel Prizes than they were entitled to on the intrinsic merit of their work" when compared to American, French, or English scientists. This type of complaint was not uncommon until Americans began to win more Nobel Prizes.

As far as Nernst's work itself was concerned, there were no criticisms from other scientists that required alterations in the heat theorem. When his work had been published, substantiations had been quick in coming. Albert Einstein had supplied a quantum theory explanation for this behavior in a paper published in 1907. R. D. Kleeman later published two articles in *Science*, in 1927, in which he stated that he had derived both the heat theorem and the third law of thermodynamics from internal energy and entropy functions for a substance; this, however, did not require revisions of the theorem. Nernst's work certainly projected the best possible understanding of the behavior of the specific heats of condensed substances that could have been made in 1906.

Biography

Walther Nernst was born on June 25, 1864, in Briesen, West Prussia. His father was a district judge. Nernst might not have become a scientist had it not been for the chemistry master at the *Gymnasium* he attended. After graduating at the top of his class, he entered the technical university. He finished with a physics thesis in 1887 under Friedrich Kohlrausch at Wurzburg. He progressed up the academic ladder, becoming a full professor at Göttingen in 1894. By this time he had a laboratory dedicated entirely to his research.

He married Emma Lohmeyer in 1892, and they settled into a state-provided mansion on university grounds. They eventually had five children during the fifteen-year period of his tenure in Göttingen. Walther and Emma became wealthy, partly because of an inheritance by Emma, partly from a special lamp that Walther invented, and partly from the proceeds of a textbook published by Walther. Emma and Walther Nernst were very much aware of the encouraging environment that they could provide through social functions. While at Göttingen, they were to host many gatherings for the faculty and research students. Life in Berlin was much more urbane, and the Nernsts were caught up in the social life of the city, which included parties where one could expect to meet people of world prominence. The Nernsts were in frequent attendance at the theater, both in Göttingen and Berlin. They also owned a series of country estates and spent as much time in the country as possible. Walther liked to hold bird shoots on the forest lands of the estates.

Nernst's world fame eventually made it inevitable that he would end up at Berlin University. The family moved to Berlin in 1905; Walther, in 1924, became the director of the physical chemistry institute at Berlin University. The Nernsts still maintained a flat in Berlin for Walther's frequent trips back to Berlin after retirement to their estate in Zibelle in 1933. He died on November 18, 1941.

Scientific Career

Nernst's scientific career really began with the influence of the chemistry master at the Graudenz Gymnasium. Nernst established a small lab for himself in his home. Following this, his first years at the university were spent determining his field of principal interest. He attended lectures at Zurich, Berlin, Graz, and Würzburg (the German government, in the mid-nineteenth century, had become increasingly supportive of the technical university system).

The German dye and pharmaceutical industries were rapidly becoming world-dominant. They required an ample supply of trained chemists and engineers, and close association developed between industry and the technical university. Students, including Nernst, were not encouraged to stay on one campus. Wanting to sharpen his interests, he attended lectures on a number of campuses. He finally settled on the electrical behavior of solutions as his primary interest. Nernst finished his studies as a transition was taking place in Germany. The country's wealth was rapidly increasing as a result of commercial success. Kaiser Wilhelm II realized this and encouraged the further development of the industrial-academic alliance. Professors, involved in consulting work, saw to it that their graduates were given ample opportunity to apply for open positions on graduation.

He began his degree research with Ludwig Boltzmann at Graz in 1886 and finished a doctorate at Würzburg under Kohlrausch. Michael Faraday had already suggested that ions were produced at electrodes during electrochemical processes. Svante August Arrhenius proposed that ions were also derived from salts that had dissolved and would be free to move about in solution. Chemists did not yet know about the structure of the outer shell of charge surrounding these ions and the manner in which it was involved with water molecules in forming a stable solution.

Nernst's research earned for him a lecturer's position at the Phisico-Chemical Institute in Leipzig. In a few years, he accepted an assistant professor's position at Göttingen. Nernst was very successful there; he expanded his research, was promoted to professor, and gained a worldwide reputation. He became well known to the Kaiser as his career advanced and was frequently called to the palace for consultations. He also wrote a textbook in physical chemistry which was so popular that it went through ten editions: *Theoretische Chemie vom Standpunkte der Avogadroschen Regel und der Thermodynamik* (1893; *Theoretical Chemistry from the Standpoint of Avogadro's Rule and Thermodynamics*, 1895).

Nernst's career research resulted in (among other things) the equation used today to express the electrode potential as a function of the concentrations of ions involved in a reaction in solution. This, in turn, is directly related to the spontaneity of a chemical reaction in the solution concerned. This equation of Nernst was adapted to the potential between the electrodes of a Daniell cell, which was a focal point of his Nobel address. He used the voltaic cell concept because everyone in the audience could immediately see that the external work was done as a result of a spontaneous chemical reaction in the cell; thus they could appreciate the use of the criteria of external work to measure the spontaneity of a chemical reaction. The Daniell cell has two halves: a zinc electrode dipped in a zinc ion solution and a copper electrode dipped in a copper ion solution. The chemical reaction proceeds as the zinc electrode dissolves to form a positive zinc ion and donates electrons (through a wire) to the copper electrode, which precipitates the positive copper ion as metallic copper. There is an internal conduit of ions that tends to keep the overall solution charge the same. The important feature is that the chemical reaction drives the electrical charge through the wire to make the external work possible. The operation of batteries is analogous to this example. That is, the automobile battery turns the starter, and the flashlight battery lights the tiny lightbulb.

Nernst's equation says that the potential difference between the zinc and copper electrodes of the Daniell cell is proportional to the concentration ratio of the zinc and copper ions in the solution. That is, the voltmeter gives a number related to the external work capability of the cell. This is, in turn, directly related to the free energy value for the cell. The free energy value, with unit concentrations of the zinc and copper ions, enables a calculation of the equilibrium constant for the reaction. This was an all-important goal of Nernst's research.

A voltmeter, with unit concentrations, would be expected to read 1.10 volts. This translates into an energy value of 212 kilojoules (a kilojoule is a unit of measurement of work or energy). This is roughly the energy required to raise the temperature of 50 kilograms of water by one degree Celsius near room temperature. If this reaction were to be carried out in a calorimeter arranged to convert a liter of unit molar concentration of copper ions into metallic copper by means of charge donated by a piece of zinc in the solution, the energy released would be expected to be 217 kilojoules, assuming that the calorimeter is carefully insulated to minimize heat transfer away from the reaction system.

Now that the physical significance of free energy has been demonstrated, the more general statement involving free energy and spontaneity may be examined. The heat released in the reaction and the external work energy available are not equal. The second law accounts for the fact that the calorimetric heat measurement and the external work energy values for the Daniell cell value do not agree: Another energy exchange process is required. In the case of the example reaction just mentioned, there were 5 kilojoules that were unaccounted for. This energy change is the result of the changes in structures in a chemical reaction and of the attendant number of microenergy states available. The number of microenergy states available is directly related to a substance's entropy value, which, multiplied by the temperature, is the related energy value. It is a natural tendency for all reactions to proceed to maximize the number of microenergy states. Not being able to count the number of microenergy states, however, chemists needed another method to measure disorder. The entropy value for a substance (at room temperature) is related to its heat capacity (heat capacity is the specific heat times the mass). These heat capacities could be measured, provided one could know how this heat capacity functioned at or near the absolute zero of temperature.

Nernst's extremely important contribution was to state that the heat capacity became zero at the absolute zero of temperature. (The absolute zero of temperature cannot be reached by any physical process.) The plots of the variation of the heat capacity with temperature could be extrapolated to absolute zero, and the entropies of substances could be measured. Thus, the final link was finally in place. Chemists would be able to determine routinely the free energy value for a chemical reaction and hence determine the equilibrium constant for that reaction by calorimetric means. The equilibrium constant gives the mass distribution expected between products and reactants in a reaction.

Nernst received the 1920 Nobel Prize in Chemistry for this contribution. As might be expected, he was also accorded other honors befitting his prominence in world science. He was even offered the ambassadorship to the United States, which he wisely declined. He did accept the presidency of the National Physical Laboratory in 1922. Nernst could not accommodate the pedantic nature of the staff, however, and returned to Berlin University. One thing that should be expected of a Nobel Prize winner is the encouragement and sponsorship of new lines of research. Nernst certainly did this. For example, he held a weekly gathering of scientists in his laboratory. New research, published and unpublished, was brought up for discussion. Research students, as well as scientists of world reputation, were in attendance. Nernst would usually be in the middle of the ensuing discussion.

Nernst was involved in the effort to bring victory to Germany in World War I. When Germany lost the initiative, something was needed to turn the tide from defensive action into an offense, and Nernst embarked on a research program to produce more powerful explosives. He was also a scientific adviser to the Kaiser during the war years. These activities led to talk of prosecution for war crimes following the war, but Nernst left the country until this talk abated.

He returned to a Germany in the midst of rebuilding. He became the director of the newly formed Physicochemical Institute at Berlin University in 1924. In this post he became a central figure in initiating new research, and his influence was instrumental in securing funding. Nernst himself began an inquiry into astrophysics to explore the application of the second law of thermodynamics to the question of the so-called entropy death of the universe. He wanted to show that the continually increasing disorder approached a limit that was actually much further off than originally postulated. Research into cosmic radiation also attracted the attention of Nernst. He immediately acquired funds to set up and operate a permanent research station at Jungfraujoch. When Nernst saw the results of these experiments on cosmic particles, he was prompted to suggest a condition of constant mass and energy production in the universe as a means of avoiding the disorder limit.

Walther Nernst finally ended a long and amazingly productive career at the center of the revolution in chemistry and physics of the early twentieth century when he retired to his country estate at Zibelle in 1933.

Bibliography

Primary
CHEMISTRY: *Theoretische Chemie vom Standpunkte der Avogadroschen Regel und der Thermodynamik*, 1893 (*Theoretical Chemistry from the Standpoint of Avogadro's Rule and Thermodynamics*, 1895); *Experimental and Theoretical Applications of Thermodynamics to Chemistry*, 1907; *Die theoretischen und experimentellen Grundlagen des neuen Wärmasatzes*, 1918 (*The New Heat Theorem: Its Foundations in Theory and Practice*, 1918).

Secondary
Atkins, P. W. *The Second Law*. New York: W. H. Freeman, 1984. This is an a excellent introduction to the physical meaning of entropy and its relation to chemical reactions. The author uses the steam engine as a very real example of the workings of the second law.

Klotz, Irving M., and Robert M. Rosenberg. *Chemical Thermodynamics: Basic Theory and Methods*. 4th ed. Menlo Park, Calif.: Benjamin/Cummings, 1986. Chapter 11 contains a very complete background discussion of the formulation of the third law. The author includes graphs that help refine one's view.

Mahan, Bruce H. *Elementary Chemical Thermodynamics*. New York: W. A. Benjamin, 1964. Contains an excellent mathematical discussion of the second law. The author introduces the reader to the molecular interpretation of the third law and its relation to the specific heat of substances. Lastly, he brings the reader to the voltaic cell as the vehicle for illustrating the second law just as Nernst did in his Nobel address.

Mendelssohn, Kurt. *The World of Walther Nernst: The Rise and Fall of German Science, 1864-1941*. Pittsburgh, Pa.: University of Pittsburgh Press, 1973. The author provides the reader with a very complete biographical portrayal of Nernst against the background of the spectacular growth of German science. The development of the university-industrial reciprocal relationship is discussed.

Pimentel, George C., and Richard D. Spratley. *Understanding Chemical Thermo-*

dynamics. Oakland: Holden-Day, 1969. The authors amplify their discussions of maximum work, randomness, entropy, free energy, spontaneity, and equilibrium with diagrams, charts, and pictorial representations. Along with well-written text, the combination creates a very understandable presentation of the second law.

Wilks, J. *The Third Law of Thermodynamics*. London: Oxford University Press, 1969. The author gives the background of some of the problems concerned with the initial implementation of the heat theorem, such as noncrystalline materials. He discusses the statistical approach to microenergy states as it relates to the entropy of substances and describes some of the experiments that demonstrate the unattainability of absolute zero.

Robert E. Whipple

1921

Chemistry
Frederick Soddy, Great Britain

Physics
Albert Einstein, Germany, Switzerland,
and United States

Physiology or Medicine
no award

Literature
Anatole France, France

Peace
Karl Branting, Sweden
Christian Lous Lange, Norway

FREDERICK SODDY
1921

Born: Eastbourne, England; September 2, 1877
Died: Brighton, England; September 22, 1956
Nationality: British
Areas of concentration: Nuclear chemistry and nuclear structure

Soddy investigated the nature of radioactivity and originated the concept of isotopes, clarifying the structure of both the periodic table and the atomic nucleus itself

The Award

Presentation

Professor Henrik Gustav Söderbaum of the Nobel Committee for Chemistry of the Royal Swedish Academy of Sciences presented the 1921 Nobel Prize in Chemistry to Frederick Soddy. He began by citing the proposal of the periodic table made by Russian chemist Dmitry Ivanovitch Mendeleyev. Söderbaum gave 1869 as the year that the principle was first published. One of the most sweeping ideas in all science, the periodic law did what all great theories do. It unified much information currently known and predicted many productive further investigations. Mendeleyev revealed striking regularities in the properties of the elements if they were arranged in order of their atomic weights. Groups of elements emerge which have similar valences, or chemical combinational ability. Obvious gaps in the sequence allowed Mendeleyev to predict the chemical behavior of then-unknown elements "with satisfactory exactitude." In the course of the 1870's and 1880's, some of his predictions were fulfilled: "Scandium was discovered by a Swede, germanium by a German, and gallium by a Frenchman," Söderbaum said. Mendeleyev's theory could even accommodate the detection of a new group of elements, the noble gases, by Sir William Ramsay (the 1904 winner of the Nobel Prize in Chemistry).

The validity of the periodic law, however, came into question. First, it seemingly had no satisfying underlying theoretical basis. Further, and much more acutely, the study of radioactivity revealed what were initially regarded as numerous new elements for which the periodic table apparently had no room. As Söderbaum expressed it, "their rapid growth in number threatened to explode irremediably the whole of the Periodical System." Söderbaum introduced the work of Frederick Soddy as having resolved this crisis and called Soddy the father of the idea of isotopy. Soddy insightfully suggested that two elements might be identical chemically but different in some physical aspects—especially atomic weight. Söderbaum concluded by briefly summarizing how Soddy came to this theory and by elaborating on its fruitfulness.

Nobel lecture

Soddy delivered his Nobel lecture on December 12, 1922. The first sentence of the lecture, which was entitled "The Origins of the Conceptions of Isotopes," immediately set a gracious tone. "The work of my students and myself, for which you have so signally honored me by the award of the Nobel Prize for Chemistry in 1921, is but a small part of much pioneering work . . . into the chemistry of radioelements and the existence and nature of isotopes." In text or footnotes, his lecture acknowledged the contributions of some sixty other researchers.

Soddy lucidly recounted the successive steps in what he termed "this long and tangled story of the conception and discovery of isotopes." He began by discussing a special aspect of the chemistry of radioactive materials recognized by 1905. One element may be spontaneously producing another by radioactive decay, and the product itself then producing a third element. Analysis of a sample at various times may therefore obtain separations of materials which may ordinarily be inseparable.

Next he cited the work of Americans Herbert N. McCoy and William H. Ross, who established in 1907 the complete chemical inseparability of isotopes, specifically in attempts to separate radiothorium from thorium. This was recognized as a much stronger restriction than difficulties previously encountered in separating chemically similar elements.

He went on to discuss the contribution of the Swedes Daniel Strömholm and Theodor Svedberg. They broke new ground in attempting to incorporate parts of the radioactive disintegration series into the periodic table, suggesting what Soddy called "a general complexity of the chemical elements concealed under their chemical identity." Soon all three natural disintegration series were incorporated into the periodic table. Sir Alexander Fleck, one of Soddy's students, was instrumental in the experimental part of this breakthrough. In the theoretical realm, Soddy recognized the efforts of Georg von Hevesy, Alexander S. Russell, and most notably the Polish-born Kasimir Fajans. Research by Friedrich A. Paneth and Hevesy showed the electrochemical identity of isotopes. Analyzing the electromagnetic radiation from isotopes, using ordinary spectroscopic techniques, Russell and Rossi corroborated this identity. Subsequently, minute spectroscopic differences were shown in very sensitive work by William D. Harkins and L. Aronberg.

In 1911, A. Van den Broek proposed that Mendeleyev's use of atomic weight to arrange the elements was in error and that, instead, successive elements in the periodic table differed by one unit of nuclear charge and by one electron in the outer shell. This was triumphantly confirmed by Henry G. J. Moseley, who Soddy later said "called the roll of the elements." Just as the discoveries of certain elements had vindicated Mendeleyev, the independent discovery in 1917 of protactinium by the team of German chemist Otto Hahn and Austrian physicist Lise Meitner and by Soddy and his student John A. Cranston supported this revision in the periodic law.

Strong evidence supporting Soddy's theory of isotopes came from careful measurements of the atomic weight of lead from various sources, such as those directed by Theodore W. Richards at Harvard University. Although all the samples were indisputably lead, their atomic weights showed marked differences. The crowning verification came from the mass spectrograph, invented by Francis W. Aston, which separated the various isotopes of an elemental sample onto a photographic plate. Soddy concluded his lecture by acknowledging this work, which earned for Aston the 1922 Nobel Prize in Chemistry. (Soddy's and Aston's awards, it may be noted, were both presented in 1922.)

Critical reception

Although two world-renowned British chemists, Soddy and Aston, were honored by being awarded the 1921 and 1922 Nobel Prizes in Chemistry, treatment of their attainments in *The Times* of London during December, 1922, was surprisingly subdued. Apparently there was considerably more interest in reporting the presentation of the Nobel Peace Prize to the Norwegian Fridtjof Nansen. A popular hero as a pioneer of Arctic exploration on his specially designed vessel *Fram* from 1893 to 1896, he had written a number of both scientific and popular books. Gripped by strong humanitarianism, Nansen had subsequently become a world leader in effective attempts to alleviate the sufferings of refugees, the famine-stricken, and prisoners of war. In its December 11, 1922, issue, *The Times* of London gave full coverage to Nansen's award, and a photo of him appeared on page 16.

There seems to have been no such article reporting Soddy and Aston's recognition. The only mention given them in *The Times* of London during the week of the Nobel ceremonies was a photograph on page 16 in the December 15, 1922, edition. Their positions were numbered in the photograph, which was accompanied by this caption: "Presentation of Nobel Prizes—Dr. F. W. Aston (1), of Cambridge, and Professor Frederic [*sic*] Soddy (2), of Oxford, in the Musical Academy, Stockholm, where they were presented by the King of Sweden with Nobel Prizes for Chemistry."

Similarly, *The New York Times* reported Nansen's triumph far more emphatically than any of the Nobel Prizes in the scientific disciplines. An article on page 4, November 10, 1922, headlined "Nobel Prize for Einstein," did record the awarding of the Nobel Prize in Physics for 1921 to the German Albert Einstein and for 1922 to the Dane Niels Bohr. There seems to have been no such reporting of the chemistry prizes that year. Further, there apparently was no reporting of the actual ceremony at which the science Nobels were presented. Again, however, Nansen was accorded full coverage by *The New York Times* in two articles around the time of his award ceremony.

The Nobel Prizes in the sciences were reported much more fully in the scientific press. In the December, 1922, issue of *Scientific Progress*, the lead article in the section entitled "The Progress of Science," by Dr. Edwin E. Slosson, was entitled "Rewards for Working Inside the Atom." After reporting the announcement of the Nobel Prizes for Einstein, Bohr, Soddy, and Aston, the article continued, "This is a striking illustration of the unity of science in spite of national divisions, for these four scientists have been in unconsidered cooperation trying to solve the same question, the most fundamental problem of the universe, what is the atom made of." The article indicated that the atom was originally believed to be indivisible, commenting that the root of the word "atom" was "uncuttable." Nevertheless, discovering that atoms contained electrons and were thus very divisible, Sir Joseph J. Thomson had opened a new arena to science, earning for himself the 1906 Nobel Prize in Physics. "Professor Soddy has not only done a large part of this work but he has given a good popular account of what it means in his book *Science and Life*," Slosson said; he then described Soddy's findings about isotopes and the relationships of his research with the contributions of fellow scientists Aston, Bohr, and Einstein.

Biography

Born on the south coast of England, Soddy was the seventh and youngest son of Benjamin Soddy, a corn merchant, and Hannah Green Soddy. His mother died only eighteen months after his birth. He was reared by his half sister and apparently had a very difficult childhood. Showing an aptitude in science from an early age, he was especially encouraged by R. E. Hughes, the science master at Eastbourne College. Having attended Eastbourne College and the University College of Wales, Aberystwyth, he entered Merton College, University of Oxford, on a science scholarship in 1895. He studied chemistry under Sir William Ramsay, was graduated with first-class honors in 1898, and remained at Oxford for two years of additional research. From 1900 to 1902, he was a demonstrator in chemistry at McGill University in Montreal, Canada. There he collaborated on the study of radioactive materials with Ernest Rutherford. In 1903, Soddy returned to London to continue his studies at University College and to resume work with Ramsay. He accepted the position of lecturer in physical chemistry and radioactivity at the University of Glasgow, Scotland, in 1904. Most of the work which immortalized his reputation in chemistry was done in Glasgow during the ensuing ten years, including the publication in 1913 of the concept of isotopes. During this period, in 1908, he married Winifred Beilby, only daughter of Sir George and Lady Beilby of Glasgow. It was a happy but childless union.

Soddy became professor of physical chemistry at the University of Aberdeen, Scotland, in 1914, continuing his research into radioactivity and aiding in the war effort. He was named Dr. Lee's Professor of Inorganic and Physical Chemistry at Oxford in 1919. As his interest increasingly shifted to economics, sociology, politics, and mathematics, realms in which he became more and more embroiled in sometimes bitter contention, his chemical research dwindled. These turmoils and the premature death of his beloved wife in 1936 led to his resignation from Oxford and his retirement the next year. Continued controversy with other scholars, especially over his ideas in economics, marked the retirement. Soddy not only espoused unpopular, radical, and often untenable positions; he frequently did so with some venom. His personality was complex and aloof; his great virtue seems to have been very pronounced generosity to those whose help he appreciated. On September 22, 1956, he died at Brighton, fifteen miles from his birthplace.

Scientific Career

In the 1890's, the University of Oxford was quite possibly the premier center of scientific scholarship in the world. Not only was the redoubtable Sir William Ramsay heading a very distinguished group in chemistry, but also the legendary Sir J. J. Thomson was Cavendish Professor of Physics and was at the center of a striking collection of physicists. Soddy thus came to work and study in the company of such brilliant scientists as Sir Ernest Rutherford, widely regarded as the father of nuclear physics; the Scotsman Charles T. R. Wilson, who shared the 1927 Nobel Prize in Physics for inventing the Wilson cloud chamber, which rendered visible the tracks of electrically charged subatomic particles; Paris-born Paul Langevin, pioneer in applying electron theory to the magnetic properties of materials; Sir Owen W. Richardson, Nobel laureate in physics in 1928; the multitalented Sir James Jeans; and Francis Aston, inventor of the mass spectrograph. It should be noted that in that era, all work with the nucleus was considered chemistry. Accepting his 1908 Nobel Prize in Chemistry, the irrepressible Rutherford commented that he had seen many remarkable transformations in his work with radioactivity, but none more rapid than his own from physicist to chemist.

During the first three years of the twentieth century, Soddy burst upon the stage of the scientific world because of far-reaching research that he had undertaken at McGill University with Rutherford. Although only six years Soddy's elder, Rutherford was already recognized as a first-rate investigator of the newly discovered phenomenon of radioactivity. While both were still in their twenties, Rutherford and Soddy combined skills and intuitions to accomplish a sensational piece of work. They provided the first acceptable explanation of radioactivity, which had been discovered in 1896 by Henri Becquerel, corecipient of the 1903 Nobel Prize in Physics. In 1898, Marie Curie, who shared in the Nobel Prize in Physics in 1903 and won the Nobel Prize in Chemistry eight years later, had coined the term "radioactivity" to describe the ability of some materials to emit steady streams of penetrating and ionizing radiation. Along with her husband, Pierre Curie, she established that two of the heaviest elements in nature, uranium and thorium, were radioactive. In addition, they discovered two new radioactive elements, radium and polonium.

Rutherford and Soddy carefully studied the "transmutations" of these elements, to use the alchemical term Soddy put forward as applicable to this case. They found that both uranium and thorium gave rise to complex series of decays, the rates of which they attempted to measure. Further, they could detect no chemical or physical means of altering the rates at which the various decays proceeded. Previously, elements had been considered by definition to be immutable. Soddy and Rutherford proposed, however, that in some of the heaviest atoms the nucleus, the minute positive core, was unstable. Such nuclei might spontaneously disintegrate into another element, emitting charged particles in the process. Some of these emanations were positive particles that Rutherford termed alpha particles. Negative emissions he called beta rays.

Rutherford and Soddy also hypothesized that radium might continuously produce helium. Partly to test this theory, Soddy rejoined Ramsay at University College. In the last years of the nineteenth century, Ramsay had discovered the rare gases argon and helium in the earth's atmosphere, attainments which earned his Nobel Prize. In 1903, his laboratory in London was probably the only facility in the world at which very small traces of gases might be studied. Because of Soddy's expertise in dealing with radioactive materials, they joined forces to show by spectroscopic methods that helium was indeed emanated from radium. This was the first unquestionable demonstration that one element could arise from another; it led Soddy to conclude that alpha particles were helium nuclei, as Rutherford later independently corroborated.

Until this stage in his career Soddy had labored, although brilliantly, in the very large shadows of Ramsay and Rutherford. Had he made no further scientific contributions, he doubtless would have become mere footnotes in the illustrious chronicles of Rutherford and Ramsay. It is a maxim in science that larger reputations tend to swallow smaller ones. His ten years at Glasgow, however, gave Soddy's name lasting prominence as a truly creative chemist. Before assuming the position at the University of Glasgow, Soddy undertook a lucrative lecture tour of Western Australia, demonstrating and discussing a sample of radium.

Soddy's first major accomplishment at Glasgow came from carefully studying purified uranium compounds. Sir William Crookes had shown in 1900 that such compounds exhibited very little radioactivity. Becquerel soon demonstrated that the radioactivity rose steadily to the usual level associated with uranium as the compounds were allowed to stand. Soddy meticulously extended this work, proving that the uranium in uranyl nitrate gradually decayed to produce radium, which was highly radioactive. He went on to propose that an intermediate element was produced in this process. In 1906, American physicist Bertram Boltwood of Yale University verified this suggestion and named the new element ionium.

In this period, Soddy also developed and delivered a series of public lectures. His "Free" lectures in the Botany Class Room of the University of Oxford reached a wide audience, introducing people in a nontechnical but very worthwhile manner to the burgeoning field of radioactivity.

Glasgow was also the site of the research that led Soddy to the breakthrough of the concept of isotopes. In his Nobel lecture, he succinctly described isotopes as atoms with "identical outsides but different insides." The chemical behavior of an atom is determined by the arrangement of its electrons, which constitute its "outside." Two atoms with the same electronic configuration should exhibit identical chemistry. It is this particular chemical activity which characterizes the unique place of each element in the periodic table. Two different isotopes, however, have different "insides," or nuclei, within the various identical layers of electrons. These isotopes thus would occupy the same place in the periodic table. (Strictly speaking, tiny differences resulting from the extra weight of the heavier isotopes are apparent upon very close examination, most noticeably among the lighter elements.) The word "isotope" is derived from Greek roots meaning "same place," and because of this classical parentage it has passed into many languages with little if any alteration. The word was actually coined in the home of Soddy's in-laws by a school-teacher named Dr. Margaret Todd, after Soddy had explained the concept to her.

En route to theorizing the existence of isotopes, he deduced three great generalizations synthesizing empirical results from many laboratories, among which his own was one of the most prominent; the scrupulous experimental contributions of his very able student Sir Alexander Fleck should be mentioned. Contained in Soddy's book *Chemistry of the Radioelements* (1911), the first generalization was the alpha displacement rule, which said that the emission of an alpha particle from an atom left an atom two below the original on the periodic chart. For example, the alpha decay of uranium would leave thorium, two spaces to the left on the periodic table.

The second generalization, given almost simultaneously by Soddy and Kasimir Fajans, was the beta displacement rule. It stated that a beta decay causes the atom to move one place higher along the periodic chart. An example of this would be the expulsion of a beta particle from thorium, leaving an atom of protactinium. In 1913, Soddy coordinated both of these rules into the group displacement law. This asserted that one alpha decay and two beta decays, in any order, would return the atom to its original place in the periodic table, although the mass of the new atom would be different from that of the original.

The culmination of this monumental effort took place later that year. The December 4, 1913, issue of *Nature* published a letter from Soddy which introduced the term "isotope" to the scientific public. The puzzle of what seemed to be more than fifty separate elements to fill twelve remaining places in the periodic table was resolved. What had been called radium B, thorium B, actinium B, and radium D, for example, were thus all shown to be various isotopes of lead. Mendeleyev's periodic law, amended by Moseley and Soddy, remains one of the foundation stones of chemistry.

During his five years at the University of Aberdeen, World War I had a serious impact on Soddy's ongoing research. Although the war effort placed great demands on the personnel and equipment of his laboratory and restricted his supply of raw materials, he achieved two very significant accomplishments. At McGill University, Soddy and Rutherford had recognized two radioactive series in nature. One originated from uranium and the other from thorium, and they were called, reasonably enough, the uranium series and the thorium series. Under Soddy's direction, John A. Cranston sought to illuminate a third series by seeking the parent element of actinium. Although they discovered protactinium in 1917, the ultimate source of the third natural radioactive series was not found until considerably later. In 1935, the Canadian-American physicist Arthur J. Dempster demonstrated that not all uranium atoms are identical. Approximately seven in each thousand represent a lighter isotope, the parent of what is called the actinium series.

Second, by this time it was widely recognized that the uranium series had as its ultimate end product one isotope of lead and that the thorium series had another. It had not yet been clearly demonstrated, however, that ordinary lead was actually a mixture of isotopes. This was done when Soddy led measurements in which the atomic weight of lead from Ceylon thorite was shown to be consistently different from the accepted value for lead.

When Soddy returned to Oxford in 1919, around the time of his forty-second birthday, few observers would have suspected that he would publish very little new research in his remaining thirty-seven years. Hopes were high that he would found a major center for radiochemistry. Nevertheless, those hopes were stillborn. Much of his energy was absorbed in wranglings with his fellow faculty members of Oxford over matters of internal politics, such as the manner of undergraduate chemistry instruction.

In addition, he was deeply embittered by World War I. The young Moseley, bright with promise, had died in battle in Italy. Much of what Soddy had seen made him believe that science was being perverted to serve what he believed were essentially evil ends. This led Soddy far afield from chemistry into such areas as economics and monetary reform, although his 1932 book *Interpretation of the Atom* was a major contribution to making its subject more accessible to the general public. Soddy became an ardent supporter of the technocratic politico-economical theories of the Belgian industrial chemist Ernest Solvay and became involved in continuous bickering over both these theories and his own.

The relationship between science and society remained of central importance to Soddy throughout his life. In 1920, he foresaw that the unleashing of nuclear energy would mean "unlimited physical power" for humanity. Thirty-five years later, at the age of seventy-seven, he was speaking out against the environmental and genetic consequences of hydrogen bomb tests. *The New York Times*, on March 21, 1955, quoted him as saying that they "are fouling the air with radioactivity. It is nonsense to say it is harmless." That same summer, only a year before his death, he was one of the eighteen Nobel science laureates from six nations who issued a warning that the use of nuclear weapons might contaminate huge portions of the earth with radioactivity and devastate entire countries.

Both the diversity of Soddy's interests and the futility of many of his efforts during the latter half of his life are illustrated by one of the provisions of his will. He left the prototype of a machine for solving a cubic equation, along with one thousand pounds, to Sir Richard Southwell in the hope that Southwell might follow through on the development and distribution of the machine to educational institutions on a nonprofit basis. His hopes were not fulfilled, as the machine was not judged to be of sufficient value.

Soddy served as president of the Röntgen Society in 1905 and 1906. The Royal Society elected him a fellow in 1910. He was awarded the Stanislao Cannizzaro Prize of the National Academy of Sciences of Italy in 1913 and the Albert Medal of the Royal Society of Arts in 1951. The University of Oxford conferred an honorary doctorate on him. A fellow of the Chemical Society, he was also a foreign member of the Swedish, Russian, and Italian Academies of Science.

Combining keen insight into theoretical chemistry and physics with meticulous attention to detail as an experimentalist, he was also a gifted writer. Although a relatively small fraction of his adult life was dedicated to chemical research—a lamentable loss to the science—Frederick Soddy contributed much to science's understanding of the nucleus.

Bibliography

Primary

CHEMISTRY: *Radioactivity: An Elementary Treatise from the Standpoint of the Disintegration Theory*, 1904; *The Interpretation of Radium*, 1909, rev. ed. 1920; *Chemistry of the Radio-Elements, Part I*, 1912; *Matter and Energy*, 1912; *Chemistry of the Radio-Elements, Part II*, 1914; *Science and Life*, 1920; *Interpretation of the Atom*, 1932; *The Story of Atomic Energy*, 1949.

ECONOMICS: *Cartesian Economics*, 1922; *The Inversion of Science*, 1924; *Wealth, Virtual Wealth, and Debt*, 1926; *The Wrecking of a Scientific Age*, 1927; *Money Versus Man*, 1931; *The Role of Money*, 1934; *British Budget*, 1938; *The Arch-Enemy of Economic Freedom*, 1943.

MISCELLANEOUS: The article on Soddy by Sir Alexander Fleck in *Biographical Memoirs of Fellows of the Royal Society*, vol. 3, 1957, pp. 203-216, contains an extensive list of Soddy's major scientific publications, lectures, and miscellany. Soddy bequeathed his papers to Muriel Howorth of Eastbourne, founder of the Institute of Atomic Information for the Layman. The Soddy-Howorth Collection is housed in the Bodleian, the library of the University of Oxford.

Secondary

Asimov, Issac. *Understanding Physics*. Vol. 3, *The Electron, Proton, and Neutron*. London: Allen & Unwin, 1966. This lucidly recounts the story of twentieth century physics through the date of its writing. Chapters 7 through 12, especially chapter 8, relate to the work of Soddy. Asimov's explanatory skills are clearly evidenced as he illuminates the historical study of radioactivity and the nucleus.

Cruickshank, A. D. "Soddy at Oxford." *The British Journal for the History of Science* 12, no. 42 (1979): 277-288. Almost any study of Soddy's life reveals even to a casual reader that he was somehow sidetracked from chemical research shortly after returning to Oxford in 1919. This source, supported by forty-six footnotes, explores that turbulent time for Soddy in careful detail.

Fleck, Alexander. "Frederick Soddy." In *Dictionary of National Biography: Supplement, 1951-1960*, edited by E. T. Williams and H. M. Palmer. London: Oxford University Press, 1971. In both this and the obituary for Soddy in *Nature* 178, October 27, 1956, page 893, Fleck brings rare insights from their long association. Fleck had worked with Soddy as a laboratory boy, as a student for graduation, and as a postgraduate research student. Few other references supply such a compassionate picture of Soddy the person.

Freedman, Michael I. "Frederick Soddy and the Practical Significance of Radioactive Matter." *The British Journal for the History of Science* 12, no. 42 (1979): 257-260. This fascinating study shows Soddy's grasp of the immediate and future practical benefits to humanity of radioactivity in medicine, commerce, and as a long-range source of energy for good or for ill. Freedman has carefully mined Soddy's writings to document these ideas, which perhaps had not been as clearly illustrated previously.

Nobelstiftelsen. "Frederick Soddy." In *Nobel Lectures: Chemistry, 1901-1921*. New York: Elsevier, 1966. This is valuable as a source of Söderbaum's presentation speech and Soddy's Nobel lecture. At the time of the awarding of the Nobel Prize, Soddy was still near his peak as a research scientist. He had always been gifted with the ability to compose very clear prose; the lecture is well worth reading.

Paneth, F. A. "A Tribute to Frederick Soddy." *Nature* 180 (November 23, 1957): 1085-1087. A unique, sympathetic treatment written not long before his own death by a contemporary of Soddy in the early twentieth century. Gives valuable anecdotal background on the idea of isotopy and Soddy's political persuasions. It also provides perceptions of what Paneth calls "Soddy's tragic scientific isolation in later years."

Rich, Louis. "Man in Conflict with Money." *The New York Times*, June 11, 1933, sec. V: 8. This is a review of an edition of Soddy's book *Money Versus Man*, which had recently become available to American readers. Rich summarizes, thoroughly but completely uncritically, Soddy's ideas on wealth, money, banking, currency reform, and the nationalization of capital.

Russell, Alexander S. "F. Soddy, Interpreter of Atomic Structure." *Science* 124 (November 30, 1956): 1069-1070. Russell also contributed the article on Soddy in *Great Chemists*, edited by Eduard Farber (New York: Interscience, 1961). As Fleck had been, Russell had been a student and friend of Soddy for many years and could bring poignant personal touches to these balanced assessments of his mentor as a scientist and a man.

Shillan, David. "Geography Benefits from a Chemist." *Geographical Magazine* 53 (November, 1980): 97-101. A thoroughly laudatory but very valuable view of Soddy the monetary reformer, thinker, and philanthropist by someone who knew him for his last twenty-two years. The text reveals Soddy as widely read, prickly, and fascinating. There are four excellent photographs, ranging from him in his Glasgow laboratory to him near the end of his life.

Trenn, Thaddeus J. "Frederick Soddy." In *Dictionary of Scientific Biography*, vol. 12, edited by Charles Coulston Gillispie. New York: Charles Scribner's Sons, 1975. This source should not be missed by anyone interested in following any of the aspects of Soddy's career. It is especially useful for its very extensive footnotes and its bibliography, in which references are organized by subject and/or time period.

Clyde J. Smith

1922

Chemistry
Francis William Aston, Great Britain

Physics
Niels Bohr, Denmark

Physiology or Medicine
Archibald Hill, Great Britain
Otto Meyerhof, Germany

Literature
Jacinto Benavente y Martínez, Spain

Peace
Fridtjof Nansen, Norway

FRANCIS WILLIAM ASTON
1922

Born: Harbonne, Birmingham, England; September 1, 1877
Died: Cambridge, England; November 20, 1945
Nationality: British
Area of concentration: Atomic chemistry

Aston developed and perfected the mass spectrograph and used it to identify and isolate more than two hundred natural isotopes of nonradioactive chemical elements. His work supported the "whole-number rule" of atomic mass

The Award

Presentation

Professor Henrik Gustav Söderbaum, a member of the Nobel Committee for Chemistry, presented the prize to Francis Aston on December 10, 1922. Professor Söderbaum began his remarks with the observation that, while radioactive elements had given science the concept of isotopes and the possibility that nonradioactive elements also possessed isotopes, the search for the latter had not been an easy one. An earlier Nobel Prize winner (in physics), Joseph John Thomson, had attempted to prove the existence of these isotopes, although his experimental results were inconclusive. His young assistant, Francis Aston, redesigned and refined the experimental instrument, later called a mass spectrograph, to identify the isotopes of neon. Following this initial discovery, Aston proceeded to demonstrate the existence of isotopes of some thirty other gaseous elements.

Francis Aston was being honored for more than an extraordinary accumulation of experimental results by extending the number of isotopes. He also provided the first conclusive evidence of a chemical law called the "whole-number rule." It had been long postulated that the atomic weight of all elements were whole-number multiples of a basic element. This idea of the unity of matter can be traced back to the ancient Greeks and had been repeatedly put forward by major figures in the history of chemistry. In 1815, William Prout revived the hypothesis that the atoms of all elements were made from the hydrogen atom, which was the lightest known element. For the next century, a number of great chemists had tried to prove this hypothesis and failed. Aston demonstrated that many elements were made of isotopes combined in certain proportions, and, although each isotope would have a whole number as its mass, the element would have a combined mass that was not a whole number.

Nobel lecture

Francis Aston began his Nobel lecture of December 12, 1922, entitled "Mass Spectra and Isotopes," by quoting the great chemist John Dalton's long-accepted rule that "atoms of the same element are similar to one another, and equal in weight."

Until Aston's experiments, there existed no body of evidence to support the second part of this rule. The history of Aston's involvement in this line of research began when he was an assistant to J. J. Thomson, who had developed a cathode ray tube that allowed him to discharge various gases, elements, and molecules of compounds through this device and measure their masses. In 1912, when neon gas was introduced into the discharge tube, they found that the instrument indicated two elements: one with an atomic weight of 20 and the other with a weight of 22. The atomic weight of neon was accepted as 20.20 and, unless there was another compound in the apparatus, the element with the weight of 22 had to be an unknown form of neon.

Aston first undertook the task of trying to separate these two forms of neon by the method of distillation. Even with the invention of a quartz balance that had an accuracy of 1 in 1,000, however, and after several thousand tests, he still came up with the atomic weight of 20.20. He then devised a more refined method of fractional diffusion, yet he could not conclusively prove that neon contained a mixture of isotopes. This work was interrupted by World War I, and when Aston returned to this research in 1919, he started to develop an instrument that would provide him with the accuracy that would prove the existence of neon isotopes.

The mass spectrograph spreads apart atoms and molecules in much the same fashion as light is broken into a spectrum through a prism. The atoms of neon were charged with energy in a cathode ray apparatus, the rays were passed through two narrow slits, and then through a magnetic field that spread the rays into a spectrum. Using the atomic mass of oxygen as the basic control, it was possible to read the spectrum of neon. Neon produced lines of atomic weight at 10, 11, 20, and 22. Those at 10 and 11, however, carried two charges and hence half the atomic weight. Using this instrument, Aston was able to show that there were two isotopes of neon, with atomic weights of 20 and 22. The atomic weight of neon is 20.20 because it contains a 10 percent concentration of the isotopes with an atomic weight of 22.

Aston's Nobel lecture proceeded to describe in some detail the more interesting aspects of his work on the atomic weights of elements, including chlorine, argon, helium, hydrogen, krypton, xenon, and mercury. Elements that exhibited less interesting results were also described, totaling a list of some thirty elements. The result of these measurements showed that the atomic weights of elements, with the exception of hydrogen, were whole numbers. Evidence was finally available to support the Prout hypothesis that all elements are made from a basic atom composed of one electron and two protons. Adding a proton and an electron to an atom would produce an isotope, although there were limits as to the number of isotopes possible for any element. The exception to the rule was hydrogen, which has one proton and one electron. Aston explained the anomalous atomic weight of hydrogen, at 1.008, in terms of the "packing fraction." Hydrogen has only one proton, and nothing else is packed in the nucleus. Other elements are packed with more than one proton, which tends to reduce the overall mass of the nucleus.

Aston concluded his lecture with a reference to the incredible energy of the nucleus and the implication of Albert Einstein's theory of relativity should such energy be released. If this energy could not be controlled, Aston hypothesized, the earth might destroy itself and explode into a new star.

Critical reception

When the Nobel Prize was awarded to Francis Aston in 1922, this was only the twentieth time that the award was given since its inception in 1901. Although all the recipients of the award up to this time were leaders in and pioneers of chemistry, neither the scientific community nor the world press saw this award as the pinnacle of achievement in chemistry. *The Times* of London, in typical understated fashion, greeted the award with a brief two-line announcement identifying the recipients' names and places of residence. *The Times* report on the Nobel awards ceremony was equally restrained, noting (in a section called "Telegrams in Brief") that the King of Sweden gave out the prizes and that "six of the seven prize winners [were] present." It stated that a banquet was given in honor of the prizewinners and mentioned the amount of the prize. *The New York Times* did not even report the award in chemistry, although it did provide brief coverage of other Nobel Prizes.

The assessment of Aston's achievement from the scientific community would come in other ways. In 1921 and 1922, *Smithsonian Reports* published extensive articles on the work by Aston and in particular on the spectacular successes of the mass spectrograph. Also in 1922, *Science*, the weekly publication of the American Association for the Advancement of Science, published Aston's findings on the spectrograph of tin. In his own country, Aston was recognized by his colleagues, who placed him twice on the Council of the Royal Society. In 1927, he was chosen to give the Bakerian Lecture, which was a singular honor. He was an honorary member of the Russian Academy of Sciences and of the Accademia dei Lincei (Italy). He received the John Scott and the Paterno medals (1923), the Royal Medal (1938), and the Duddell Medal of the Physical Society (1941). He was also a prominent member of the International Atomic Weights Committee.

Biography

Francis William Aston, the third child and only surviving son of George and Fanny Aston, was born on September 1, 1877. His father and grandfather were involved in the metal trade in Birmingham. His mother was the youngest daughter of Isaac Hollis, who was a gunmaker in the same city. Francis was reared on a small farm called Tennal House in the village of Harbonne; he showed an early interest in mechanical and scientific activities, including fireworks and glass blowing. In 1899, he attended Harbonne Vicarage School and two years later went to Malvern College. In 1893, he entered Mason College, which later became the University of Birmingham, and studied chemistry. He not only excelled in chemistry but also did well in mathematics; he spent his spare time in the carpenter's shop and became skillful in the use of tools. Aston passed the London matriculation in 1896 and at about the same time created a laboratory in the loft of his father's house, where he spent many hours practicing glassblowing and working on problems of vacuum research. Needing employment, Aston studied fermentation and began to work for a brewery in 1900.

When the discovery of X rays was announced to the world, Aston became convinced that his future lay in this area of science. While working at the brewery, he had developed both a more efficient vacuum pump and a discharge tube. In 1903, he returned to the University of Birmingham on a scholarship to work on properties of gas discharges. He published two papers on his research there. In 1908 his father died, and with his inheritance Aston was able to take a trip around the world. When he returned the following year to take up the position of lecturer in physics at Birmingham, he was invited by Joseph John Thomson to work at the Cavendish Laboratory and Trinity College of the University of Cambridge.

Francis Aston never married, and he indulged in many hobbies, including travel and sports. Although sea travel was his favorite, Aston combined these pleasures with science. He participated in a number of expeditions to view eclipses, went to conferences in distant places, and gave lectures in a number of countries. He engaged in ice skating and skiing, was an early participant in rock climbing, and toured much of England and Wales on a bicycle. He was a man with broad and abiding interests and enjoyed life to the fullest until his death on November 20, 1945.

Scientific Career

Francis Aston was ideally suited for the line of research that would lead him eventually to a Nobel Prize. He possessed the temperament of an experimenter who could patiently repeat a series of experimental procedures many times while making minute adjustments in his instruments. He possessed the mechanical skills to make instruments that could produce the desired results and, in particular, was an expert glassblower who could create the discharge tubes necessary for atomic research. The publication in 1903 of J. J. Thomson's book *Conduction of Electricity Through Gases* opened up a world of new challenges for Aston. He was captivated by the new phenomena of cathode rays and X rays. He became interested in an effect called "Crookes' dark space," which existed between the cathode and the negative glow. By designing a discharge tube with a movable cathode, Aston was able to define one of the dark spaces mathematically, and it was subsequently named for him. Aston continued to work on the variables between current, pressure, electrode materials, and dark space until well into 1923.

J. J. Thomson had a reputation for inviting gifted scientists to work at the Cavendish Laboratory. The invitation he extended to Aston in 1910 was such a case. Recommended by J. H. Poynting, who taught Aston physics at Mason College, Aston began a lifelong association with Cavendish, and Trinity College became his home. By 1906, Thomson had discovered the electron and turned his attention to positive rays generated by the cathode of the discharge tube. When the electrons were stripped from an atom, the atom became positively charged. By the use of magnetic and electric fields, it was possible to channel these positive rays into parabolic tracks. Thomson was able to identify the atoms of different elements by examining photographic plates of these tracks.

Aston's first contributon at the Cavendish Laboratory was to improve this instrument by blowing a spherical discharge tube with a finer cathode and making a better pump to create the vacuum. He also devised a camera capable of producing sharper photographs of the parabolic tracks. By 1912, the improvements to this apparatus provided proof that individual molecules of a substance have the same mass. While working on the element neon, Thomson obtained two parabolas: One had a mass of 20, and the other had a mass of 22. Aston was given the task of resolving this mystery. To separate the two constituents of neon, Aston decided to try fractional distillation and diffusion. The fractions of the distillation were in such minute quantities, however, that he had to invent a new balance to measure the differences. The quartz microbalance used a sealed quartz bulb balanced on a liquid of known density. By measuring the degree to which the bulb floated or sank, it was possible to compare the density of a known gas with that of an unknown one. He started with a quantity of neon, and after several thousand operations he was able to extract a minute amount of the heavier element of neon. Unfortunately, the change in density was barely outside the realm of experimental error and hence was too doubtful to prove his case.

The next four years gave Aston time to ponder this problem. During World War I, Aston worked as a chemist at the Royal Aircraft Factory at Farnborough, improving the canvas that covered the aircraft. These were not unproductive years, however, since a number of other scientists were housed at the same facility. Here the recent developments in physics and chemistry were openly discussed, and Aston, who was normally shy, was encouraged to discuss his work under these intimate living conditions. In addition, neon discharge tubes were a source of research here, because they were an excellent source of light for the stroboscope. After the war, Aston briefly continued with the attempt to distill the heavier part of neon but failed to achieve the necessary results.

In 1919, Aston began to build a mass spectrograph, an idea he had developed while at Farnborough. The idea was to treat ionized or positive atoms like light. Light can be dispersed into a spectrum and analyzed through its constituent colors, and Aston thought the same could be achieved with atoms of an element such as neon. By using magnetic fields to focus the stream of particles, he was able to create a mass spectrum and record this on a photographic plate. The heavier mass of neon was collected on one part of the spectrum, and the lighter neon appeared on another part. This was a magnificent apparatus, since the masses could be analyzed without reference to the velocity of the particles, which was a problem with the parabola method devised by Thomson. Neon turned out to possess two isotopes: one with a mass of 20 and the other with a mass of 22, in a ratio of 10:1. When combined, this gave the atomic weight 20.20, which was the accepted weight of neon.

The years following 1919 were charged with excitement, since month after month new isotopes were announced. Chlorine had two; bromine had isotopes with weights of 79 and 81, which gave almost an exact atomic weight of 80; krypton had six isotopes; xenon had even more. In addition to the discovery of these nonradioactive isotopes, the "whole-number rule" for chemistry was verified: Protons were the basic building blocks of different atoms, and these occurred in whole numbers. In 1920, Aston found that the hydrogen atom had a mass about 1 percent greater than a whole number. At the time, it was thought reasonably certain that when four atoms of hydrogen were brought together they would produce one atom of helium. This means that in "packing" the nucleus, about 1 percent of the mass would be lost. Aston's original mass spectrograph had an accuracy of 1 in 1,000. In 1927, he built a more accurate instrument that gave ten times greater accuracy. Using this instrument, he was able to determine the packing fractions of many elements. In 1935, Aston began to build an instrument with yet another ten times greater accuracy. His instrument proved to be of great value to nuclear chemistry, since accuracy of the chemical masses was critical to the success of the discipline.

His accomplishment in developing the mass spectrograph was immediately recognized by the scientific community, since it was a simple device that was capable of accomplishing a large amount of research quickly. In 1920, he was awarded the first research fellowship at Trinity College. He subsequently received many honors, including the Mackenzie Davidson Medal of the Röntgen Society (1920), Fellow of the Royal Society (1921), and the Hughes Medal of the Royal Society (1922). He was awarded the American John Scott Medal, the Italian Paterno Medal, and Fellow of the Institute of Chemistry all in one year (1923). In 1922 Aston saw the publication of his book *Isotopes*, which was favorably received by the scientific community and over the years was revised under a number of editions. The popularity of the book prompted a major revision in 1933, entitled *Mass-Spectra and Isotopes*.

After achieving success with isotopes of elements gained through gas discharges, Aston hardly broke step to receive his honors and to continue with his research. In 1925, he turned his attention to metal elements and mastered the technique of analyzing these isotopes. In all, he analyzed fifty-six elements in this group. By 1927, he had constructed the second-generation mass spectrograph and, with its greater accuracy, was able to determine that the whole-number rule was at best an approximation. The apparatus was also sensitive enough to measure Einstein's law of mass energy conversion during a nuclear reaction. Between 1927 and 1935, Aston reviewed all the elements upon which he had worked earlier and published updated results. After 1935, he began work on the third-generation mass spectrograph, which had reached the operational stage shortly before war broke out in 1939. After World War II, he had very little time left to complete his apparatus and was unable to deal with the problem of poor resolutions. Aston died in Cambridge on November 20, 1945.

Bibliography

Primary

CHEMISTRY: "Experiments on the Length of the Cathode Dark Space," *Proceedings of the Royal Society of London*, vol. 79A, 1907; "Sir J. J. Thomson's New Method of Chemical Analysis," *Science Progress*, vol. 7, 1912; "A Micro-Balance for Determining Densities," *Proceedings of the Royal Society of London*, vol. 89A, 1914; "The Possibility of Separating Isotopes," *The London, Edinburgh and Dublin Philosophical Magazine*, vol. 37, 1919; *Isotopes*, 1922; "Problems of the Mass-spectrograph," *The London, Edinburgh and Dublin Philosophical Magazine*, vol. 43, 1922; "Photographic Plates for the Detection of Mass Rays," *Proceedings of the Cambridge Philosophical Society*, vol. 22, 1923-1925; "A New Mass-Spectrograph," *Proceedings of the Royal Society of London*, vol. 115A, 1927; *Mass-Spectra and Isotopes*, 1933.

Secondary

Chalmers, W. T. *Historic Researches: Chapters in the History of Physical and Chemical Discovery*. New York: Charles Scribner's Sons, 1952. A number of chapters cover experimental work done through the 1920's. Although Aston is only briefly mentioned, the book provides an overview of experimental work during this period. Aston remarked in 1935 that he doubted if his researches would have passed any planning committee; his work was done during more informal and less controlled times.

Crowther, James G. *The Cavendish Laboratory, 1874-1974*. New York: Science History Publications, 1974. While this work covers the history of the laboratory and has limited material bearing directly on Aston, there are extensive sections on the working environment where Aston spent the greater part of his life. There are also extensive sections on J. J. Thomson and his work on the electron, which led directly to Aston's investigations.

Ihde, Aaron J. *The Development of Modern Chemistry*. New York: Harper & Row, 1964. This is a long and comprehensive history of various aspects of chemistry. Aston's contribution is described in a brief three pages. All of chapter 18 is worth reading, however, since it covers the developments in "radiochemistry" that led directly to Aston's. These topics include the Dalton atom, gas discharge tubes, X rays and X-ray spectra, radioactivity, and isotopes.

Thomson, George Paget. *J. J. Thomson and the Cavendish Laboratory in His Day*. London: Thomas Nelson, 1964. This volume attempts to detail the work done by Thomson and those who worked around him. Although the bulk of the information in this volume is also covered by Crowther, this book describes experiments in greater detail and provides excellent drawings of the experimental equipment and photographs of the experimental results.

Victor W. Chen

1923

Chemistry
Fritz Pregl, Austria

Physics
Robert Andrews Millikan, United States

Physiology or Medicine
Sir F. G. Banting, Canada
J. J. R. Macleod, Great Britain

Literature
William Butler Yeats, Ireland

Peace
no award

FRITZ PREGL
1923

Born: Laibach, Austria (modern Yugoslavia); September 3, 1869
Died: Graz, Austria; December 13, 1930
Nationality: Austrian
Area of concentration: Microanalysis of organic compounds

Pregl invented and perfected methods that required very small amounts for the accurate analysis and measurement of organic substances. His microanalysis made possible great advances in organic chemistry in the twentieth century in pure science, medicine, and industry

The Award

Presentation

Professor Olof Hammarsten, Chairman of the Nobel Committee for Chemistry of the Royal Swedish Academy of Sciences, delivered the presentation speech, pointing out that Alfred Nobel himself wanted the chemistry prize to be awarded for "the most important chemical discovery or improvement." Fritz Pregl's work, he stressed, was "the most important chemical improvement" in an extremely important field of chemistry. He emphasized the fact that while older methods for quantitative analysis required relatively large quantities, Pregl's new methods and the new apparatus he introduced made it possible to reduce the needed amounts of materials under investigation to 5 to 3 milligrams or even less. Pregl first concentrated on methods of analyzing carbon and hydrogen; later, he extended his micromethods to determine nitrogen, chlorine, bromine, iodine, sulfur, phosphorus, and many metals found in organic compounds. He also devised and constructed a microapparatus that could determine the proportionate amounts of the elements in a molecule of an organic substance.

In physiological or pathological chemistry, Hammarsten stated, materials to be investigated often are available only in limited quantities, and new materials are unavailable or only obtainable with great difficulty. Pregl's microanalysis can be used in all branches of organic chemistry; its future prospects extend to the vast field of biochemistry, including enzymes, vitamins, and hormones—a thorough chemical study of which is of extreme importance.

Nobel lecture

Pregl gave his Nobel lecture on December 11, 1923; its title was "Quantitative Micro-Analysis of Organic Substances." He began by mentioning that in 1921 he had given two lectures on his quantitative organic microanalysis, with demonstrations, to experts in the Kemiska Sällskapet (the Swedish Chemical Society).

When Pregl was working on an investigation of a substance available only in extremely small quantities, he decided to search for new methods of analysis. It became necessary to weigh the substance with far greater accuracy than the analytical balances allowed. Wilhelm Kuhlmann in Hamburg, the designer and manufacturer of assay balances for precious metals, followed suggestions made by Pregl and greatly improved the accuracy of his scales. Various other serious problems stood in the way of microanalysis, however, especially in the determination of nitrogen, carbon, and hydrogen. Pregl had to make major modifications and adjustments to the equipment and apparatus: Even the slightest impurities caused errors, and the absorption of water vapor from the air increased the weight in an apparatus. Only when a number of strict conditions were observed could accurate analytic results be obtained. Within a span of ten years, Pregl's microanalysis method was able to reduce the quantities required for determination to about one-hundredth part, while maintaining at least the same accuracy that traditional methods achieved. Not only were there economies in materials used, but also identical results could be obtained in at least one-third of the time required by macroanalysis. Pregl also worked out methods to identify halogens and sulfur. His assistant, Hans Lieb, developed methods to determine phosphorus and arsenic in organic substances.

Determining molecular weights through the boiling-point method was also made possible through microanalysis. This method also enabled Pregl to discover that the yellow color in corpora lutea of cattle ovaries was carotin, the same substance that is found in carrots. His methods helped in the determination of molecular structures and were applied in technology for electrolytic metal analysis. New microanalytical methods, he said, had also been developed for the analysis of wine. Pregl expressed great confidence that his microanalysis would find many fields of application and expansion.

Critical reception

Nobel Prizes in Chemistry have normally been awarded for an important discovery of something previously unknown. This was not the case in 1923: Pregl received the undivided award for a breakthrough and a decisive improvement in analytical methods. The Nobel Committee has not awarded the prize every year; in 1924, for example, there was no Nobel Prize in Chemistry. The committee therefore must have been strong in its belief that Pregl's improvements in the methodology of quantitative analysis merited the award.

Pregl developed his analytical methods in his laboratory for many years; unlike many university professors, he did not believe in publishing many preliminary studies. His major work, the definitive text on quantitative organic microanalysis, appeared in 1917, during World War I. Although it had been translated into English, not much was known about Pregl when the 1923 Nobel Prizes were announced. His name was often misspelled by the press. As might be expected, the Austrian press was not critical; it was full of pride over the first Austrian Nobel Prize winner in chemistry. The international reaction was simply to give quiet recognition to a somewhat newsworthy item that did not, however, seem to need the critical comments that the Peace Prize or the prize for literature require. After World War I,

Austria was facing devastating inflation and was in economic and political turmoil. *The Chicago Tribune* and *The New York Times* mentioned that Professor Pregl lost two-thirds of the prize to the Austrian government—that is, 2.25 billion Austrian crowns (about $32,000) went to taxes, and he kept only 1.5 billion crowns (approximately $21,000).

Biography

Fritz Pregl was born in the capital of the Austrian duchy of Carniola on September 3, 1869; its German name was Laibach, its Slovenian name is Ljubljana. He attended German schools in his hometown where his father, Raimund Pregl, was an official with a savings and loan institution; his mother was the former Friederike Schlacker. Fritz Pregl, who had no brothers or sisters, was an excellent student and received complete support from his parents when he chose an academic career. After the early death of his father, who left a small amount of money, he and his mother moved to Graz, a university town not far away, where he enrolled in the university as a medical student in 1887 and was graduated with an M.D. degree in 1894, with highest honors and distinction.

Although Pregl decided to make Graz his permanent home, he seemed to have some attachment to his place of birth, with its beautiful environs. A nature lover, outdoorsman, fisherman, and experienced mountain climber, he frequently returned to the region where he had been born—there were not many mountaintops in that area that he had not conquered. Hiking through the Alps relaxed him and recharged his energy. He also loved sports, such as bicycling, was a good and enduring swimmer, and was a soccer fan. He enjoyed the company of people and was known for his sense of humor, yet he never married. Besides teaching and being involved in research, he practiced medicine for a number of years as an ophthalmologist and eye surgeon. For almost thirty years, he was a medical expert for the courts and frequently had to give testimony at trials. Much chemical testing was done in Pregl's institute for the police departments. He was a member of top medical committees of the government, and during wartime he served his country as a consultant and officer in the army reserve. Later in life he learned to drive and developed a love for the automobile. Ironically, he was involved in a minor traffic accident that caused circulatory complications, and he died on December 13, 1930, at the age of sixty-one.

Scientific Career

When still a medical student at Graz, Pregl became an assistant in the Institute of Physiology in 1890, then an assistant professor of physiology in 1899, and an associate professor in 1903. Already as a young assistant he had become thoroughly familiar with laboratory work and learned how to use all kinds of instruments. More and more he became interested in research, primarily in physiological chemistry, and thus he devoted much time to the formal study of chemistry, which he continued during a one-year study leave at several German universities. There he had the opportunity to work under famous chemists such as Wilhelm Ostwald (University of Leipzig) and Emil Fischer (University of Berlin), who received Nobel Prizes in 1909 and 1902, respectively. After his return to Graz, and later in Innsbruck, he reorganized the curriculum in chemistry for medical students by placing more emphasis on physiological chemistry. He was an extremely popular and interesting teacher, who lived for science and for his students. Most of his days were spent working in his laboratory. After a long day, he often would go to a café and discuss experimental results with one of his assistants or make a sketch for new instruments; his work and the improvement of his methods were constantly on his mind. On a vacation trip through the South Tyrol, for example, he was struck by the idea of replacing a mercury gas meter with a Mariotte flask for doing carbon and hydrogen analysis. He immediately interrupted his trip, canceled his room reservation, and headed back to Innsbruck and straight to his laboratory to test his idea. He never worked with a big team and actually enjoyed working alone; at crucial times he would sleep in his laboratory. Pregl often was a generous and kind man. During hard times he organized help for needy students, and in his later years he donated much of his Nobel Prize money for scientific purposes, such as laboratory equipment for his university.

From 1910 to 1913, he was professor of medical chemistry at the University of Innsbruck (in the Tyrol). During this exciting and productive time in his life, he concentrated on the development of his new methods in analytical chemistry. In 1913, the University of Graz invited him back, and he was happy to return to his old friends and familiar surroundings. Here he stayed for the rest of his life, despite tempting offers from other universities, building his institute into what some called a mecca of microchemistry.

Pregl's early research dealt with, among other topics, the gastric juices of sheep, various aspects of human urine and bile acids, and—together with the work of Emil Abderhalden—the hydrolysis products of egg albumin. The investigation of certain bile acids, which could be isolated only in such small amounts that a traditional quantitative analysis was not possible, presented Pregl with only three alternatives: secure an enormous supply of the material to be analyzed, develop new analytical methods, or give up the research.

Pregl was not the only pioneer of microchemistry in Graz. Friedrich Emich, professor of analytical chemistry at the Graz Institute of Technology, was developing analytical methods in the field of microchemistry beginning in the 1890's. While Emich's work was in inorganic chemistry, Pregl set out to determine the composition of organic substances—primarily compounds containing carbon, hydrogen, nitrogen, and sulfur. To accomplish his goal of reducing quantities to a few milligrams, many laboratory instruments had to be adjusted and adapted. Pregl understood the problems of microchemistry; he realized that the common notion of simply miniaturizing available instruments was misguided. He would have to invent and test totally new processes for standard laboratory procedures such as distillation, filtration, and handling of crystals. His many talents made it possible for him to do much of the manual work himself. Since he was familiar with carpentry and was an expert glassblower, technician, and mechanic, he could design, redesign, and build a number of instruments and appliances. Thus, in order to improve the carbon and hydrogen analysis he was able to construct an automatic combustion furnace.

Pregl clearly understood that he could not accomplish his goals in microanalysis with the available balances. He first saw a Kuhlmann assay balance in Emich's laboratory and realized its even greater potential value for his own work, a potential that designer Wilhelm Kuhlmann himself had not foreseen. Pregl's suggestions on improving the accuracy of this balance were decisive for the field of microchemistry, because this improved balance was able to register one-millionth of 1 gram. Its sensitivity was so great that it reacted to the opening of the door to the room as well as to extremely minute differences in temperature. The room containing it had to be kept as free of dust as was possible. A matter of amusement among students were Pregl's very detailed directions on exactly how to wipe the absorption tube, lest an inadvertent electrical charge become a source of error.

In Innsbruck, Pregl had his own institute and was able to equip his laboratory according to his needs. In his analytical methods he followed the traditional concepts of elementary analysis developed by Justus von Liebig and Jean-Baptiste-André Dumas. While much of Liebig's work had focused on the determination of carbon and hydrogen, the combustion method of Dumas became a standard quantitative analysis of organic substances and especially of nitrogen. These methods, however, required relatively large quantities for analysis. For example, scientists in Richard Willstätter's laboratory in Zurich needed six thousand chicken eggs to extract the 2,600 milligrams of lutein (the coloring matter of egg yolk) they needed in order to conduct their experiments. Already in February, 1911, Pregl was able to report that his exact micromethods required quantities of only 7 to 13 milligrams. In subsequent years, he was able to reduce these small quantities further and still produce equally accurate measurements.

Not until 1917, however, did Pregl publish his *Die quantitative organische Mikroanalyse* (*Quantitative Organic Microanalysis*, 1920), after at least seven years of concentrated work and constant testing and retesting. He lived to see revised and expanded second and third editions (1923 and 1930) as well as English editions. French and Russian translations also appeared; a fifth English edition was published in 1951, and a seventh German edition—revised by Hubert Roth—appeared in Vienna in 1958. It is indeed a rare event in the field of organic chemistry that a work is kept on the market for more than four decades. Shortly after its publication, the book was favorably reviewed and was recognized as a major contribution. Despite the difficult subject matter, it is clearly written.

It was not long before scientists realized the advantages of this new method, and Pregl's institute became a popular gathering place for both students and experts. Pregl himself guided, helped, and taught hundreds of professional colleagues from all over the world, some of whom, such as Carl Peter Henrik Dam (winner of the Nobel Prize in Physiology or Medicine, 1943), would later become famous. Regular seminars in microchemical methods were held at Graz; they continued for many years, even after Pregl's death. A journal, *Mikrochemie*, was founded. Other scientists, such as Fritz Feigl in Vienna, further developed the microanalytical methods of Emich and Pregl.

As a physician, Pregl was proud of his many contributions to modern medicine. He developed a simple method to test the functions of the individual kidneys. The ordinary Austrian knew his name because of an iodine solution named for him, a mild but highly effective disinfectant. Microanalysis revolutionized the determination of blood sugar, urea, uric acid, lactic acid, various salts, and even metabolic processes. Microanalysis has also been used in the testing of water, soil, air, foods, pharmaceuticals, and the purity of technical products.

The Nobel Prize was not the only honor bestowed upon Pregl. He was awarded the Lieben Prize (in 1914); the Austrian government gave him an honorary title; the University of Göttingen awarded him an honorary doctorate. The city of Graz made him an honorary citizen, and he became a member of the Academy of Sciences in Vienna. His sixtieth birthday was marked by a festive official celebration, and he was honored by a special publication to which Friedrich Emich contributed. He served the University of Graz as dean of its medical school and later as president. He donated a large sum of money for the establishment of a prize that the Academy of Sciences in Vienna awards annually for the most important work in the field of microchemistry. It was fittingly named the Pregl Prize; its first recipient was Fritz Feigl in 1931. Pregl's methods, which repeatedly were called the biggest progress in organic elementary analysis since that made by Justus von Liebig, meant for scientific research substantial savings in time, material, and effort. They contributed significantly to the steadily increasing tempo of modern scientific development.

Bibliography

Primary

CHEMISTRY: *Die quantitative organische Mikroanalyse*, 1917 (*Quantitative Organic Microanalysis*, 1920). Preceded by a short article in the *Handbuch der biochemischen Arbeitsmethoden*, this was Pregl's only significant publication. It went through many editions and revisions and was translated into English in five different editions.

Secondary

Farber, Eduard. *Nobel Prize Winners in Chemistry, 1901-1961*. Rev. ed. New York: Abelard-Schuman, 1963. A brief biographical sketch is followed by a description of Pregl's work which earned for him the Nobel Prize. Some of this is a partial translation from *Les Prix Nobel en 1923*, and the final section is a short evaluation of the consequences of his contributions in theory and practice.

Kainz, Gerald. "Friedrich Emich, Fritz Pregl, Fritz Feigl: Three Austrians as Pioneers in Microanalytic Research." *Journal of Chemical Education* 35 (1958): 608-611. This article summarizes the scientific career and accomplishments of

Pregl and points out that he was not a lone star in his field but rather was a brilliant representative of a group of noteworthy Austrian scientists in the field of microchemistry. Emich was, in a sense, Pregl's predecessor.

Lieb, Hans. "Fritz Pregl, 1869-1930." In *Great Chemists*, edited by Eduard Farber. New York: Interscience, 1961. Lieb was Pregl's main assistant for about twenty years and became his successor at the University of Graz. He worked on the major projects that made scientific history. His recollections are one of the main sources on Pregl's life and work. Lieb gives a simple account, but he admired and respected Pregl.

Szabadváry, Ferenc. "Fritz Pregl." In *Dictionary of Scientific Biography*, vol. 11, edited by Charles Coulston Gillispie. New York: Charles Scribner's Sons, 1975. A short and simply written article from the point of view of a historian of science. About half is on Pregl's life, and the other half concerns the highlights of his scientific work, giving a fair amount of detail. Includes a short bibliography.

Julius M. Herz

1925

Chemistry
Richard Zsigmondy, Germany

Physics
James Franck, Germany
Gustav Hertz, Germany

Physiology or Medicine
no award

Literature
George Bernard Shaw, Great Britain

Peace
Sir Austen Chamberlain, Great Britain
Charles G. Dawes, United States

RICHARD ZSIGMONDY
1925

Born: Vienna, Austria; April 1, 1865
Died: Göttingen, Germany; September 24, 1929
Nationality: German
Area of concentration: Colloid chemistry

Zsigmondy, with the assistance of physicist H. F. W. Siedentopf, invented a device he called the ultramicroscope, which allowed individual particles in colloid solutions to be identified and studied for the first time

The Award

Presentation

In the presence of the Swedish royal family and the members of the Royal Swedish Academy of Sciences, Professor Henrik Gustav Söderbaum presented the 1925 Nobel Prize in Chemistry to Richard Zsigmondy in December, 1926. After defining colloid substances and giving a brief account of research in the field during the nineteenth century, Söderbaum lauded Zsigmondy for the invention of the ultramicroscope, a device which made possible substantial progress in the study of colloids.

Söderbaum succinctly described the operation and purpose of the ultramicroscope. The ultramicroscope shines a very bright light through the substance or solution being studied. The microscope itself then focuses on the light shaft from the side, much as an observer sitting in an enclosed room might view a narrow shaft of sunlight shining through a small window. As the observer in the room would be able to see dust particles in the shaft of sunlight that are not usually visible, so the scientist using the ultramicroscope is able to view colloidal particles ordinarily invisible even to the strongest conventional microscope.

Söderbaum then turned to the important discoveries concerning colloids that Zsigmondy made using the ultramicroscope. Zsigmondy first proved that earlier hypotheses that colloids are made up of microscopic particles are correct. He further showed that all colloidal substances are heterogeneous in nature, and he even managed to measure the size of the particles. He succeeded in explaining the mechanism of the so-called "coagulation phenomenon" (the tendency of primary particles in colloidal solutions to join together to form large aggregates). Other scientists, drawing on Zsigmondy's work, subsequently formed a mathematical theory of coagulation, which Zsigmondy and his students verified through laboratory experiments. Söderbaum concluded by pointing out the great importance of Zsigmondy's work and deeming him worthy of the Nobel Prize in Chemistry.

Nobel lecture

Zsigmondy delivered his Nobel lecture, entitled "Properties of Colloids," on

December 11, 1926. He began with a definition of colloidal solutions, including the familiar examples of coagulating blood and curdling milk. He then gave a synopsis of the research on colloids accomplished in preceding centuries, beginning with the experiments of the Swedish scientist Carl Scheele, whom he characterized as the greatest chemist of the Middle Ages. After mentioning the pioneering work of several other chemists, the laureate turned to his own work.

Zsigmondy related that he first became interested in the study of colloids through commercial work that he was doing in gold orpiment glass and ceramic dyes. He became particularly interested in the then-raging controversy in the scientific community concerning the nature of a colloidal substance called "purple of Cassius." Many chemists held that it was a chemical compound in its own right, while others held that it was a mixture of small particles of gold and stannic acid. He subsequently devised experiments which showed conclusively that the latter view was the correct one, while at the same time demonstrating that a colloid mixture sometimes behaves exactly like a chemical compound.

Many scientists were not able to replicate Zsigmondy's experiments, he said, because of poor techniques in the laboratory. Their criticisms of his work in the professional journals stimulated his greatest discovery: the ultramicroscope. With the help of numerous assistants, all of whom Zsigmondy recognized by name in his Nobel lecture, he developed a device which allowed colloidal substances to be observed and measured for the first time. After describing the nature and function of his invention, Zsigmondy turned to its practical uses and the discoveries already made possible through its use by other scientists, many of whom he named. Here the laureate showed how his own work integrated with that of the world community of scientists.

Critical reception

The Nobel committees did not announce the 1925 recipients until November, 1926. Announcements of the awards in American newspapers were extremely brief. On November 12, 1926, *The New York Times* merely mentioned Zsigmondy on page 8 as being the 1925 laureate in chemistry, without giving any exposition of the work which won the prize for him. (This was not unusual; American newspapers typically paid little attention to foreign Nobel Prize winners during the interwar era.) *The Times* of London and *Le Temps* (Paris) carried equally perfunctory announcements of the awards on the same day that they were announced in *The New York Times*.

German newspapers on November 12 contained, predictably, more thorough accounts of the award itself and of the work that won it for Zsigmondy. The *Berliner Tageblatt* ran a full-column, front-page article which included a short biography of the laureate and a brief account of his most notable achievements in the field of colloid chemistry. The *Frankfurter Zeitung* carried a similar account; the satisfaction that the writers of these articles felt that a German had won the award was evident throughout their stories.

None of the English-language professional journals in chemistry even mentioned the award, much less commented on whether the recipient deserved it. Outside the German newspaper press, Zsigmondy's award seems to have been greeted with virtual indifference both by his peers and by the world at large.

Biography

Richard Adolf Zsigmondy, born April 1, 1865, was the second of four children born to Dr. Adolf Zsigmondy and Irma Zsigmondy (née von Szakmary). His father, a prominent Viennese dentist, gained considerable fame as an inventor of surgical instruments. Richard demonstrated an early interest in chemistry. His parents encouraged this interest by providing him with a small laboratory at home, where he performed many of the experiments described in university-level chemistry texts. After his father's death when Richard was fifteen years old, his mother continued to support her son's scientific proclivities; she also introduced him to mountain climbing, a sport in which he continued to participate for the rest of his life.

Upon completion of his studies at the Technische Hochschule in Vienna in 1887, Zsigmondy enrolled at the University of Munich to study chemistry. After completing his doctorate there in 1890, under Wilhelm von Miller, he remained at Munich for a year as von Miller's assistant before accepting a similar position with the physicist Adolf Kundt in Berlin, where he worked on inorganic inclusions in glass. In 1893, he moved to Graz as a lecturer at the Technische Hochschule there. In 1897, he joined the Schott Glass Manufacturing Company, where he worked with turbid and colored glasses. While there, he invented the famous Jena milk glass, which is still prized by collectors. Zsigmondy left the Schott company in 1900 to pursue private research that resulted in the invention of the ultramicroscope and in his widely acclaimed work on gold solutions.

In 1903, Zsigmondy married Laura Louise Müller, who eventually bore him two daughters. He accepted a position as professor of inorganic chemistry at the University of Göttingen in 1907. He remained at Göttingen for the rest of his life. He died there on September 24, 1929, three years after receiving the Nobel Prize in Chemistry.

Scientific Career

Zsigmondy's scientific reputation rests primarily on his investigations into the nature of colloids. He was actually trained as an organic chemist, in which discipline he took his Ph.D. at the University of Munich under Wilhelm von Miller in 1890 after having also studied for a year with Eduard Ludwig at the University of Vienna. While working as an assistant to the physicist Adolf Kundt in Berlin in 1892, he became interested in the lustrous colors that may be impressed upon porcelain surfaces by painting them with an organic mixture containing very fine particles of gold. He subsequently abandoned organic chemistry and devoted his life to the study of colloids.

In 1893, Zsigmondy returned to his native Austria to accept a post as lecturer at the Technische Hochschule at Graz. (Although *technische Hochschule* translates literally as "Technical High School," the actual level of instruction is more nearly comparable to an American university.) While at Graz, he began a rigorous and thorough study of the nature of the lustrous colors producible through the use of organic solutions liberally endowed with tiny gold particles. These fine dispersions of a material or substance in a solution of another material or substance are called "colloidal"; thus Zsigmondy undertook the study of colloids.

He was especially drawn, by his own admission, to gold-ruby glass, the accidental invention of the seventeenth century alchemist Johann Kunckel. Kunckel, while pursuing the alchemists' chimera of transmuting base substances into gold, discovered instead a method of producing glass with a beautiful deep red luster through the suspension of very fine particles of gold throughout the liquid silica before it was cooled to become glass. This led Zsigmondy, while still at Graz, into the study of "purple of Cassius," a colloidal pigment invented by another alchemist of the seventeenth century, Andreas Cassius.

Zsigmondy quickly discovered that Cassius' purple was indeed a colloidal solution and not, as many chemists believed at the time, a chemical compound. This discovery allowed him to develop techniques for glass and porcelain coloring that had potentially great commercial value, leading directly to his appointment in 1897 to a research post with the Schott Glass Manufacturing Company in Jena, Germany. While with the Schott company, Zsigmondy concentrated on the commercial production of beautifully colored glass objects. His most famous achievement during this period was the invention of the Jena milk glass.

Between 1900 and 1907, Zsigmondy pursued private research. During this period, he completed most of the work that eventually won for him the 1925 Nobel Prize. In pursuing his investigations into colloids, he encountered a number of problems unresolvable with available scientific equipment. The presence of colloidal particles in an organic solution can usually, but not always, be ascertained through the observation under a microscope of a cone of scattered light called the Faraday-Tyndall cone. A microscope does not, however, permit the observer to see the individual particles suspended in the solution. Using the facilities of the Zeiss Company of Jena, and assisted by a number of the employees of that firm (especially the physicist/optician H. F. W. Siedentopf), Zsigmondy developed an ingenious device that would permit direct observation of individual colloidal particles. This device, which its developers named the ultramicroscope, made colloidal gold particles as small as one ten-millionth of a millimeter visible in sunlight.

The principle utilized by Zsigmondy and his associates in the development of the ultramicroscope was not new. Sometimes called "dark-field illumination," the method utilizes a bright light (usually sunlight focused by mirrors) shining through the solution under the microscope at right angles from the observer rather than directly from the observer into the solution. The resulting effect is similar to that of a beam of sunlight admitted to a closed room through a small aperture. If an observer stands back from, and at right angles to, such a beam, even with the unaided eye he will observe many dust motes suspended in the air. Zsigmondy and those who helped him made a number of refinements and improvements in dark-field illumination procedures, and the result was the ultramicroscope.

Using the ultramicroscope, Zsigmondy and his staff quickly made a number of important discoveries concerning colloidal gold solutions in particular and colloidal substances in general. They found that color changes in colloidal gold solutions occurred because of coagulation—that is, changes in the size and number of gold particles in the solution. Coagulation occurs, Zsigmondy found, when the negative electrical charge of the individual particles is removed by the addition of salts. Coagulation can be prevented or slowed by the addition of protective colloids. These observations made possible the determination of the speed at which coagulation takes place as well as of the number of particles in the colloidal substances being studied. With the assistance of the theoretical physicist Marian Smoluchowski, Zsigmondy worked out a complete mathematical formula of colloidal coagulation that is valid not only for gold colloidal solutions but also for all other colloids. These observations and discoveries were instrumental in Zsigmondy's receiving the Nobel Prize in Chemistry for 1925.

After Zsigmondy's invention of the ultramicroscope and his subsequent observations concerning colloidal solutions, the University of Göttingen in 1907 appointed him professor of inorganic chemistry and director of its Institute for Inorganic Chemistry—positions he occupied for the remainder of his life. At the institute, Zsigmondy and his students developed another tool for the investigation of colloidal substances, which he called ultrafiltration. Using the ultramicroscope and ultrafiltration, Zsigmondy's team at Göttingen undertook a detailed study of gels, particularly silica and soap gels (which are essentially coagulated colloidal solutions), that led ultimately to many important discoveries with numerous commercial applications.

In later years, Zsigmondy directed several of his students at Göttingen in the study of the electrical conductivity of colloidal particles. This sort of investigation was only made possible by the ultrafiltration methods developed earlier, which permitted the separation of colloidal solutions from the admixed electrolytes, not only in gold solutions but also in other colloidal solutions. Again, the discoveries resulting from these investigations had broad commercial applications.

Toward the end of his life, Zsigmondy turned his attention to the structure of colloidal particles, and he was engaged in that investigation when he died on September 24, 1929. His scientific career was long and productive, and his discoveries and innovations in the field of colloidal chemistry were integral to the modern development of the field.

Bibliography

Primary
CHEMISTRY: *Zur Erkenntnis der Kolloide*, 1905 (*Colloids and the Ultramicroscope*, 1909); *Kolloidchemie: Ein Lehrbuch*, 1912 (*The Chemistry of Colloids*, 1917); *Das kolloide Gold*, 1925 (with P. A. Thiessen); "Membrane Filters and Their Uses"

and "The Immersion Ultramicroscope," in Jerome Alexander, ed., *Colloid Chemistry*, 1926.

Secondary

Farber, Eduard. *Nobel Prize Winners in Chemistry, 1901-1961*. Rev. ed. New York: Abelard-Schuman, 1963. Farber's book, suitable for all reading audiences, includes a brief biography of Zsigmondy and an account of the work for which he was awarded the Nobel Prize. The account of the prizewinning work is drawn entirely from Zsigmondy's Nobel lecture.

Hatschek, Emil, ed. *The Foundations of Colloid Chemistry*. London: Ernest Benn, 1925. Hatschek mentions Zsigmondy's work briefly, putting him into the context of his predecessors in the field. The reader will need a considerable background in chemistry to understand this book.

Hauser, Ernst. *Colloidal Phenomena*. New York: McGraw-Hill, 1939. Hauser mentions Zsigmondy and his work numerous times in his book, which is an exploration of the then-current status of colloid research. A knowledge of chemical terms and concepts is necessary.

Kruyt, H. R. *Colloids*. London: Ernest Benn, 1930. This book is still a standard reference in colloid chemistry. Kruyt discusses Zsigmondy's contributions in the field at some length, but the reader will need an extensive knowledge of chemistry to appreciate it.

McBain, James W. *Colloid Science*. Lexington, Mass.: D. C. Heath, 1950. McBain includes an extensive and admiring overview of Zsigmondy's work and his contributions to the field of chemistry. The book is replete with technical terms and scientific terminology that will foil any reader without a background in chemistry.

Paul Madden

1926

Chemistry
Theodor Svedberg, Sweden

Physics
Jean-Baptiste Perrin, France

Physiology or Medicine
Johannes Fibiger, Denmark

Literature
Grazia Deledda, Italy

Peace
Aristide Briand, France
Gustav Stresemann, Germany

THEODOR SVEDBERG
1926

Born: Fleräng, Valbo, Sweden; August 30, 1884
Died: Örebro, Sweden; February 25, 1971
Nationality: Swedish
Area of concentration: Colloid chemistry

Svedberg advanced the study of disperse systems (colloid solutions) by developing improved purification and analytical techniques for colloidal particles, most notably by the invention of the ultracentrifuge. His contributions were valuable for the identification and physical characterization of biochemical molecules

The Award

Presentation

Henrik Gustav Söderbaum, secretary of the Royal Swedish Academy of Sciences, presented the Nobel Prize in Chemistry to Theodor ("The") Svedberg on Friday, December 10, 1926. In his address, Söderbaum summarized the history of colloid chemistry, beginning with the work of English botanist Robert Brown. Colloids are small particles suspended in liquid solvent, and Brown studied the curious motion of microscopic plant particles suspended in liquid.

This "Brownian movement" was initially attributed to molecular and atomic vibration. Albert Einstein, the 1921 Nobel physics laureate, and Marian Smoluchowski proposed an alternative hypothesis, in which the motion of disperse particles was attributed to random collisions between molecules. They developed an elaborate mathematical description of Brownian movement. Svedberg and 1926 Nobel physics laureate Jean-Baptiste Perrin of France confirmed the Einstein-Smoluchowski interpretation by determining the speed and distribution of colloid particles.

Svedberg's single most important contribution to colloid research was the ultracentrifuge, a device whose rapid rotation (40,000-100,000 revolutions per minute) can create gravitational forces hundreds of thousands of times greater than that of the Earth. Centrifugation of dispersed colloidal solutions proved to be an effective separation tool for purifying and characterizing distinct species of colloidal molecules. The determination of the molecular weight for the protein hemoglobin served as a prime example.

Nobel lecture

Svedberg delivered his Nobel lecture, appropriately entitled "The Ultracentrifuge," on Thursday, May 19, 1927. His lecture emphasized precision measurement and detailed instrument design. Svedberg began by honoring his colleagues, in particular Richard Zsigmondy, winner of the 1925 Nobel Prize in Chemistry. Zsigmondy advanced the study of colloid solutions by observing illuminated colloid samples with the ultramicroscope. Unfortunately, the ultramicroscope failed to provide accurate resolution of particle sizes. Svedberg, Perrin, and others improved these measurements.

Svedberg and Herman Rinde initially obtained accurate size distributions for large particles by sedimenting them through a gravitational field, a technique pioneered by K. Oden. Nevertheless, Svedberg realized that thousandfold magnifications of gravitational force would be necessary for the analysis of smaller particles. This observation led to his study of 20-micrometer-diameter gold colloids using a 150-g centrifuge (150 times the earth's gravitational attraction), an instrument developed in collaboration with J. Burton Nichols at the University of Wisconsin in 1923. For better resolution of smaller particles, Rinde and Svedberg developed the first ultracentrifuge (7,000-g, 12,000 revolutions per minute) in 1924. Svedberg topped this achievement with a 100,000-g ultracentrifuge (42,000 revolutions per minute) in 1926.

Because of the tremendous forces produced at high rotation speeds, each ultracentrifuge is an elaborate instrument crafted to the finest detail. The primary component is a cylindrical rotor carefully constructed for a precise center of gravity along the spin axis. Colloid samples are placed within crystal cells, which are balanced by weight on opposite sides of the rotor. The rotor spins within a hydrogen atmosphere, which reduces friction. Svedberg's ultracentrifuge utilized a built-in camera system and ultraviolet illumination for photographing samples during centrifugation; the ultracentrifuge was extremely well-designed for its time.

Centrifugation of colloid solutions can be used to determine molecular weights and particle sizes. Colloid particle molecular weights are determined by the rate of migration of particles in the centrifuge cell. Colloid particle sizes are determined based upon the concentration distribution of particles after various sedimentation times. Svedberg and his colleagues developed comprehensive mathematical models for making these measurements.

Although Svedberg initially used the ultracentrifuge to study the properties of gold colloids, he proceeded to the study of biological and industrially important molecules. Robin Fahraeus, Nichols, and Svedberg utilized the ultracentrifuge for the molecular weight determination of hemoglobin. Centrifugation of a carefully purified hemoglobin suspension yielded a mean molecular weight of approximately 68,000 daltons (one dalton is about the mass of one hydrogen atom). Centrifugation of the protein ovalbumin yielded a molecular weight of approximately 34,500 daltons. They also measured the proteins phycocyanin and phycoerythrin.

Svedberg's development of the ultracentrifuge had effects extending well beyond the study of colloid suspensions. The determination of molecular weights and particle sizes had immediate applications to the structural analysis of low and high molecular weight molecules such as proteins, carbohydrates, and nucleic acids.

Critical reception

The Svedberg's many contributions to physical chemistry culminated in his being awarded the 1926 Nobel Prize in Chemistry at the age of forty-two. His achievement continued the rich tradition of Swedish science, in particular chemistry, established by individuals such as Jöns Jakob Berzelius and Svante August Arrhenius. His prize was greeted with considerable favor, both at home and abroad. Arne Tiselius, his student, and Stig Claesson, writing in the *Annual Review of Physical Chemistry*, described Svedberg as a dominant force in Swedish science and in physical chemistry throughout the world.

The award came at a critical time in twentieth century Swedish and European history. World War I had created a climate of apathy throughout the continent. The Swedish government had cut funding for many programs, including science. Financial scarcity, coupled with inadequate, outdated laboratory equipment, signaled a bleak scientific future for the country. Svedberg's Nobel Prize stemmed this downward trend and produced an academic renaissance at Sweden's University of Uppsala.

The Nobel Prize revitalized Swedish chemistry. Svedberg's proposed Institute of Physical Chemistry was approved and completed at Uppsala in 1930. Furthermore, funding for science increased, leading to considerable chemical research and a major influx of students from all parts of the world.

Additionally, the award was important for its elevation of colloid chemistry as a science. The 1926 Nobel Prizes in Chemistry and Physics, awarded to Svedberg and Perrin respectively, plus the delayed 1925 Nobel Prize in Chemistry to Zsigmondy, emphasized the importance of colloid chemistry to a better understanding of biological and physical processes. The simultaneous awarding of Nobel Prizes to three giants of the field served as a testament to this fact. In his introductory speech to the winners on December 10, 1926, Söderbaum defended the importance of colloid chemistry, citing its applications in physical chemistry, organic chemistry, physiology, and medicine.

The New York Times and *The Times* of London, on December 11, 1926, each listed the various Nobel Prize winners, including Svedberg, but neither elaborated upon the science winners. Instead, their focus was placed upon the 1926 Peace Prize, awarded to Aristide Briand of France and Gustav Stresemann of Germany for the Pact of Locarno, which brought a tentative peace to Europe. Postwar tensions were very high.

Svedberg was appointed director of the new Institute for Physical Chemistry at Uppsala in 1931. His prominence in Swedish science allowed his research to flourish for the remainder of his career. When he reached mandatory retirement age in 1949, the Swedish government honored him with a unique action: He was promoted to emeritus professor and appointed permanent director of the Gustav Werner Institute for Nuclear Chemistry.

Furthermore, physical chemists honored Svedberg with the centrifuge sedimentation coefficient "s," whose unit is the "svedberg." One svedberg (1 s) is equal to 1×10^{-13} second, or 0.0000000000001 second. Svedberg's Nobel Prize was a fitting tribute to a brilliant career, which continued for more than four decades after the award.

Biography

Theodor Svedberg was born on August 30, 1884, in Fleräng, Valbo, near Gavleborgs Lan, Sweden. He was the only child of Elias and Augusta (née Alstermark) Svedberg. His father was a civil engineer who had an intense love for nature, an interest acquired by the young Svedberg.

Svedberg enrolled at the University of Uppsala in January, 1904, to study chemistry. He earned a bachelor's degree in September, 1905, and received his doctorate in chemistry in 1908. His doctoral dissertation concerned colloids, the principal research focus for his entire scientific career.

His rise at Uppsala was rapid, beginning with a lectureship in physical chemistry from 1907 to 1912. He became professor of physical chemistry in 1912, the first individual to hold the position. He retained this appointment until mandatory university retirement in 1949. In 1922, he was a visiting professor at the University of Wisconsin, where he began work on his crowning achievement, the ultracentrifuge.

Svedberg was married four times, first to Andrea Andreen in 1909, then to Jan Frodi Dahlquist in 1916, Ingrid Blomquist Tauson in 1938, and Margit Hallén Norback in 1948. He was a member of the Royal Society, the National Academy of Sciences (United States), the Academy of Sciences of the U.S.S.R., and numerous other scientific organizations. He held honorary doctorates from the Universities of Delaware, Gröningen, Oxford, Paris, Uppsala, and Wisconsin, and from Harvard University. He was active in the Swedish Research Council for Technology and the Swedish Atomic Research Council.

Svedberg served as director of the Gustaf Werner Institute of Nuclear Chemistry from 1949 to 1967. He died in Örebro, Sweden, on February 25, 1971, at the age of eighty-six.

Scientific Career

Theodor Svedberg's scientific research could be described as innovative, detailed, and cross-disciplinary. His work was innovative because he devised new techniques and equipment for tackling previously unsolvable problems. It was detailed because he applied painstaking thought to the proper design and conduct of experiments. It was cross-disciplinary because his research proved to be useful in many fields other than colloid chemistry, further demonstrating his diverse interests.

While Svedberg's interests included both biology and chemistry, he chose the latter as a career. He believed that biological processes were explainable at the chemical level, a concept to which he returned in his later studies. At the time of his doctoral research, the composition of colloidal solutions was poorly understood. Many scientists believed that understanding colloids would be useful for modeling biological systems.

This impetus stimulated Svedberg to conduct the first quantitative analyses of colloidal solutions. He obtained the first high purification of gold and platinum colloids by passing an alternating electric current between two electrodes (either gold or platinum) immersed in water. Gold or platinum colloidal solutions resulted from the dispersion of metal particles from the electrodes into the water. Svedberg's purification experiments were an improvement upon a similar technique developed by Gregor Bredig. Svedberg observed the purified colloid particles using high illumination coupled with the ultramicroscope developed by Zsigmondy. He extended his observations of colloids beyond metals to organic molecules.

Using the ultramicroscope, Svedberg studied the Brownian movement of colloid particles, the random motion of particles in solution. He and Perrin studied the quantitative effects of particle size, temperature, and other factors upon the movement of colloids. In 1906, these studies verified the Einstein-Smoluchowski interpretation of Brownian movement, that particle motion was caused by random collisions between particles and solvent molecules.

In collaboration with Professor D. Stromholm of Uppsala, Svedberg studied the separation of radioactive compounds in a gravitational field. They found that certain radioactive elements solidified with certain salts (for example, barium), but not with others. These experiments were among the first to verify the existence of radioactive isotopes—atoms of elements that, because of a neutron imbalance, achieve stability by emitting a radioactive particle. Frederick Soddy, the winner of the 1921 Nobel Prize in Chemistry, performed decisive experiments concerning the existence and nature of radioactive isotopes; he cited the importance of Stromholm and Svedberg's work in his Nobel lecture.

Therefore, Svedberg's early work on colloidal solutions not only yielded improved purification and analysis of various substances but also generated crucial data to support two important breakthroughs in chemistry and physics. Svedberg's brilliance as a student and his major research achievements early in his professional career led to a rapid rise in status. He was appointed to the first Swedish chair of physical chemistry at Uppsala in 1912.

Svedberg continued his colloid studies on inorganic substances during the years prior to World War I; he and colleagues provided considerable evidence that molecules existed as particles. He visited chemical institutes throughout Europe, including Berlin in 1913, Vienna in 1916, and Paris in 1922.

During and following the war years, funding for science was very limited in Sweden. Furthermore, the laboratories at Uppsala had been inadequately supplied in terms of the large equipment necessary for physical chemistry experiments. Svedberg often had to improvise equipment; his ingenuity was usually successful. Svedberg's success in colloid chemistry, however, eventually became limited with the available instrumentation. The ultramicroscope had been valuable, yet it lacked the resolution necessary for observing particles smaller than 100 micrometers in diameter. In 1923, Svedberg and Herman Rinde developed a technique for determining the particle size distribution in a sedimenting colloidal solution. Their experiment involved the measurement of sediment accumulating in a colloidal system suspended on a balance. K. Oden had pioneered the experiment but had only distinguished between 1-gram particles. Svedberg and Rinde improved the resolution by controlling factors (air currents, for example) that disturbed the balance scale. They also determined the particle size distribution for gold colloids, based upon the variation of colloid concentration with colloid migration distance in the sedimenting system.

Even as these experiments were proceeding, Svedberg was thinking of other methods to improve colloid analysis. One approach was centrifugation, which he would pursue later that year. The other approach was electrophoresis, the separation of particles based on size and charge in an electric field. Svedberg performed preliminary work on electrophoresis with Eric R. Jette.

Following these studies, Professor J. H. Matthews of the University of Wisconsin at Madison invited Svedberg to spend eight months teaching and doing research in Madison. Svedberg capitalized on this opportunity, which would produce the major breakthrough of his career. He began more advanced studies in centrifugation, electrophoresis, and diffusion of colloidal solutions. With J. Burton Nichols, Svedberg constructed the first ultracentrifuge, an instrument which could spin at the rate of 20,000 to 30,000 revolutions per minute. The centrifugal force generated by such high speeds could sediment colloidal solutions far better than a traditional centrifuge, with gravitational forces thousands of times greater than the earth's gravity. Svedberg and Nichols' ultracentrifuge was elaborate, incorporating both a camera and illumination for photographing samples during the centrifugation process. They obtained particle size distributions and particle radii for gold sols, clay, barium sulfate, and arsenous sulfide.

Upon returning to Uppsala, Svedberg concentrated upon using the ultracentrifuge for determining the molecular weights of proteins. Initially, he and Nichols attempted a molecular weight determination for ovalbumin by centrifuging the molecule with a force of 5,000-g. At first, they were unsuccessful. Undeterred, Svedberg and Robin Fahraeus used the same procedure on hemoglobin, obtaining a molecular weight of approximately 66,800 daltons.

To achieve greater accuracy in determining molecular weights by sedimentation, Svedberg began experimenting with higher-speed ultracentrifuges. His first oil turbine centrifuge produced centrifugal forces around 100,000-g at 45,000 revolutions per minute. These experiments were not without drawbacks: The centrifuges often exploded because of the rotor instabilities generated at such high speeds. Nevertheless, Svedberg and his students persevered with steadily improved ultracentrifuge designs, achieving 200,000-g in 1931, 300,000-g in 1932, 400,000-g in 1933, and eventually 750,000-g in 1935. Svedberg was determined to push the limits of the ultracentrifuge as far as possible to realize its full potential.

Beyond hemoglobin, Svedberg applied the ultracentrifuge to the study of other proteins, working toward the elucidation of their structures. Molecular weights were obtained for proteins from many species, ranging from humans to plants. Among the biologically relevant molecules were cytochrome c, pepsin, myoglobin, insulin, albumin, globulin, catalase, urease, and hemocyanin. Svedberg's invention was an invaluable tool eventually used by most protein chemists.

The Nobel Prize propelled Svedberg to the forefront of Swedish science. His work attracted many students, including Arne Tiselius, who continued Svedberg's earlier work on electrophoresis of proteins; Tiselius was awarded the Nobel Prize in Chemistry in 1948.

Svedberg's extensive molecular weight analyses of proteins yielded an intriguing pattern. Virtually all proteins examined had molecular weights that were multiples of 17,600 daltons. The multiples were 2, 4, 8, 16, 24, 48, 96, 192, and 384, yielding protein molecular weights of approximately 35,200, 70,400, 281,600 daltons, and so on. These results were questioned by many scientists; corroborative studies, however, initially confirmed Svedberg's observations. Nevertheless, his results were based on incomplete data in that the proteins studied were mostly respiratory and circulatory in nature. Later studies of other organ system proteins failed to support this pattern, thereby disproving Svedberg's multiple molecular weight hypothesis. His hypothesis did, however, stimulate a period of extensive protein research that advanced the field of protein chemistry.

Ultracentrifuge studies of large molecules (macromolecules) continued with carbohydrates (that is, complex sugars such as starch). Svedberg combined his interest in biologically relevant molecules with his interest in botany; the result was a pioneering study in the complex sugars of the Liliifloreae family, which includes lilies and irises. Svedberg and Nils Gralen ultracentrifuged the bulb juices of seventy-five species. They obtained two major sedimentation classes of carbohydrates. These two groups of carbohydrates were remarkably similar from species to species within the same genus. The similarities declined, however, between species of different genera. This work not only contributed to the structural analysis of carbohydrates but also provided a useful analytical tool for later evolutionary studies by biologists.

During World War II, Svedberg was forced to divert his research toward the Swedish war effort. His laboratory played a major role in the development of polychloroprene (synthetic rubber). He also worked on the development of other synthetic polymers. In addition to these important contributions, he still found time to focus on new methods for analyzing colloids. He used the electron microscope and X-ray diffraction to study the properties of cellulosic materials. He developed the osmotic balance, a device used to weigh colloid particles accurately by separating the particles through a permeable, or penetrable, membrane. He ultracentrifuged cellulosic materials, including cereals and malts, to determine molecular size and shape. This was a period during which Svedberg could innovate and experiment with new technologies which would later be invaluable for the structural analysis of molecules.

Svedberg reached mandatory retirement age in 1949. In honor of his many achievements, the Swedish administration made a special exception for him. He was appointed lifelong director of the Gustaf Werner Institute of Nuclear Chemistry, newly created with funds from Swedish textile magnate Gustaf Werner. Appointment to this position returned him to his early interest in radiation. The construction by 1951 of a 200-mega-electron-volt synchrocyclotron had tremendous applications. As usual, he seized the opportunity and directed use of the instrument toward biological and medical applications, investigating radiochemotherapy and the effects of radiation on macromolecules. Svedberg always demonstrated tremendous foresight into the applications of science toward human welfare.

Bibliography

Primary

CHEMISTRY: "The Determination of the Distribution of Size of Particles in Disperse Systems," *Journal of the American Chemical Society*, vol. 45, 1923 (with Herman Rinde); "The Cataphoresis of Proteins," *Journal of the American Chemical Society*, vol. 45, 1923 (with Eric R. Jette); "Determination of Size and Distribution of Size of Particles by Centrifugal Methods," *Journal of the American Chemical Society*, vol. 45, 1923 (with J. Burton Nichols); "A New Method for the Determination of the Molecular Weight of the Proteins," *Journal of the American Chemical Society*, vol. 48, 1926 (with Robin Fahraeus); "Sedimentation of Molecules in Centrifugal Fields," *Chemical Reviews*, vol. 14, 1934; "A Discussion on the Protein Molecule," *Proceedings of the Royal Society of London*, vol. B127, 1939; "Soluble Reserve Carbohydrates in the Liliifloreae," *Biochemical Journal*, vol. 34, 1940 (with Nils Gralen); *The Ultracentrifuge*, 1940 (with Kai O. Pedersen).

Secondary

Claesson, Stig, and Kai O. Pedersen. "The (Theodor) Svedberg." In *Dictionary of Scientific Biography*, edited by Charles Coulston Gillispie. New York: Charles Scribner's Sons, 1970. This short article, written by two of Svedberg's colleagues, provides an intimate look at his life and scientific career. It provides glimpses at Svedberg's childhood and personal interests and informative coverage of his work with the ultracentrifuge.

Debus, Allen G., ed. *World Who's Who in Science*. Chicago: Marquis-Who's Who, 1968. This reference work provides concise, one-paragraph summaries of the lives of major twentieth century world scientists, including information on marriages, children, and honors.

Farber, Eduard. *Nobel Prize Winners in Chemistry, 1901-1961*. Rev. ed. New York: Abelard-Schuman, 1963. An informative reference, this book provides short synopses of the first sixty Nobel Prize winners in chemistry. Each laureate is discussed with a biographical sketch, description of his scientific work, and importance of the work.

Findlay, Alexander. *A Hundred Years of Chemistry*. 3d rev. ed. London: Gerald Duckworth, 1965. Findlay's book is an extensively detailed description of the development of chemistry from the middle 1800's through the early 1960's. Emphasis is placed upon the atomic, organic, and physical branches of chemistry.

Ihde, Aaron J. *The Development of Modern Chemistry*. New York: Harper & Row, 1964. Presents an extensive, lively discussion of the history of chemistry in the twentieth century. It begins with background information concerning the great chemists of the eighteenth and nineteenth centuries, then proceeds into comprehensive presentations of the major branches of twentieth century chemistry.

MacCallum, T. W., and Stephen Taylor, eds. *The Nobel Prize-Winners and the Nobel Foundation, 1901-1937.* Zurich: Central European Times, 1938. Although dated, this reference work provides an early perspective on the Nobel Prizes in all fields. Brief, one-page biographical sketches are provided for each laureate.

Nobelstiftelsen. *Nobel: The Man and His Prizes.* 2d ed. New York: Elsevier, 1962. This comprehensive reference work discusses the life of Alfred Nobel and the history of the Nobel Prize winners. Each laureate's contributions are discussed in terms of importance to the respective discipline.

Tinoco, Ignacio, Kenneth H. Sauer, and James C. Wang. *Physical Chemistry: Principles and Applications in Biological Sciences.* Englewood Cliffs, N.J.: Prentice-Hall, 1978. A book of physical methods in molecular biology experiments, this textbook is aimed primarily at advanced undergraduate and graduate students. The book presents a mathematical discussion of basic physical concepts, including Svedberg's ultracentrifuge and electrophoresis.

Tiselius, Arne, and Stig Claesson. "The Svedberg and Fifty Years of Physical Chemistry in Sweden." *Annual Review of Physical Chemistry* 18 (1967): 1-8. This introductory article for an annual journal is a tribute to The Svedberg by two of his students and colleagues. The article vividly discusses his life, his scientific research, and his contributions to Swedish academia.

David Wason Hollar, Jr.

1927

Chemistry
Heinrich Otto Wieland, Germany

Physics
Arthur Holly Compton, United States
Charles Thomson Rees Wilson, Great Britain

Physiology or Medicine
J. Wagner von Jauregg, Austria

Literature
Henri Bergson, France

Peace
Ferdinand Buisson, France
Ludwig Quidde, Germany

HEINRICH OTTO WIELAND
1927

Born: Pforzheim, Germany; June 4, 1877
Died: Starnberg, West Germany; August 5, 1957
Nationality: German
Area of concentration: Structure of bile acids

It had long been known that bile acids were fundamental to the process of digestion, but how they contributed was only vaguely understood. Wieland extracted from bile a saturated acid that is the quintessential component of all bile acids; he studied this acid, describing its structure and function in full detail

The Award

Presentation

On Monday, December 10, 1928, the Secretary of the Royal Swedish Academy of Sciences, Henrik Gustav Söderbaum, presented Heinrich Otto Wieland and Adolf Windaus to King Gustav V as recipients, respectively, of the 1927 and 1928 Nobel Prizes in Chemistry. Wieland's award, withheld in the preceding year, was bestowed, as sometimes happens, in the following year.

Söderbaum first addressed the question of the increasing specialization of scientific research, using this observation as the basis for pointing out that the two current recipients had deviated from that characteristic specialization to pursue research in broad areas that cut across several subspecialties of organic chemistry. In Wieland's case, although the work he did had a strong basis in organic chemistry, it had broad implications for biochemists, physicians, and physiologists as well.

Söderbaum outlined the extent to which the bile acids had been studied thoroughly for more than a hundred years but noted that, despite this investigation, previous researchers had produced little information about the connections among the bile acids and almost nothing about their structure. Identifying this area of study as one of the most challenging and difficult in organic chemistry, he credited Wieland with extracting from bile the saturated acid that is the underlying substance of all bile acids and with accurately ascertaining its structure.

Acknowledging the complex composition of the substances with which Wieland was working, Söderbaum indicated how difficult it was to produce even in minute quantities the material that Wieland required for his investigations and experimentation. That Wieland, having designed his experiments, was able to generate and isolate these materials for analysis provided evidence of his remarkable skill as an organic chemist.

Nobel lecture

Wieland delivered his Nobel lecture, "The Chemistry of the Bile Acids," on December 12, 1928. Replete with diagrams to illustrate the atomic structures of many molecules related to bile, it began by reviewing the study of bile acids in the nineteenth and early twentieth centuries, noting particularly Hans Fischer's discovery in 1911 that the lithocholic acid he found in the gallstones of oxen is an essential component in the bile of humans as well.

Wieland showed the centrality of desoxycholic acid to the understanding of bile. This acid combines easily with esters, hydrocarbons, alcohols, ethers, and phenols to form well-defined compounds that generally contain two molecules of desoxycholic acid that lend themselves to the sort of analysis that his research necessitated. He observed further that whereas cholic acids that contain neutral compounds that are insoluble in water do not decompose when they are absorbed by alkalis, the alkali salts of desoxycholic acid can absorb some neutral substances that are not soluble in water. This unlocked one of the mysteries of how bile acids work.

In order to study the structure of bile acids, Wieland had to study chemically the various stages of decomposition as they take place. The process of this study was monotonous and, according to Wieland, unattractive from an experimental standpoint. He observed that nitrogen is absent from the decomposition process, in which carbon and hydrogen figure prominently with little oxygen present.

He detailed how, in order to gain the broad view of biological relationships of the chemically related natural substances similar to bile that he needed in order to conduct his research, he had to investigate such substances as sterols, vegetable cardiac poisons (saponins), and similar poisons from the secretions found on the skins of toads, determining the basic chemical structures of each.

Wieland indicated one of the most pressing problems of his research in his explanation that in order to obtain a mere five grams of tricarboxylic acid, which was extremely important to his research, he had to begin with a kilogram of desoxycholic acid, reducing it, through a process that lasted more than a week, into the substance he required. This problem contributed significantly to the difficulty of conducting the research on which he had embarked.

When Wieland discovered that the four most crucial bile acids are extremely closely related to one another both in basic structure and in the distribution of hydroxyl (OH) groups, he had to make minute calculations to determine the almost imperceptible differences among the four, which led to his most important conclusions about the bile acids. Wieland found that bile acids conjugated with glycerin and taurine have predictable relationships with natural amino acids, which explains to some extent how digestion takes place in animals.

Acknowledging that much remains to be learned about bile acids, Wieland ended his address by saying that, when the final mysteries in the field are understood, chemists should be able to synthesize the compounds necessary to digestion, although he repudiated this as one of the more valuable activities that might grow out of his research.

Critical reception

The announcement of the 1928 Nobel Prizes included the name of Heinrich Wieland as recipient of the 1927 Nobel Prize in Chemistry, which had been withheld the previous year. Neither *The New York Times* nor *The Times* of London for November 14, 1928, paid much attention to the awards made that year in the sciences, although they did name the recipients. *The Times* of London focused its attention on Henri Bergson, winner of the 1927 Nobel Prize in Literature, which had also been withheld in 1927. The 1928 recipient in literature, Sigrid Undset, also evoked considerable attention from the British press.

The announcements of the actual awards in the newspapers of December 11, 1928, were brief and provided a mere identification of most of the laureates, giving their fields of research and identifying the specific areas in which they had received the prize. The field in which Wieland had worked was one about which most people outside the field knew little, and this situation probably accounted for the lack of immediate attention in the popular press.

In 1930, however, the *Journal of Chemical Education* published Gulbrand Lunde's "The 1927 and 1928 Nobel Chemistry Prize Winners, Wieland and Windaus," an article that focused on the contributions that Wieland and Windaus made to the field of organic chemistry and the implications of their research for other areas of scientific inquiry. This piece was complimentary, emphasizing the experimental difficulties that their respective research tasks entailed. It pointed out that Wieland and Windaus had isolated a bile acid isomeric with desoxycholic acid at about the same time, although they had worked independently. Also, Wieland was much aided in his work by Windaus' earlier research studies on cholesterol.

The new *Annual Review of Biochemistry*, first published in 1932, contained Windaus' "The Chemistry of the Sterols, Bile Acids, and Other Cyclical Constituents of Natural Fats and Oils," in which Windaus gave full credit to Wieland for his research, which was complementary to his own research of about the same period. He clearly applauded Wieland's being given the Nobel Prize for his pioneering work, which involved some of the most arduous experimental research that an organic chemist could undertake.

The popular magazines of the day, if they mentioned the prizes at all, paid scant attention to Wieland other than to mention his name and the basis for his award. Because his work was technical and because an understanding of it necessitates understanding molecular structures at a quite advanced level, it was little recognized by the public, although its implications—particularly its biochemical implications—were such that few human beings have failed to benefit from the discoveries he made.

Biography

Heinrich Otto Wieland learned his earliest lessons in chemistry from his father, Theodor Wieland, a pharmaceutical chemist, whose wife was Elise (née Blom) Wieland. Upon completing his *Gymnasium* studies in Pforzheim, Wieland attended the universities of Munich, Berlin, and Stuttgart, moving from one university to another to attend the lectures of each school's most distinguished faculty members, as was the custom in Germany in his day. He returned to the University of Munich in 1899 to proceed with doctoral studies under Johannes Thiele, receiving the doctorate in organic chemistry in 1901.

By 1904, he had passed his *venia legendi*, which made him eligible to teach, and in that year he was duly appointed a *Privatdozent* at the University of Munich, the rough equivalent of an instructor in a higher institution in the United States. Always considering Munich his spiritual home, Wieland spent most of his life there, except for a year during World War I when, on leave from Munich's technical university (at which he was now a professor), he spent a year at the Kaiser-Wilhelm Institute for Physical Chemistry and Electrochemistry in Berlin. He also spent the years from 1921 to 1925 at the University of Freiburg, but returned to the University of Munich in 1925 as director of the renowned Baeyer Laboratory, where he had done his own doctoral work, and as chair of the department of organic chemistry. He remained at the University of Munich until 1950, when he assumed emeritus status.

Wieland was editor of the *Justus Liebigs Annalen der Chemie* (annals of chemistry) for more than twenty years, and was himself a prolific writer, producing more than fifty technical reports between 1912 and 1943 on the mechanisms of oxidation alone. His laboratory work was continually concerned with isolating and determining the molecular structure of such natural products as cardioactive toad poisons, morphine alkaloids, mushroom poisons, and strychnine alkaloids.

Wieland married Josephine Bartmann in 1908, and they had three sons, all of whom pursued careers in science, and a daughter, Eva, who married Feodor Lynen, Nobel laureate in physiology or medicine in 1964. A kindly man who lived for his work, his students, and his family, Wieland died in Starnberg, West Germany, on August 5, 1957, shortly after his eightieth birthday.

Scientific Career

Wieland's scientific interests were far-ranging, but early were focused on the chemistry in compounds of nitrogen, especially on what happens when nitrogen oxides are added to carbon-carbon double bonds. He was also concerned with the nitration of aromatic hydrocarbons, which were being studied extensively at the time by Hermann Staudinger, Nobel laureate in chemistry in 1953.

Wieland studied the color reactions of hydrazines and in so doing discovered the nitrogen-free radicals, groups of extremely volatile atoms that have a peculiar unpaired electron. His work on nitrogen compounds yielded almost one hundred scholarly papers and, in itself, would have assured Wieland's professional reputation as an organic chemist.

Simultaneously, Wieland was pursuing extensive laboratory research on oxidation. For 150 years, people had accepted Antoine-Laurent Lavoisier's explanation that oxidation was caused by activated oxygen, which is highly reactive and has little stability. Wieland produced a well-documented opposing theory of dehydrogenation caused by the activation of hydrogen. He also showed how dehydrogenation occurs in living cells, how acetates are converted to succinic acid in yeast cells bereft of oxygen.

His work reestablished the unity between organic chemistry and biochemistry at a time when scientific studies were becoming increasingly fragmented as, because of the growing proliferation of information with which they were confronted, scientists were pushed more and more into the kinds of specialization that Wieland, with his broad view of his discipline and with his variety of research interests, eschewed.

Wieland's work on bile acids for which he received the Nobel Prize is considered his greatest achievement. He sought to explain how these substances that are found in the gallbladders of humans and other vertebrates react to help in the digestion of lipids. It must be remembered that when Wieland began his work, many of the research tools that organic chemists now take for granted—spectrometry, X-ray analysis, and chromatography—were not available to researchers, meaning that they had to carry out their experiments arduously and tediously over long periods of time.

Proceeding slowly and with incredible care, Wieland showed that three of the most significant bile acids—cholic acid, lithocholic acid, and deoxycholic acid—could be converted to cholanic acid, clearly indicting that all of them have the same basic structure and differ in only one particular, the number of attached hydroxyl groups. Just as Wieland was making these research findings, Adolf Windaus, the 1928 Nobel laureate in chemistry, had succeeded in converting cholesterol into cholanic acid, which indicated a strong relationship between it and the bile acids with which Wieland was working.

Wieland demonstrated that bile acids combine with fats (cholesterol) and hydrocarbons to form colloidal solutions in water and that their function physiologically is to turn fats in the diet into compounds that are soluble in water, thereby making efficient digestion possible. He also unraveled the complex question of the molecular structure of the various bile acids.

This work led him into his investigation of such vegetable cardiac poisons as digitalis and strophantus, both of which are used medicinally in limited quantities as cardiac tonics. These vegetable poisons are called sterols and are found in deathcap mushrooms as well as in the skin secretions of poisonous toads. Their production in a pure state had not been achieved prior to Wieland's work; therefore their structure and chemical relationships were unknown.

The vegetable sterols found in plant organisms are called phytosterols and are closely related to cholesterol, which is found only in animal organisms, occurring in the brain, nerve substance, blood, and presumably all cells of all such organisms. Just as many kinds of bile acids exist, so cholesterol is found in many forms. In Wieland's day, little was known about what role it plays in biological processes; the mystery intrigued Wieland and led his fellow Nobel laureate, Windaus, to the discovery and isolation of cholesterol. Nevertheless, Wieland drew some of the initial parallels between the phytosterols and cholesterol, realizing early the close relationship that both of these compounds have to the bile acids.

Advances in understanding cholesterol and the functioning of the bile acids have been of particular use to nutritionists and have led in the United States to a society that is highly cholesterol-conscious, as it has been made clear that some types of cholesterol accumulate on the walls of the arteries, leading to coronary occlusions in some people. Gallstones and kidney stones are also known to have high cholesterol content and to be related both to diet and to genetic predispositions. Much of this information has been derived from the basic information Wieland and Windaus made available to the public in the 1920's and 1930's.

Wieland's work with fulminic acid and his discovery of how it turns into a polymer are also significant. Work that Hermann Staudinger was pursuing at the same time, much of it at the University of Freiburg in the position that Wieland had vacated in 1925, postulated the existence of macromolecules (large molecules), a most unpopular theory in its day because it flew in the face of what most chemists of that day believed and thought that they had proved. Wieland, however, was moving in the direction of similar conclusions in his experimentation with polymers.

Wieland's professional career continued for a quarter of a century after he received his Nobel Prize. His work extended into areas that focused on such things as the pigmentation of butterflies, which led to his discovery of an important class of compounds called pterins. Although much of his initial work on bile acids necessarily had to be done with synthetic products in order to control the experiments in ways that made them manageable in his later career, Wieland worked increasingly on natural compounds, many of them related to bile acids.

During the years when he directed the Baeyer Institute and worked closely with students, guiding them into important research channels and always showing a tremendous interest in them and in their work, Wieland also contributed more broadly to organic chemistry internationally through his editorship of the *Justus Liebigs Annalen der Chemie*, in itself a daunting job. Wieland was perfectly suited to both his directorship and his editorship because of his encompassing knowledge of the whole field of chemistry rather than of the small, specialized corner of that field with which most scientists of his age were acquainted.

Wieland's fame was international. During his lifetime, he held membership in the Royal Society of London, in the American National Academy of Sciences, in the American Academy of Arts and Sciences, and in the chemical societies of half a dozen countries, including India and Japan. In his own country, he was a member of the science academies of Munich, Berlin, Heidelberg, and Göttingen. Two years before his death, he had bestowed upon him the first Otto Hahn Prize for Physics and Chemistry of the German Chemical Society. He also received honorary degrees from the universities of Freiburg and of Athens.

Bibliography

Primary

CHEMISTRY: "Die Knallsäure," *Sammlung chemischer und chemishtechnischer Vortrage*, vol. 14, 1901; *Die Hydrazine*, 1913; "Die Chemie der Gallensäuren," *Zeitschrift für angewandte Chemie und Zentralblate für technische Chemie*, vol. 42,

1929; "Recent Researches on Biological Oxidation," *Journal of the Chemical Society*, vol. 64, 1931; *On the Mechanism of Oxidation*, 1932; "Die Konstitution der Gallensäuren," *Berichte der deutschen chemischen Gesellschaft*, vol. 67, 1934.

AUTOBIOGRAPHY: "Autobiography," *Nachrichten aus Chemie und Technik*, 1955.

Secondary

Huisigen, Rolf. "The Wieland Memorial Lecture." *Proceedings of the Chemical Society*, 1958: 210-219. This lecture, delivered the year after Wieland died, presents an overview of his work, focusing significantly upon the work for which the Nobel Prize was awarded. Although the tone is laudatory, Huisigen presents an accurate and balanced view of Wieland's major contributions in terms reasonably comprehensible to those not well acquainted with organic chemistry.

Jones, Daniel P. "Heinrich Otto Wieland." In *Dictionary of Scientific Biography*, vol. 14, edited by Charles Coulston Gillispie. New York: Charles Scribner's Sons, 1976. This brief biographical sketch covers the high points of Wieland's career both before and after he was awarded the Nobel Prize. Although the article aims to be accessible to nonspecialists, the nature of Wieland's work makes achieving such accessibility difficult.

Lunde, Gulbrand. "The 1927 and 1928 Nobel Chemistry Prize Winners, Wieland and Windaus." *Journal of Chemical Education* 7 (1930): 1763-1771. Lunde's article is quite technical, but it is valuable to the nonspecialist for the information it gives about the complementarity of Wieland's and Windaus' work. In their ongoing research in the mid-1920's, they were working on different corners of the same puzzle, Windaus concentrating on animal substances, Wieland including the phytosterols as well.

Die Naturwissenschaften 30 (1942). The bulk of this issue in commemoration of Wieland's sixty-fifth birthday is devoted to an assessment of his overall contributions to chemistry. The article by Elisabeth Dane is the best starting point; the articles by Wilhelm Franke, Friedrich Klages, and Clemens Schöpf—all in German—deal with his work on oxidation, on pterins, on alkaloids, and on bile acids and are considerably more technical.

Schlessinger, Bernard S., and June Schlessinger, eds. *Who's Who of Nobel Prize Winners*. Phoenix, Ariz.: Oryx Press, 1986. The coverage in this book is concise, direct, and largely bibliographical. Designed with librarians and students in mind, it is accessible and, to the greatest extent possible, directs users to resources in English.

Wasson, Tyler, ed. *Nobel Prize Winners*. New York: H. W. Wilson, 1987. Although most of the brief biographical sketches in this book are directed to the general reader rather than to the specialist, the entry on Wieland is more technical than most and is not easily accessible, due largely to the complex nature of Wieland's research. Despite this caveat, the piece is worth reading and its bibliography is useful.

Windaus, Adolf. "The Chemistry of the Sterols, Bile Acids, and Other Cyclical Constituents of Natural Fats and Oils." *Annual Review of Biochemistry* 1 (1932): 109-134. Although this article largely comments upon Windaus' own work, it gives full credit to the pioneering efforts of Wieland and those who worked in the Baeyer Laboratory as they worked toward isolating and determining the structure of the major bile acids. Very technical.

R. Baird Shuman

1928

Chemistry
Adolf Windaus, Germany

Physics
Sir Owen Willans Richardson, Great Britain

Physiology or Medicine
Charles Nicolle, France

Literature
Sigrid Undset, Norway

Peace
no award

ADOLF WINDAUS
1928

Born: Berlin, Germany; December 25, 1876
Died: Göttingen, West Germany; June 9, 1959
Nationality: German
Area of concentration: Sterol and vitamin structure

Through his investigation of cholesterol and other sterols, Windaus worked out the initial structural and chemical model of cholesterol and in further research demonstrated the close relationship between sterols and vitamins

The Award

Presentation

Henrik Gustav Söderbaum, Secretary of the Royal Swedish Academy of Sciences, presented the Nobel Prizes for the years 1927 and 1928 to Heinrich Wieland and Adolf Windaus, respectively, on December 10, 1928. He opened his remarks with a comment that the problem of specialization in science appeared to destroy any possibility of overall unity. Professor Söderbaum then pointed out that this diversification into limited areas of research was merely the maturing growth of science. It was no longer possible for the broad problems of science to be investigated by a single individual. Once the specialists complete their work, their contributions become part of a chain of scientific knowledge—the current awards providing a case in point.

Wieland and Windaus, through their work, brought together several separate fields of chemical knowledge. The areas of specialized work included bile acids, central to the process of digestion and studied for several hundred years (yet little was known about this group of substances); cardiac poisons, found in the skin secretions of certain toads and in plants such as digitalis and used in the treatment of cardiac conditions (their chemistry was largely unknown); sterols, found in vegetables and animals and identified in bile, brain tissue, nerve cells, egg, and blood; cholesterol, the part it played in organic life unknown; and vitamins, a recent discovery that had come to the attention of both chemists and the public. The contributions of Wieland and Windaus not only provided greater knowledge in each of these areas but also created significant links among them.

Wieland extracted cholanic acid, which proved to be the basic compound of all bile acid, and his further work demonstrated the mechanism of digestion. Windaus independently extracted cholanic acid from cholesterol and gave the world the first link between their two fields of chemistry. Windaus produced several digitalis compounds in their pure state and found that they were related to both cholesterol and bile acids. While working on another sterol, ergosterol, Windaus found that, when this compound was treated with ultraviolet light, it assumed the same property as vitamin D.

Professor Söderbaum concluded his remarks with the observation that it was fortunate that the Academy had two awards for chemistry that year, since it prevented the difficulty of deciding which of these men deserved the prize more.

Nobel lecture

Adolf Windaus thanked the Royal Academy and delivered his lecture, entitled "Constitution of Sterols and Their Connection with Other Substances Occurring in Nature," on December 12, 1928. He began by observing that sterols were widely distributed throughout nature and that the best-known sterol was cholesterol. This compound was first found in gallstones and later identified in the brain, adrenal cortex, blood serum, and other organs of the body. Sterols occurred in animals, insects, sponges, all members of the vegetable kingdom, and fungi. The single exception seemed to be bacteria.

Of the sterols, chemists had the greatest knowledge about cholesterol. This was a complex compound, and synthesis of this material had not been accomplished. Consequently, the question of whether cholesterol was synthesized in the organism or absorbed from food had been left unanswered. Working on the assumption that cholesterol was absorbed through the food supply, experimental evidence showed that herbivores digested plant sterol and converted it to cholesterol. Also, when cholesterol was introduced into their food supply, rabbits developed a disease pattern in their blood vessels similar to arteriosclerosis in the human population.

While both carnivores and herbivores can absorb cholesterol from their food supply, experimental evidence showed that rats fed on a sterol-free diet maintain a level of cholesterol many times greater than that of newborn rats. This suggested that cholesterol was formed in the organism from compounds other than sterols. Consequently, organisms had the capacity to synthesize cholesterol. There were a number of compounds found in animals that were chemically similar to cholesterol, and Windaus in his lecture described how he had explored the structure of these compounds for the possible existence of a basic sterol. There were only three atoms' difference between cholesterol and Wieland's cholanic acid, which was the basic form of bile acids. The close chemical structure of these two compounds suggested a parent compound which Windaus named allocholesterol. Yet a number of experiments had proved inconclusive as to the possible role of this parent sterol, and part of the problem lay in the obscure biological function of cholesterol. Future exploration of its organic functions might well provide answers to synthesis in the organism.

One known property of cholesterol was its ability to detoxify a class of cardiac poisons (haemolytic) including digitalis and make pure and nontoxic forms of these compounds. In the future it might be possible to reverse the process and evaluate the properties of cholesterol. Another property of cholesterol which created intense interest was the connection between sterols and vitamin D. This vitamin, which is effective in the treatment of rickets, can be produced from fish-liver oil after exposure to ultraviolet light. Later experimental evidence showed that food exposed to ultraviolet light would produce the same effect. Indeed, rickets, a disease that softens the bones of developing children, resulting in abnormal bending, can be treated by sunlight alone, which suggested that light activated some chemical process. It was also believed by chemists that sterols were activated by ultraviolet light, and that this connection with vitamins had experimental corroboration. One sterol (ergosterol) was radiated and mixed with food for rats; it provided as much protection as 100,000 times the effect of fish-liver oil.

Windaus concluded his lecture with a detailed description of his work on the relationship between sterols and vitamins. This information included descriptions of experimental methods and equipment and several proposals of structural similarities between these two groups of chemicals. Although he demonstrated that cholesterol was not identical with provitamin (non-irradiated form of vitamin D), he was able to show that provitamin was identical with ergosterol.

Critical reception

By the end of the 1920's, the Nobel Prizes had acquired not only international recognition but also aspects of national character, power, and prestige. In 1929, *The New York Times* tabulated the number of Nobel winners by country: Germany had the lead in chemistry and physics, with England coming in a close second. There was a clear suggestion that Americans needed to try harder in competition for these international prizes, and, further, that these awards reflected the talents and resources of a nation.

In 1928, after the Nobel Prize in Chemistry was awarded to Windaus, *The Scientific Monthly* (April, 1929) devoted an article to questioning why a number of American and British scientists were overlooked in the award. The article began with the theme that scientific activity was no longer solitary research undertaken by individuals, but an international activity linked by lines of communication. Despite the intensive effort on the part of American scientists in solving the problem of rickets, it came as a surprise that Windaus of Germany should have received credit for this work. At the end of World War I, a hypothesis from England suggested the possibility that rickets might be the result of vitamin A deficiency. This idea was picked up by two groups of American scientists, who identified vitamin D as effective against rickets. Then Alfred Hess and Harry Steenbock discovered the process of exposing either food or living animals to ultraviolet light and achieving the same prevention of the disease. Hess continued this line of investigation based on cod-liver oil, and his research led him to cholesterol. A number of British scientists were also working on other sterols along with ultraviolet radiation.

The article now came to Windaus. He had worked for twenty-five years on sterols and was recognized as a world authority on the subject. When Hess encountered difficulties in his research on cholesterol, he wrote to Windaus and suggested that they collaborate on this research. Windaus received similar requests from his colleagues in England. Since his interest was in sterols and not vitamins, he turned to this problem only after some period of consideration. Thus, the article said,

"Windaus has been a key man in the team playing in a given contest. . . . His exaltation casts no dishonor on his team mates and he has himself been quick to accredit those who consulted him for what they accomplished." *The New York Times* (November 15, 1928) published a brief announcement of the award, with a reference to vitamin D and rickets. The announcement managed to include the name of Hess and O. Rosenheim of London as "pioneers" in this field of research.

Biography

Adolf Otto Reinhold Windaus was born on December 25, 1876, in the city of Berlin, Germany, to Alfred Windaus and the former Margarete Elster. His father's side of the family had been weavers and clothing manufacturers for more than two hundred years, and his mother's family boasted artisans and craftsmen. He received his early education at the French *Gymnasium* in Berlin, where the emphasis was on German and foreign literature; virtually no science was taught. During his final year at school, he came across the work of Robert Koch and Louis Pasteur and decided to begin his professional career in medicine. By this time, his father had died, and although his mother wanted him to take over the family business, she did not stand in his way as he pursued a medical career. He entered the University of Berlin in 1895 and found that much of medical education was of little interest to him, but the chemistry lectures of Emil Fischer awoke a vocation that was to last a lifetime. Windaus received his *Physikum* (bachelor's degree) in 1897, and decided to continue his education in chemistry at the University of Freiburg im Breisgau, where he worked with Heinrich Kiliani. Although he continued to study medicine, in time he shifted completely to the field of chemistry. Working with Kiliani, he began to study the structure of digitalis compounds and received a Ph.D. in 1899 with a dissertation on these substances. Windaus spent two years in military service and in 1901 returned to Freiburg.

Windaus began his research in chemistry with a substance that eventually made him famous. At Kiliani's suggestion, he began to study an unknown substance called cholesterol, which was commonly found in animal cells. Upon the publication of "Cholestrin," which was his initial research on the substance, Windaus was placed on the permanent staff in Freiburg and three years later was awarded a professorship. In 1913, Windaus moved to Innsbruck, where he spent two years. In 1915, he went to the University of Göttingen, where he would remain the rest of his professional life. Windaus married Elizabeth Resau in 1915, and they had three children—two sons and one daughter. He died in Göttingen at the age of eighty-two in 1959.

Scientific Career

At the age of twenty-four, Windaus began work on a major scientific problem, and it occupied his attention for the next thirty years. Heinrich Kiliani suggested to his young assistant that he unravel the structure of cholesterol, a substance found in all animal cells. In 1901, the importance of this substance was not known, and a number of able chemists had tried their hands at determining the makeup of this substance without success. Cholesterol was one of a large group of related compounds called sterols, which are found in animal and vegetable cells. Windaus began by comparing this group of substances and found that they shared a common feature in a tetracyclic carbon skeleton. Windaus was convinced that other natural products should share in this basic skeleton. By 1919, he had demonstrated through a series of experiments that cholesterol could be transformed into cholanic acid, which was the basic acid that Wieland had recently produced from bile acids. This important result was announced to the Göttingen Scientific Society on May 16, 1919, and from this point on these two lines of investigation became joined, since the results from one area would profit the other.

Once it became clear that the differences between sterols and bile acids could be found, Windaus began his work on two derivatives of cholesterol. After breaking down the cholesterol molecule one atom at a time, he was able to arrive at a formula. Along the way, Windaus found that cholesterol would form an insoluble compound with a digitalis chemical related to sterols. Although this line of research was useful for his investigation, his work also contributed to the analysis of the therapeutic effects of cardiac poisons, which included toad venom and animal cardiac poisons. By 1932, the work of Wieland and Windaus had led to the correct structure of the sterol ring.

Windaus' contribution to the study of sterols alone was enough to give him a permanent place in the history of science. Yet in 1925, already recognized as the great living authority on sterols, he was invited by Alfred Hess of New York to take part in the work on vitamin D. The story of the vitamin began much earlier, when Christiaan Eijkman demonstrated that the disease beriberi was caused by a dietary deficiency, which was later found to be the lack of a substance called thiamine, or vitamin B. In 1906, Frederick Hopkins proposed that several substances were essential for the maintenance of health and, together with Casimir Funk, created the term vitamin. By the 1920's, vitamin research was being pursued in a number of laboratories. One line of research involved the disease rickets and the discovery that fish-liver oil could prevent its occurrence. By the early 1920's, it was discovered that the active agent in the fish-liver oil was vitamin D. Although vitamin D could effect a cure for rickets, exposure to sunlight was also effective—hence the problem of whether there were several paths toward a cure or whether these paths were all part of a single therapeutic process. In 1924, Hess and Harry Steenbock exposed certain foods to sunlight and found that these were also effective in the cure of rickets. Somehow, light converted chemicals in food into vitamin D. At the invitation of Hess, Windaus began a collaborative effort on the study of vitamin D. Windaus believed that cholesterol was the source of vitamin D, since cholesterol exhibited similar properties when exposed to ultraviolet light. Robert Pohl, working at Göttingen, had identified an impurity in cholesterol, called ergosterol, which Hess and Windaus later proved could convert to vitamin D. Thus, by 1927, the major features of both the chemistry and the structure of sterols and vitamin D had become clear.

The following year Windaus received the Nobel Prize in Chemistry.

With further research, Windaus found several variations of vitamin D and eventually isolated one form, which was identical to the one purified from tuna fish-liver oil. This confirmation was done by Hans Brockman, working in Windaus' laboratory. Windaus continued his work on the photochemical nature of sterols and, over the years, he identified a number of other compounds with similar characteristics. Once the sterol ring structure of cholesterol was established, it was possible to determine the structure of other sterols. Adolf Butenandt, an assistant to Windaus, began work on the structure of sex hormones and found that these substances were related to sterols; later they were to receive the name "steroids." Steroids include not only the sex hormones but also the hormones of the adrenal cortex, such as cortisone.

In view of Windaus' substantial career, one of his earlier contributions could easily be overlooked. Upon his appointment at Freiburg in 1901, when he began his work on cholesterol, he also collaborated with the biochemist Franz Knoop on a project to convert sugar into amino acids. Working with glucose and ammonia, he obtained a derivative of a compound called imidazole. Further study showed that the amino acid histidine was also a derivative of imidazole. Thus Windaus is also credited with the discovery of histamine; this chemical became commercially available as a result of his work. Windaus soon became immersed in cholesterol research and did not return to imidazole until 1929, when two Dutch chemists claimed that vitamin B contained an imidazole ring. Windaus was convinced that they were mistaken, isolated pure vitamin B, and proved the true structure for this substance.

Windaus was an unassuming man who quietly went about his research activities. During his active career, a number of his colleagues considered him primarily as the greatest authority on cholesterol. In retrospect, he extended the knowledge of the chemistry and the role of sterols in biological functions, provided an analysis of the photochemical process of sterols, determined the structure of vitamins D and B, opened the way for future investigations into hormones, and contributed to the chemistry of cardiac poisons. Any one of these areas of research would justify a lifetime's work, and yet he encompassed them all. As professor of chemistry at Göttingen and director of the chemistry laboratory, his influence upon students and workers was through his strength of character; he remained a man of few words. Even though he rejected National Socialism (the program of the Nazi Party), his international reputation allowed him to continue his research in the 1930's after the Nazis came to power. He ended his research career in 1938 and retired in 1944. Several of his students became important figures in the field of chemistry, including Adolf Butenandt, who received the Nobel Prize in 1939 for his work on sex hormones. Windaus received many honors, including the Baeyer Medal (1928), the Pasteur Medal (1938), the Goethe Medal (1941), and recognition by his country in the Grand Order of Merit (1951) and Grand Order of Merit with Star (1956). He received honorary degrees from the universities of Göttingen, Munich, Freiburg, and Hannover.

Bibliography
Primary

CHEMISTRY: "Cholestrin," *Berichte der deutschen chemische Gesellschaft*, vols. 36, 37, 39, 40-42, 50, 1903-1909, 1917; "Gitonin, ein neues Digitalis-Glykosid," *Berichte der deutschen chemischen Gesellschaft*, vol. 46, 1913 (with A. Schnechenburger); "Die Umwandig. der Cholesterins in Cholansaure," *Berichte der deutschen chemische Gesellschaft*, vol. 52, 1919 (with K. Neukirchen); "Sapogenin d. Quillajasre," *Hoppe-Seylers Zeitschrift für physiologische Chemie*, vol. 160, 1926 (with E. Hampe and H. Rabe); "Antirachitis Vitamin," *Naturwissenschaften*, vol. 14, 1926; "Antirachitis Vitamin aus bestrahtem Ergosterin," *Hoppe-Seylers Zeitschrift für physiologische Chemie*, vol. 203, 1931; "Chemistry of Irradiated Ergosterol," *Proceedings of the Royal Society of London*, vol. 108, 1931.

Secondary

Bailey, Herbert. *The Vitamin Pioneers*. Emmaus, Pa.: Rodale Books, 1968. This work covers the medical and historical development of vitamins. The sections on vitamins B and D are comprehensive and not overtly technical. Although recommended for the general reader, copies are rarely found in most libraries and are shelved in the biomedical section.

Farber, Eduard. *Nobel Prize Winners in Chemistry, 1901-1961*. Rev. ed. London: Abelard-Schuman, 1963. This book is available in moderate-sized libraries and is a useful source for standard information on major twentieth century chemists. The section on Windaus includes a biographical sketch and extracted sections from his Nobel Prize lecture.

Florkin, Marcel. *A History of Biochemistry*. New York: Elsevier, 1972. This is the first major effort to cover all aspects of biochemistry. Volumes 30-36 are part of a multivolume set that covers the history of biochemistry in great detail. The history of enzymes and sterols can be found in volume 30. The text is highly detailed and probably too technical for the general reader, although those with high school biology and chemistry backgrounds could read parts of these sections and gain valuable information.

Ihde, Aaron J. *The Development of Modern Chemistry*. New York: Harper & Row, 1964. This is a long and comprehensive history of the different aspects of chemistry. Windaus' contribution is described in two to three pages. All of chapter 24 is worth reading, since it covers the developments in biochemistry that led directly to Windaus' work. These topics include nutrition, the search for vitamins, and metabolism. Although Windaus' research is part of the sections on vitamin and sterols, he was also involved in the rickets problem that is covered in the two earlier sections.

Leicester, Henry M. *Developments of Biochemical Concepts from Ancient to Modern Times*. Cambridge, Mass.: Harvard University Press, 1974. While this book attempts to cover much information, there are several good chapters that provide the reader with a valuable overview of biochemical concepts. Chapters 15-17 cover enzymes and cell constituents, energy production and biological oxidation, and intermediary metabolism.

Victor W. Chen

1929

Chemistry
Sir Arthur Harden, Great Britain
Hans von Euler-Chelpin, Germany and Sweden

Physics
Louis de Broglie, France

Physiology or Medicine
Christiaan Eijkman, The Netherlands
Sir F. Hopkins, Great Britain

Literature
Thomas Mann, Germany

Peace
Frank B. Kellogg, United States

SIR ARTHUR HARDEN
1929

Born: Manchester, England; October 12, 1865
Died: Bourne End, Buckinghamshire, England; June 17, 1940
Nationality: British
Area of concentration: Biochemistry

Harden, in his research on the fermentation process of sugar, discovered that enzymes were the key physiological mechanism of fermentation

The Award

Presentation

Professor Henrik Gustav Söderbaum, Chairman of the Nobel Committee for Chemistry of the Royal Swedish Academy of Sciences, presented the 1929 Nobel award to Sir Arthur Harden. Professor Söderbaum opened his remarks with a reference to the ancient beginning of fermentation, when various sugars were used to produce alcoholic drinks. This transformation had such magical qualities that sometimes it was attributed to the intervention of divinities. Two hundred years ago, science began to unravel the mechanism by which this process took place. Progress was slow, and by the end of the nineteenth century, there were two schools of thought on the mechanism of fermentation. One school, represented by Justus von Liebig, thought that fermentation was a chemical process whereby a ferment substance brought about the decomposition of sugar. The other school, represented by Louis Pasteur, argued for an organic process whereby a fungus was responsible for change in sugar.

An earlier Nobel Prize laureate, Eduard Buchner, marked a decisive turning point in this investigation by providing evidence for both points of view. He destroyed living yeast cells and from the juice identified a substance called "zymase." When Harden began his research on fermentation, his starting point was this yeast juice. By using different methods of filtration, he found two different substances, neither of which produced fermentation; when they were mixed together, however, they would again start fermentation. Harden identified one of these as an organic enzyme called cozymase and the other component as a phosphate acid. Although Harden was the first to recognize the importance of phosphoric acid, it was left to the other recipient of the Nobel Prize in Chemistry, Hans von Euler-Chelpin, to discover its function in fermentation. As it turned out, in the presence of enzyme and sugar, the phosphate triggered a chemical process to create carbonic acid and ethyl alcohol. The combined research efforts initiated by Harden and von Euler-Chelpin led to important conclusions on the nature of fermentation within the metabolism of all organic life.

Nobel lecture

Arthur Harden began his Nobel lecture, "The Function of Phosphate in Alcoholic Fermentation," delivered on December 12, 1929, with a reference to a former colleague, Allan Macfadyen, who had picked up the line of research started by Buchner and stimulated his own interest in this subject. As a result of the work by von Euler-Chelpin, there was no longer any doubt that phosphate had to be present for fermentation to take place. The conclusions of a series of experiments showed that under conditions of rapid fermentation, when the available phosphate was depleted, the process became a slow fermentation. In this second process, the phosphate ester (an ester is an acid in which the hydrogen has been replaced by a hydrocarbon) was reconverted back to a phosphate, and the reaction would go on for some time. In a third series of experiments, a compound (phosphatase) was added to increase the rate of ester conversion, which then increased the rate of fermentation but would eventually end. In order to create laboratory conditions that reproduced living yeast cells, Harden found that if he substituted an arsenate for a phosphate, the reaction could be permanently raised as there was no longer an accumulation of phosphate ester.

Harden turned his attention in his lecture to the problems associated with the rate of fermentation. Experiments with the cell-free yeast juices proceeded at between 2 percent and 5 percent of the rate of living yeast. He offered several possibilities for this decrease in laboratory fermentation rate: The phosphatase may have been destroyed when the cell was killed, the disruption of the cell may have produced a heavier concentration of inhibitors, or a substance that accelerates the action of the phosphatase may have been inactivated by the process of making yeast juice. After describing several ongoing experiments that might eventually resolve this problem of fermentation rate, Harden proceeded to describe the role of phosphate esters in fermentation. There are a number of different ester compounds (hexosediphosphate, hexosemonophosphate, and others) that play an intermediate part in the reaction that converts sugar to alcohol. Harden speculated on the emergence of several chemical formulas that attempted to explain the action of these compounds in producing fermentation. He found none of these completely satisfactory or superior to the ones derived by himself and William John Young.

At the conclusion of his lecture, Harden touched on the importance of the cozymase in yeast respiration and the similarity between fermentation and metabolism of muscles. There existed a high degree of similarity in almost all the details between the production of lactic acid by muscle enzymes and the production of alcohol by yeast enzymes. Harden thought that future research in the action of enzymes in bacteria, molds, and plants would reveal a universal organic process that was originally revealed by alcohol fermentation.

Critical reception
The presentation of the Nobel awards for 1929 was a major international event that did not focus only on the merits of Arthur Harden. The literature award was given to German author Thomas Mann, who had acquired an international reputation. The physics prize for 1929 was given to Louis de Broglie of France, who had

proposed the wave-matter theory that had significant consequences in nuclear physics. Owen Richardson of England was awarded the physics prize for 1928, reserved from the year before, based on his work on ions and electrons which form the basis of vacuum tubes, wireless telephones, and broadcasting. Arthur Harden's work on fermentation, while by no means meager, became more prominent as a result of the other recipients. *The Times* of London covered the awards in a major column describing the ceremony and recipients in some detail and gave Harden a paragraph at the end of the article (November 13). *The New York Times* devoted several columns to a lengthy description of the Nobel awards; Mann captured the headlines and the bulk of the story, but Harden and von Euler-Chelpin both received several paragraphs that described their contributions to biochemistry and their professional associations. The article commented that "Englishmen have thus placed their country in the forefront by winning one full award (Richardson) and sharing in two others (Harden and Frederick Hopkins for medicine)." In an article printed on the following day, *The New York Times* tabulated the number of Nobel winners by country. Germany had the lead in chemistry and physics, with England coming a close second (November 14). There was a clear suggestion that America needed to try harder in competition for these international prizes, and further that these awards reflected the talents and resources of a nation.

Science, the weekly publication of the American Association for the Advancement of Science, reprinted an article originally published in the *British Medical Journal*, which recognized the awards in biochemistry and medicine (December 20, 1929). In describing Harden and Hopkins, the article noted: "Both of the English workers are biochemists and both are notable as pioneer workers in various fields, which, once opened up by their efforts, have produced an increasingly rich crop of knowledge." Harden was awarded the Davy Medal of the Royal Society in 1935 and knighted in 1926. He received several honorary degrees and was elected to memberships in several scientific societies.

Biography

Arthur Harden was born on October 12, 1865, in Manchester. He was the third child and only son of Albert Tyas Harden, a local businessman, and Eliza Macalister of Paisley. He was brought up in a strict Puritan environment, which influenced him throughout his life. At the age of seven he went to a private school in Victoria Park, and later to Tettenhall College, where he remained until he was sixteen. In 1882, he entered The Owens College in the University of Manchester, and three years later he was graduated with first-class honors in chemistry. In 1886, he was awarded the Dalton scholarship, completed his first independent chemical research, published his work, and began graduate work at the University of Erlangen under Otto Fischer. He completed his Ph.D. and returned to Manchester to become first junior and then senior lecturer in chemistry. He enjoyed teaching chemistry and, in particular, an honors class in the history of chemistry. This led to a joint research project with Henry Roscoe on the notebooks of John Dalton and eventually resulted in a book entitled *A New View of the Origins of Dalton's Atomic Theory* (1896). His interest in Dalton continued for many years, and he contributed to the scholarship in this area.

Until 1896, Harden concentrated his efforts on teaching and writing. He wrote a textbook with Roscoe to help students pass the South Kensington chemistry examination, and he coauthored a book with F. C. Garrett entitled *Practical Organic Chemistry*. He also wrote several journal articles and unsuccessfully applied for two administrative positions. In 1897 Harden's life changed when he was appointed at the British (later Lister) Institute of Preventive Medicine in London. In 1900, he married Georgina Sydney Bridge of Christchurch, New Zealand. Their marriage was childless and she died in 1928. Although Harden retired from the Lister Institute in 1930, he continued his daily routine in the laboratory and served as coeditor of *The Biochemical Journal*. One or two years before his death, he contracted a progressive nervous disease, and he died on June 17, 1940, at his home at Bourne End.

Scientific Career

Arthur Harden possessed personal characteristics that would enhance his scientific career. He was careful, logical, and patient, and he exhibited a distrust of the imagination, which might make claims far beyond the available facts. Until 1897, he showed few signs of an interest in biochemistry. Harden was a well-liked teacher who had a wide range of interests, including the history of chemistry, the investigation of the composition of iron and bronze instruments found in ancient sites, and photochemistry. At the age of thirty-two, he did not seem to possess an urgent desire for a life of scientific research and in fact applied for two separate administrative positions, as a principal of a school and as a scientific inspector. His application to the British (later Lister) Institute was successful, and he taught chemistry to those students interested in becoming public health officials. His classes consisted largely of chemical analysis in the areas of foods and water. Because of changes in the requirements for public health officials, however, Harden's classes were dropped, and he became solely occupied with research.

In 1898, Harden became acquainted with Allan Macfadyen in the biology department and began work on the fermentation of sugar by bacteria. His initial project was to find a means of differentiating among the ways different bacteria broke down sugar through fermentation. In the course of the investigation, he discovered a number of by-products of fermentation. He published his first paper on this subject in 1899. Harden continued his work on bacterial chemistry for more than a decade but attracted little attention from either biologists or chemists. Harden's pioneer work in bacterial metabolism was overshadowed by his discoveries in alcohol fermentation, which he began in 1900.

Eduard Buchner had accomplished a series of significant experiments that set aside the controversy on fermentation between those who insisted that live yeast cells were necessary and those who believed that fermentation was a purely inorganic chemical reaction. Buchner killed the yeast cell and from the juice was able to produce fermentation. From these experiments Buchner found an enzyme compound called zymase. Yet there were two problems with the yeast juice: Fermentation occurred without any addition of sugar and then quickly lost its ability to continue fermentation. Harden's first investigation was to discover the cause of these two problems. He found that zymase by itself would not convert sugar to alcohol and carbon dioxide but required a second substance, and then fermentation would occur only in the presence of phosphate.

Harden was able to make advances in his research because he abandoned the experimental procedures of others, who relied on weighing the amount of carbon dioxide given off during the experiment in favor of measuring the volume of the gas. Since the release of carbon dioxide determined the rate of fermentation, weighing the gas occurred infrequently and was a complex procedure. Harden determined the rate of fermentation by volume and was able to test this in as short a time as ten-minute intervals. The discovery of cozymase, the other substance necessary for fermentation, occurred fortuitously. He had added boiled yeast juice, which would no longer trigger fermentation, to a mixture in the process of fermentation and found that the reaction increased rapidly. Using a special gelatin filter, he was able to separate zymase from cozymase. The name cozymase was suggested by von Euler-Chelpin, who was able to separate the substance into its constituent parts and as a result of this work shared the Nobel Prize with Harden.

Harden found that the new cozymase contained phosphate, leading to the idea that phosphate was necessary in fermentation. Harden added potassium phosphate to fermentation and found that the rate was increased seven times. Over time, the reaction would return to the rate set prior to the addition of the phosphate. Harden and his associate, William John Young, came to the conclusion that the active phosphate was removed from the reaction by the formation of a compound. Later Young found that the phosphate combined with sugar formed a compound called hexosediphosphate. In the living yeast cell, the process of fermentation continued until all free sugar was used up; while in laboratory experiments with yeast juice, the phosphate was removed by combining with sugar. Harden and Young worked on a hypothesis that live yeast contained a phosphatase that quickly broke down the sugar-phosphate compound and released the phosphate for further reaction. They worked on an experiment in which fermentation had almost ceased after the addition of phosphate. To this they added phosphatase, and the rate of fermentation immediately increased. Yet the rate could not be sustained. In 1914, working with Robert Robinson, Harden found that another compound, monophosphate, was necessary in the chain of reaction to imitate the action of live yeast.

Except for the period of four years during World War I, Harden continued to work through the complex and intricate series of reactions that would finally produce a systematic understanding of the process of fermentation. Harden's discovery of cozymase and of the role of phosphates and its derivatives in alcohol fermentation also contributed to an understanding of how muscle enzymes work. He discovered a high degree of similarity between the production of lactic acid by muscle enzymes and the production of alcohol by yeast enzymes; both include the essential presence of phosphates. Without Harden's discoveries, the future of muscle chemistry would have been bleak.

When Harden arrived at the Lister Institute, there were two areas of chemistry— chemistry and biochemistry. In 1905 the two leading figures in biochemistry left the institute, and Harden became the head of the combined areas. In 1912, in recognition of his work, Harden was named professor of biochemistry at the University of London. When war began two years later, few male staff members or students remained at Lister, and Harden was made head of the institute during the military service of the director. For the next five years, Harden gave up his research on alcohol fermentation and concentrated his efforts on discovering the causes of beriberi and scurvy. These two diseases plagued Allied forces in Africa and Asia. There were good reasons for believing that food factors, or the lack of vitamins, produced both diseases. Working with several colleagues, Harden contributed to medical interventions for both diseases: In one case, he helped in the creation of an antiberiberi compound from yeast; in the case of scurvy, he was able to remove sugar, organic acid, and proteins from lemon juice and prepare a compact and durable substance that treated the disease. Harden's work on nutrition during the war years provided him with a wide range of knowledge on food factors and resulted in his editing three editions of a book entitled *Present Knowledge of Accessory Food Factors* (1919).

Harden was honored for his contribution to biochemistry. He was elected a Fellow of the Royal Society in 1909 and awarded the Nobel Prize in 1929. He received honorary degrees from Manchester, Liverpool, and Athens, was awarded the Davy Medal in 1935, and was knighted in 1926. Literary work also occupied much of his time. His contribution to the literature of his field was significant and diverse, and by serving as editor of *The Biochemical Journal* from 1913 to 1938, he remained at the forefront of research throughout his life.

Bibliography

Primary
CHEMISTRY: *A New View of the Origins of Dalton's Atomic Theory*, 1896 (with Henry Enfield Roscoe); "Composition of Some Ancient Iron and a Bronze Found at Thebes," *Transactions of the Manchester Library and Philosophical Society*, vol. 41, 1897; *Practical Organic Chemistry*, 1897 (with F. C. Garrett); *Inorganic Chemistry for Advanced Students*, 1899 (with H. R. Roscoe); "The Alcohol Ferment of Yeast Juice," *Proceedings of the Royal Society*, vol. 77B, 1907 (with W. J. Young); *Alcohol Fermentation*, 1911; "John Dalton's Lectures and Lecture Illustrations. Part III. The Lecture Sheets Illustrating the Atomic Theory," *Memoirs and Proceedings of the Manchester Literary and Philosophical Society*, vol. 59, 1915 (with H. F. Coward).
EDITED TEXT: *Present Knowledge of Accessory Food Factors*, 1919.

Secondary

Farber, Eduard. *Nobel Prize Winners in Chemistry, 1901-1961*. Rev. ed. New York: Abelard-Schuman, 1963. This book is available in moderate-size libraries and is a useful source for standard information on major twentieth century chemists. The section on Harden includes a biographical sketch and extracted sections from the Nobel Prize lecture.

Florkin, Marcel. *A History of Biochemistry*. New York: Elsevier, 1972. This is the first major effort to cover all aspects of biochemistry. Volumes 30-36 are part of a multivolume set and cover the history of biochemistry in great detail. The history of enzymes and metabolism can be found in volume 30. The text is highly detailed and technical.

Ihde, Aaron J. *The Development of Modern Chemistry*. New York: Harper & Row, 1964. This work gives a long and comprehensive history of the different aspects of chemistry. Harden's contribution is described in less than a page. All of chapter 24 is worth reading, since it covers the developments in biochemistry that led directly to Harden. These topics include nutrition, the search for vitamins, and metabolism. Although Harden's research is part of the section on metabolism, he was also involved in the beriberi and scurvy problems which are covered in the two earlier sections.

Leicester, Henry M. *Developments of Biochemical Concepts from Ancient to Modern Times*. Cambridge, Mass.: Harvard University Press, 1974. While this book attempts to cover much information, there are several good chapters which provide the reader with a valuable overview of biochemical concepts. Chapters 15-17 cover enzymes and cell constituents, energy production and biological oxidation, and intermediary metabolism.

Victor W. Chen

1929

Chemistry
Sir Arthur Harden, Great Britain
Hans von Euler-Chelpin, Germany and Sweden

Physics
Louis de Broglie, France

Physiology or Medicine
Christiaan Eijkman, The Netherlands
Sir F. Hopkins, Great Britain

Literature
Thomas Mann, Germany

Peace
Frank B. Kellogg, United States

HANS VON EULER-CHELPIN
1929

Born: Augsburg, Germany; February 15, 1873
Died: Stockholm, Sweden; November 6, 1964
Nationality: German; later Swedish
Area of concentration: Biochemistry

Euler-Chelpin advanced knowledge of the fermentation process and of the bio-chemistry of sugars and phosphates. He studied coenzymes and the chemical linkage between an enzyme and the substance upon which it acts

The Award

Presentation

Professor Henrik Gustav Söderbaum, Chairman of the Nobel Committee for Chemistry of the Royal Swedish Academy of Sciences, presented the 1929 Nobel Prize in Chemistry to Hans von Euler-Chelpin. Söderbaum began his address by recounting the history of research on the nature of fermentation. Even though scientists had discovered two centuries earlier that sugar was the fermenting substance, the catalyst that brought about the process remained unknown for many years. One of the first breakthroughs in the understanding of this process was made by Eduard Buchner, who was awarded the Nobel Prize in Chemistry in 1907 for his discovery of noncellular fermentation. Söderbaum credited Buchner's work with deciding the validity of the two schools of thought regarding fermentation: the earlier school, which viewed fermentation as a purely chemical process, and the newer school, which saw it as physiological. Neither school, it turned out, was entirely correct or entirely wrong. The greatest value of Buchner's research, however, lay in the impact that it had on the work of scientists such as Hans von Euler-Chelpin and Arthur Harden.

The Swedish Academy of Sciences decided to divide the 1929 Nobel Prize in Chemistry between von Euler-Chelpin and Harden for the great advances that they had made toward understanding the process of fermentation. By filtering yeast juice through a gelatin filter, Harden discovered the agent of fermentation, called cozymase, which was left as a residue on the filter itself. Although Harden's work also demonstrated the importance of phosphoric acid to the process of fermentation, von Euler-Chelpin and his pupils made the primary contribution toward knowledge of the mechanism of phosphorization; they also conducted a more precise study of the properties of cozymase.

Söderbaum concluded his speech by putting each scientist's accomplishments in the proper perspective. Harden, he said, provided the groundwork for von Euler-Chelpin's research which, in turn, established the validity and worth of Harden's discovery. Together, the two men helped unravel the mysteries of carbohydrate metabolism in both vegetable and animal organisms.

Nobel lecture

Hans von Euler-Chelpin's lecture, delivered on May 23, 1930, was concerned primarily with the way organic cells decompose into sugar and provide energy for life and growth; it was entitled "Fermentation of Sugars and Fermentative Enzymes." It is particularly difficult to study enzymes, because enzyme molecules are unstable and are easily destroyed by acids and alkalines. When poisons such as mercury salts and hydrocyanic acid inactivate dissolved enzymes, the results are often fatal to the organism.

Poisons also work on enzymes in other ways. Fermentation from sugar to alcohol or carbon dioxide proceeds through several stages, each of which has its own enzyme. Although it is difficult to separate these partial reactions, it is possible to poison the series of reactions partially in order to cleanse the other reactions. The addition of fluoride, for example, inactivates that part of the reaction in which cozymase operates.

Von Euler-Chelpin stated that although scientists have known for years that many organisms recover their energy through sugar decomposition, which generates heat, how this energy is transferred to other processes within a cell has not received much attention from physiologists. It is clear, however, that respiration energy which is developed in the form of heat within the cell is not as important as the energy that is used for reproduction, growth, and regeneration. Thus, an energy-rich decomposition product must be involved in the energy-absorbing reaction.

This activator, known as cozymase, is one of the most biologically important activators within both the plant and animal worlds. Because of its considerable dilution, cozymase is difficult to isolate. Yeast provided the best starting material, even though 1 kilogram of yeast did not yield more than 2 centigrams of cozymase.

In addition to this chemical method, von Euler-Chelpin continued, enzyme research was evolving in a different direction—toward biology. The first problem here involved the relationship of the enzyme to the living cell, and dried yeast had become the focus of this research. Scientists wanted to determine whether a difference exists between the fermentation and reproductive abilities of dried-yeast cells and fresh-yeast cells. Professor C. Barthel found that a catalyst participating in the reproduction process was destroyed in dry yeast, although the fermentation enzymes were retained. Von Euler-Chelpin deduced that the enzyme system within the living cell is combined with the protoplasm and is dependent upon the structure of the protoplasm.

Von Euler-Chelpin concluded his lecture by explaining how enzymochemical processes and methods can be aplied to other fields of biology. The study of adaptation lends itself to this approach because, when an organism adapts itself to new conditions, the first measure it takes is to develop the required enzyme system. He also stated that it was time to begin the study of antigens and antibodies by purification and concentration. He cited immunity and heredity as fields in which new discoveries would be made by the application of enzyme chemistry.

Critical reception

Although most of the media focused its attention on Sir Arthur Harden, von Euler-Chelpin's cowinner, the importance of their research did not go unnoticed. An article in *Science* (December 20, 1929) hailed both of them as pioneers in studies of bacterial enzymes and metabolism. In a profile of Sir Arthur Harden that appeared in *Scientific Monthly* (November, 1930), the author pointed out that the work of both men had advanced knowledge of metabolic processes in all living forms. *The New York Times* of November 13, 1929, credited von Euler-Chelpin with advancing the entire field of biochemistry when it reported that the Rockefeller Foundation gave $65,000 which, along with an equal sum contributed by Swedish patrons, helped to establish a biochemical institute in Stockholm dedicated to his work.

Indeed, the greatest value of his work lay in the impact that it had on later research. By elucidating the chemical structures of several vitamins, von Euler-Chelpin had a major influence on synthetic chemists such as Robert Burns Woodward, who reproduced the chemical structure of vitamin B_{12}. His work with the coenzyme also advanced knowledge of the biochemistry of sugar and contributed to the unraveling of the mechanism of phosphorization.

Biography

Hans Karl August Simon von Euler-Chelpin was born on February 15, 1873, in Augsburg, Germany. His father, Rigas von Euler-Chelpin, had been a captain in the Royal Bavarian Regiment. Because his father was transferred to Munich, von Euler-Chelpin was reared primarily by his grandmother at Wasserburg. Ironically, von Euler-Chelpin's interest in science was a direct result of the art training that he had received between 1891 and 1893 at the Munich Academy of Painting. By the time he was graduated from high school, he had transferred his artistic interest in colors to a scientific interest in the spectrum, and he set his sights on a career in science.

After enrolling at the University of Berlin, von Euler-Chelpin studied physics under Max Planck and Emil Warburg. His chemistry instructors—Emil Fischer and A. Rosenheim—were equally prestigious. He took his doctorate in chemistry at the University of Berlin in 1895. Between 1896 and 1897, he worked at the University of Göttingen under Walther Nernst, who greatly influenced his scientific development. In 1897, he assisted Svante Arrhenius in Stockholm. A year later, von Euler-Chelpin was appointed *Privatdozent* in physical chemistry at the university there. In the summers of 1899 and 1900, he worked with another eminent scientist who shaped von Euler-Chelpin's approach to research, Jacobus Henricus van't Hoff in Berlin.

Over the next five years, von Euler-Chelpin's focus shifted from physical chemistry to organic chemistry, largely as a result of visits that he made to the laboratories of Arthur Hantzsch and Johannes Thiele. All of his remaining research was conducted in Sweden. During 1902, he became a citizen of Sweden, and he married Astrid Cleve, who assisted him in his research into fermentation. In 1906, he became professor of general and organic chemistry at the University of Stockholm.

He remarried in 1913, this time to Baroness Elisabeth Ugglas. Between 1916 and 1917, von Euler-Chelpin was allowed to compress his teaching activities into a six-month period so that he could serve in the military during World War I.

After the war, von Euler-Chelpin returned to the university to teach and conduct research. In 1923, he began what was to become a decade of research into the role played by cozymase in the process of fermentation. In 1929, the year that he won the Nobel Prize in Chemistry, von Euler-Chelpin became director of the Vitamin Institute and Institute of Biochemistry, which was founded by the Knut and Alice Wallenberg Foundation and by the International Education Board of the Rockefeller Foundation. Although he retired from teaching in 1941, he carried on his research for the rest of his life. Because of his intense patriotic fervor, von Euler-Chelpin briefly interrupted his research activities to serve in a diplomatic capacity for Germany during World War II. He died in Stockholm, Sweden, on November 6, 1964.

Scientific Career

When von Euler-Chelpin shifted his interest from inorganic chemistry to organic chemistry, he concentrated his studies on the enzymes associated with fermentation. His work with enzymes formed the basis of most of the research that he conducted throughout the rest of his career. His examination of metabolic problems, for example, was an extension of his work with the chemistry of plants. In addition, his studies of enzyme factors led him to the study of vitamins.

Von Euler-Chelpin's most important research was conducted between the years 1923 and 1929, with the assistance of K. Myrbäck and R. Nilsson. For nearly a decade, he and his associates examined the role played by cozymase in fermentation. To a large extent, the work of Stanislao Cannizzaro became a point of departure for von Euler-Chelpin. He attempted to prove that the coenzyme that Cannizzaro had identified as being instrumental in the reaction of acetaldehyde in liver was identical with cozymase. Once this similarity was established, he would have proved that the fermentation phase requires the presence of the cozymase.

Von Euler-Chelpin's research also relied heavily upon the work done by his corecipient of the Nobel Prize, Arthur Harden, who acted upon Eduard Buchner's discovery that cell-free yeast juice that had been strained through a gelatin filter separated into two parts, neither of which could ferment sugar. When combined, however, the two fractions regained the power of fermentation. Working on his suspicion that cozymase was the mysterious enzyme that brought about the reaction, von Euler-Chelpin and Myrbäck demonstrated that glucose splits into two three-carbon fragments when it reacts with phosphoric acid. The other two fragments combine to form glucose diphosphate, while the nonphosphorylated fragment breaks down even further. Myrbäck and von Euler-Chelpin concluded that the sugar molecule splits into energy-rich and energy-poor fragments while undergoing fermentation.

Von Euler-Chelpin began with Nilsson's discovery that the part of the fermentation reaction in which the cozymase cooperates is inactivated by fluoride. Von Euler-Chelpin arrested certain stages of the enzyme-catalyzed reactions through the toxic effects of fluoride, thereby "cleansing" each stage so that it could be studied independently from the others. In 1924, Myrbäck's poisoning experiments revealed that the fermentation reaction phase requiring the cooperation of cozymase is a very early one that precedes the combination with phosphoric acid. By applying salts of the alkaloids and of the alkaline-earth metals to his starting material, yeast, von Euler-Chelpin was able to isolate cozymase to the extent that it could be recovered with practically unchanged activity. He and his associates began with an extract with 200 units of activity, which they concentrated into a substance possessing 85,000 units. This product possessed the characteristics of a nucleotide; it contained sugar, a phosphate, and a purine base. He then tested for nicotinamide in cozymase, obtaining positive results. Von Euler-Chelpin and his coworkers proved that the chemical structure of cozymase was that of diphosphopyridine nucleotide (DPN).

Through his examination of the presence of cozymase in organic materials, von Euler-Chelpin concluded that it was one of the most important catalysts within both the plant and animal kingdoms. He and Nilsson also noticed that the majority of tissues and organs with high carbohydrate metabolism, such as the working muscle, the retina, and parts of the brain, are particularly rich in cozymase.

Von Euler-Chelpin also studied the relationship between the enzyme and the living cell. With the assistance of C. Barthel, von Euler-Chelpin found that after treatment with alcohol, less than one-tenth of 1 percent of dried yeast cells are capable of reproduction, but that dried yeast still had the same fermentation power as fresh yeast. They deduced that the fermentation enzymes were retained in the dry cells (freed of lipoids) but that a catalyst participating in the reproduction process was destroyed. They concluded that the enzyme system in the living cell is combined with protoplasm.

Von Euler-Chelpin also tried to elucidate the chemical structures of several vitamins. In 1924, he began his studies of vitamins in collaboration with his wife, Paul Karrer, and Margaret Rydom. In 1928, they studied the vitamin A activity of carotene. His research also helped clarify the role of nicotinamide and thiamine (vitamin B_1) in metabolically active compounds. During his tenure as director of the Vitamin Institute and Institute of Biochemistry, he investigated the use of enzyme chemistry for the study of heredity and blood serum.

Von Euler-Chelpin's work with coenzymes advanced knowledge of the biochemistry of sugar and phosphates. His later work helped clarify the structure of several important vitamins. Von Euler-Chelpin will be remembered primarily, however, as the man who dispelled the cloud of mystery that had enveloped the process of fermentation for centuries.

Bibliography

Primary
CHEMISTRY: *Chemie der Hefe und der alkoholischen Gärung*, 1915 (with Paul Lind-

ner); *Chemie der Enzyme,* 1920-1927; *Biokatalysatoren,* 1930; *Biochemie der Tumoren,* 1942; *Reductone, ihre chemischen Eigenschaften und biochemischen Wirkungen,* 1950; *Chemotherapie und Prophylaxe des Krebses,* 1962.

Secondary

Duddington, Charles Lione. *Micro-organisms as Allies.* New York: Macmillan, 1961. Concerned primarily with the way microorganisms such as fungi and bacteria are used in industry, this book is a useful supplement to von Euler-Chelpin's work.

Farber, Eduard. *Nobel Prize Winners in Chemistry, 1901-1961.* Rev. ed. New York: Abelard-Schuman, 1963. Contains a brief biographical sketch and a description of von Euler-Chelpin's prizewinning work. Includes an excerpt from his Nobel lecture discussing his work.

Ihde, Aaron J. "Hans Karl August Simon von Euler-Chelpin." In *Dictionary of Scientific Biography,* vol. 4, edited by Charles Coulston Gillispie. New York: Charles Scribner's Sons, 1971. This article presents the most thorough biography of the scientist in English. While the emphasis is on von Euler-Chelpin's scientific achievements, it does trace his life and career up to his winning of the Nobel Prize in 1929. Includes an extensive bibliography.

Schlessinger, Bernard S., and June Schlessinger, eds. *Who's Who of Nobel Prize Winners.* Phoenix, Ariz.: Oryx Press, 1986. Contains a very brief description of von Euler-Chelpin's life and publications. The entry is valuable, however, because of its bibliography. The "Commentary" section explains the nature of von Euler-Chelpin's research and shows why he won the Nobel Prize.

Alan Brown

1930

Chemistry
Hans Fischer, Germany

Physics
Sir Chandrasekhara Venkata Raman, India

Physiology or Medicine
Karl Landsteiner, United States

Literature
Sinclair Lewis, United States

Peace
Nathan Söderblom, Sweden

HANS FISCHER
1930

Born: Höchst am Main, Germany; July 27, 1881
Died: Munich, Germany; March 31, 1945
Nationality: German
Area of concentration: Blood and chlorophyll structure

Fischer's investigations into the nature and structure of the red pigment of blood and the green pigment of chlorophyll led to fundamental discoveries about both substances that were instrumental in their eventual syntheses

The Award

Presentation

In the presence of the royal family of Sweden and the members of the Royal Swedish Academy of Sciences, Professor Henrik Gustav Söderbaum presented the 1930 Nobel Prize in Chemistry to Hans Fischer. Söderbaum began his citation by pointing out the importance of determining the nature of blood and the tremendous difficulties encountered by chemists in its study. He then gave a brief account of the direction of chemical research into the blood, beginning with the invention of the microscope in the seventeenth century, and showed how Fischer's investigations integrated with the work of his predecessors.

In unusually laudatory terms, Söderbaum then explained in some detail the nature and importance of the discoveries for which Fischer was being awarded the Nobel Prize in Chemistry. The presenter noted not only Fischer's synthesis of hemin (a major component of blood) but also his demonstration that hemin is closely related to chlorophyll; he called them "two of the most fundamental processes of organic life." Söderbaum expressed special admiration for the enormous perseverance and dedication displayed by Fischer and expressed the gratitude of all scientists for Fischer's achievements. Those achievements were, in the estimation of Söderbaum and the members of the Nobel Committee for Chemistry, full worthy of the Nobel Prize.

Nobel lecture

Hans Fischer delivered his Nobel lecture before the Royal Swedish Academy of Sciences on December 11, 1930. Entitled "On Haemin and the Relationships Between Haemin and Chlorophyll," it was a succinct synopsis of the research and discoveries for which Fischer won the Nobel Prize in Chemistry. Fischer prepared the lecture for an audience with a substantial background in chemistry.

Translated into nontechnical language, Fischer in his lecture said this: He drew in his research on the works of many of his predecessors in chemical analyses of the blood in seeking to understand and ultimately to synthesize hemoglobin, the pigment that gives blood its red color. Drawing on the concurrent work of many of his colleagues, Fischer related, he was able finally to arrive at an understanding of the exact chemical nature of hemin, one of the two components of hemoglobin, and ultimately to synthesize it. He pointed out that the achievement of synthesis was a monumentally laborious process.

His investigations into the synthesis of hemin led directly into the study of chlorophyll. Fischer told how he and his coworkers eventually proved a close relationship between the life processes followed by the two substances and concluded consequently that they had a common evolutionary history. They further concluded, he said, that chlorophyll must be as amenable to synthesis as is hemin, and he encouraged them to pursue his idea that the two pigments necessary for plant and animal life share a common evolutionary origin.

Critical reception

Hans Fischer's Nobel Prize in Chemistry in 1930 went virtually unnoticed outside Germany and Sweden. English-language newspapers such as *The New York Times* and *The Times* of London carried only the barest mention of Fischer's honor, and the Parisian newspaper *Le Temps* little more. American professional journals in chemistry ignored the award completely. This indifference to the Nobel Prize typified the American press in the interwar period: Unless an American were involved in the prize, editors apparently considered it to be of little interest to their readers.

The reaction to the award in the German press and the German scientific community contrasted markedly with the reactions outside that country. Both the *Berliner Tageblatt* and the *Frankfurter Zeitung* carried two substantial articles concerning the prize, one each on November 14 (following the announcement of the winners by the Nobel Committees) and another on December 13, immediately after the awards ceremony.

The greatest newspaper coverage of Fischer's honor, however, came in his adopted hometown of Munich. The *Völkischer Beobachter* (people's observer), the principal organ of Adolf Hitler's National Socialist German Workers Party, had its main offices in Munich, the birthplace of the movement. The *Völkischer Beobachter* predictably hailed Fischer's award as further evidence of Aryan superiority. In several feature articles in November and December of 1930, anonymous *Völkischer Beobachter* writers gave an exhaustive (and confusing) description of the work for which Fischer received the prize. The articles also included comments from interviews with Fischer and with several other scientists. Several German scientific journals commented very favorably on Fischer's selection for the award, including *Verhandlungen der deutschen Gesellschaft für innere Medizin*.

Biography

Anna Fischer (née Herdegen) gave birth to Hans Fischer on July 27, 1881, at Höchst am Main, a village near Frankfurt. His father, Dr. Eugen Fischer, worked for Meister, Lucius and Bruning, a large chemical firm in Höchst. The elder Fischer took over the position of laboratory director at the Kalle Dye Works in the village of

Bierbach (near Wiesbaden) a few years later. Hans Fischer thus grew up near the chemical pigment industry and developed a lifelong interest therein.

Fischer also developed an early interest in medicine and began his university career in that discipline at the University of Lausanne in 1899. He transferred to the University of Marburg the next year, where, influenced by Theodor Zincke, he changed his concentration to chemistry. He received his doctorate at Marburg in chemistry in 1904, then again took up the study of medicine at the University of Munich, from which he received an M.D. in 1908. In that year he became an assistant in the chemical laboratory of Emil Fischer (no relation) in Berlin, then returned to Munich in 1911, where he worked in the Physiological Institute as a research assistant for five years. In 1916 he accepted the chair of medical chemistry at the University of Innsbruck.

Fischer did not serve in the armed forces during World War I because of ill health. During the war he underwent a kidney-removal operation, necessitated by tuberculosis. Despite the frailty of his health, Fischer was an expert skier and an avid mountain climber until the tragic death of his father in a climbing accident. Shortly before the end of World War I, Fischer accepted the chair in chemical medicine at the University of Vienna. During the next three years, unfortunately, research funds and facilities were not available in Vienna. In 1921, Fischer was appointed head of the Institute of Organic Chemistry at the Technische Hochschule in Munich, where he spent the remainder of his life.

In 1925, the Bavarian government conferred upon Fischer the title of Geheimer Regierungsrat (approximating the rank of secretary in an American state government). In 1929, he won the Liebig Memorial Medal for distinguished scientific research, and he won the Nobel Prize in Chemistry the next year. In 1935, he married Wiltrud Haufe, who was thirty years his junior. Despite the disparity in the ages of the partners, the marriage was, by all reports, a happy one. In 1936, Harvard University awarded him an honorary doctorate, and a year later he received the Davy Medal.

He continued his research during World War II, but as Allied strategic bombing became more intense, he witnessed the almost total destruction of his laboratory facilities. Despondent over what he perceived to be the ruination of both his life-work and his country, Hans Fischer took his own life on March 31, 1945.

Scientific Career

Hans Fischer's scientific career began when he was working as Emil Fischer's assistant at the First Berlin Chemical Institute in 1908. In Berlin, he concentrated his efforts on peptides and sugars, but upon taking a position at the Physiological Institute in Munich under the direction of Friedrich Müller, he began the study of pigments that occupied him for the remainder of his career. He first investigated the bile pigment bilirubin, the study of which he did not complete until the last years of his life. His first important scientific paper, published in 1915, concerned bilirubin. Müller allowed Fischer to devote all of his efforts to pure research without the burden of teaching duties, as did Otto Frank, in whose laboratory Fischer took an assistantship shortly before the outbreak of World War I. At this time and throughout his entire career, Fischer worked completely independently, never seeking counsel from his colleagues and seldom discussing his scientific work, even with close friends. His first published paper demonstrated another lifelong characteristic: the inability to express himself well with the written word.

Shortages of money and material during the war and the immediate postwar period and his own ill health effectively checked Fischer's research until 1921. In that year he assumed the position of head of the Institute of Organic Chemistry at the Technische Hochschule at Munich (although "Technische Hochschule" may be literally translated as "Technical High School," the level of study is more nearly equivalent to that of an American university). Research facilities and funds in the Munich institution enabled Fischer to return to serious investigations of pigments.

Fischer arrived in Munich during a period of enormous political and scientific activity. Adolf Hitler's National Socialist movement was beginning to make large numbers of converts in the city of its birth; street battles in Munich between Hitler's followers and members of the various Marxist parties were not uncommon. In the midst of this political turmoil, no fewer than seven past or future Nobel laureates besides Fischer were working in the various academic and scientific institutions in Munich—surely the highest concentration of scientific luminaries in the world. Fischer himself remained aloof from politics, concentrating instead on his research with a dedication that many of his friends regarded as bordering on obsession. He spent an incredible number of hours in his laboratory each day, and he demanded so much from his students that they were often driven to despair. Despite his reputation as a "slavedriver," however, his students loved and respected him to the point of reverence. Fischer returned their affection by taking greater pride in the dozens of his students who went on to brilliant careers in industry, medicine, and academe than he took in his Nobel Prize or the many other honors bestowed upon him.

Fischer rapidly proved to be as able at administration as he was at research. In a very short time he organized his laboratory at Munich so well that it became a model of efficiency. No other research facility had ever carried out as many analyses or created as many new compounds as did Fischer's. One of his most important innovations was based on the principle of the division of labor, whereby specific laboratory procedures were carried on simultaneously in several separate laboratories. In Munich, Fischer returned to his study of bile pigment and related substances. He discovered that bilirubin, the subject of his investigations, is derived from hemin, the active portion of the hemoglobin molecule. He correctly identified it as a porphyrin, related examples of which are present in a number of living sources, including chlorophyll. By 1929, he succeeded in synthesizing hemin, after completely deciphering its chemical composition. This work led to his being awarded the Liebig Memorial Medal in 1929 and to his Nobel Prize in 1930.

After accepting the Nobel Prize, Fischer continued his study of porphyrins. He had already concluded that porphyrins from widely differing life forms differed from one another only in the presence of differing substances in the molecules that surrounded them, their "pyrrole rings." For the next decade he devoted all of his energies to pyrrole chemistry. During this period, he published the definitive study on pyrroles in three volumes. Entitled *Die Chemie des Pyrrole*, it remains a standard work on the subject. In this tumultuous era, Fischer continued to be publicly indifferent to the foreboding events taking place in Germany, neither endorsing Hitler's regime nor condemning it. Privately he expressed great reservations about the direction in which the Nazis were taking his country, and he was greatly depressed by the outbreak of war in 1939. He buried himself ever more deeply in his work.

Much of Fischer's work involved microanalysis. He and his students and colleagues worked out microanalytical techniques in their research that remain impressive achievements. Using those techniques, Fischer finally determined the structure of bilirubin, the study of which had launched his career. Fischer completed this work in the midst of World War II, finally achieving the synthesis of bilirubin in 1944.

During the later years of his career, Fischer continued to work on chlorophyll, but he did not manage to synthesize it before his death. Other scientists, drawing heavily on Fischer's work (of his more than 300 published papers, 129 concerned chlorophyll), finally were successful in 1960 in achieving synthetic chlorophyll, which eluded Fischer before his premature death in 1945.

Bibliography

Primary
CHEMISTRY: "Hemin und Porphyrine," *Verhandlungen der deutschen Gesellschaft für innere Medizin*, vol. 45, 1933; *Die Chemie des Pyrrole*, 3 vols., 1934-1940.

Secondary
Carter, C. W., et al. *Biochemistry in Relation to Medicine.* New York: D. C. Heath, 1959. This book contains several references to Fischer's research and his laboratory techniques but offers no biographical material. It is highly technical, designed for those with extensive backgrounds in chemistry.
Farber, Eduard. *Nobel Prize Winners in Chemistry, 1901-1961.* Rev. ed. New York: Abelard-Schuman, 1963. Farber includes a very brief biographical sketch of Fischer and an account of the work that won for him the Nobel Prize in Chemistry that is drawn entirely from Fischer's Nobel lecture.
Fieser, Louis F., and Mary Fieser. *Reagents for Organic Synthesis.* New York: John Wiley & Sons, 1967. The Fiesers, obviously admirers of Fischer, include numerous references to his life and his work. Like most works on chemistry, the work is intended for readers with broad backgrounds in the field.
Roberts, John. *Basic Principles of Organic Chemistry.* New York: W. A. Benjamin, 1965. Roberts includes a brief and very technical account of Fischer's work on chlorophyll. The book is valuable primarily because it shows the relationship of

Fischer's research to that of his predecessors and successors in the field.

Wieland, Heinrich. "Hans Fischer." Translated by Ralph E. Oesper. In *Great Chemists*, edited by Eduard Farber. New York: Interscience, 1961. Wieland was a personal friend and colleague of Fischer in Munich. His brief account of the life and career of his friend is both touching and informative and is not overburdened with technical or scientific terms. Suitable for high school and college readers.

Paul Madden

1931

Chemistry
Carl Bosch, Germany
Friedrich Bergius, Germany

Physics
no award

Physiology or Medicine
Otto Warburg, Germany

Literature
Erik Axel Karlfeldt, Sweden

Peace
Jane Addams, United States
Nicholas Murray Butler, United States

CARL BOSCH
1931

Born: Cologne, Germany; August 27, 1874
Died: Heidelberg, Germany; April 26, 1940
Nationality: German
Areas of concentration: Industrial and high-pressure chemistry

Bosch developed the high-pressure techniques necessary for industrial production of ammonia, a key ingredient in nitrogenous fertilizer and explosives. He also experimented with the synthesis of fuels, including methanol, and the production of gasoline from coal

The Award

Presentation

Carl Bosch was presented with the 1931 Nobel Prize in Chemistry, which he shared with Friedrich Bergius. In his presentation speech, Professor Wilhelm Palmær, a member of the Nobel Committee for Chemistry of the Royal Swedish Academy of Sciences, reminded the audience of Alfred Nobel's desire to reward chemists for achievements of great benefit to mankind. Bosch's pioneering inventions and research represented such an achievement, since one result was the possibility of large-scale industrial production of ammonia, a key ingredient of nitrogenous fertilizer.

Palmær noted that fertilizer could now be produced using abundant nitrogen from air as its raw material rather than the expensive and nonrenewable resources (such as South American nitrate deposits) that were needed for the older methods. Apart from its direct impact, the new ammonia process could also be appreciated as the first high-pressure chemical process carried out on an industrial scale. Future workers would find that many fundamental problems had been identified and solved by Bosch and his coworkers. For example, Bosch designed a reactor that was able to contain high-pressure hydrogen at a high temperature without corrosion of the metal, and he also made systematic studies to find the optimum steel alloys for use in various parts of the reactor. At the time of the presentation, further high-pressure processes for manufacture of methanol (wood alcohol) and formaldehyde were under development, and Palmær concluded by predicting that many additional valuable substances would become available on a commercial scale because of Bosch's work.

Nobel lecture

Carl Bosch began his Nobel lecture of May 21, 1932, "The Development of the Chemical High Pressure Method During the Establishment of the New Ammonia Industry," by referring to the work of Fritz Haber (1868-1934), who had studied the effect of pressure on the nitrogen/hydrogen/ammonia equilibrium and had discovered catalysts that speeded up the approach to equilibrium. In his 1920 Nobel lecture in Stockholm, Haber had mentioned approaching a German chemical firm, Badische Anilin und Sodafabrik (BASF), in 1908 to propose the commercial production of ammonia by the high-pressure reaction of nitrogen with hydrogen. Bosch then told how, as an employee of BASF, he had been entrusted with the task of developing the Haber process on an industrial scale. He began work simultaneously on three major problems: supply of raw materials, provision of suitable catalysts, and construction of a large-scale high-pressure apparatus. The first two of these were solved fairly readily, but the third was a more difficult problem. The major part of the lecture was therefore devoted to a discussion of the problem of working on a large scale with high-pressure gas mixtures containing hydrogen.

In order to make preliminary tests on materials of construction and catalysts, Haber's laboratory converter was redesigned, and two dozen of these improved reactors were used to complete more than twenty thousand separate test runs over several years of day and night operation. Upon expanding the scale of operations for the first time, a surprising setback occurred. After roughly eighty hours of operation at high pressure, two tubes in the apparatus burst. Examination of the tubes after the accident showed the effects of corrosion and swelling of the metal caused by high-pressure hydrogen gas at temperatures of 400-450 degrees Celsius in the reactor. Extensive tests were done to determine the mechanism of this corrosion problem and to evaluate possible alternative materials of construction. It was found that the iron carbides present in steel reactor walls were being attacked by hydrogen, causing the production of gaseous hydrocarbons, which tended to expand and cause swelling and cracking of the metal. This problem was overcome in an ingenious manner by providing the reactor with a thin, perforated iron liner, protecting the pressure vessel itself from attack.

Bosch continued by describing the monitoring instruments that were developed to ensure the purity of the gas streams used in the ammonia process and the arrangements that were made to control the temperature and heat flow in the reactors, as they were made in ever larger sizes. From 1910 to 1915, the size of the ammonia converters increased from 0.3 ton to 75 tons. A huge plant was constructed at Oppau, and later another at Leuna, for the commercial exploitation of the ammonia synthesis and other high-pressure processes.

Near the end of his lecture, Bosch alluded briefly to the high-pressure methods for making urea (used in fertilizer), methanol, and gasoline. The gasoline process, which involves hydrogenation of oil or of coal, was discussed in more detail in the lecture given by cowinner Friedrich Bergius. Bosch concluded by noting that probably no project had ever been described that required the participation of more colleagues, but he singled out two for his special praise: Alwin Mittasch, head of the scientific laboratory, and F. Lappe, in charge of technical development.

Critical reception

By the time he was awarded the Nobel Prize for Chemistry in 1931, Carl Bosch had already been the recipient of numerous honors in Germany, if not elsewhere.

The University of Heidelberg and the Technische Hochschulen in Karlsruhe, Darmstadt, Munich, and Berlin all awarded him honorary status. He had advanced to the highest levels of management at BASF and at IG Farben. All these honors attest the high regard that Bosch enjoyed in Germany. The Nobel Prize was a crowning achievement that he well deserved.

In the United States, Bosch was praised in somewhat muted terms. People remembered World War I and felt that Bosch's work had been too helpful to the Kaiser's Germany and perhaps not quite so helpful to the world in general. *The New York Times*, on November 13, 1931, reported that "Two German Chemists Share Nobel Prize," stressing that the synthetic ammonia process had virtually saved German agriculture during the war. An editorial in that paper noted the growing importance of industrial chemistry as shown by the award to Bosch and Bergius. Later, upon Bosch's death in 1940, *The New York Times* printed "His Discoveries of Chemical Substitutes Credited with Aiding Imperial Army."

Bosch was known in Europe and in the United States for his activities in support of the German chemical industry, and of IG Farben and BASF in particular. While he was respected as a scientist and engineer, and for his personal honesty, he was a hard bargainer and was very devoted to Germany's interests. There were people with long memories who felt that no German should ever be honored. Fritz Haber suffered much from this sort of attitude in relation to his work with chemical warfare. Bosch did not suffer so much as Haber, but there were some editorial comments in *Journal of Industrial and Engineering Chemistry* when the two men were awarded the Bunsen Medal. Those Americans who actually met Bosch and knew him were better inclined, and Frank A. Howard, chairman of Standard Oil Company of New Jersey, remarked on the occasion of Bosch's death that Bosch had been the only person left in German public life who still spoke out honestly on political issues.

Biography

Carl Bosch was born on August 27, 1874, in Cologne, Germany. He was one of six children in the family of Carl Bosch senior and his wife Paula. Bosch (senior) had come to Cologne from the south of Germany, near Ulm, and his brother, Robert (young Carl's uncle), was the founder of a large industrial firm that still bears his name. Bosch (senior) ran a plumbing business and workshop in Cologne, and young Carl grew up in a household where fine workmanship and practical talents were valued. As a youth, he loved nature and would take long walks from which he would bring back plant and animal specimens. He also developed an interest in chemical experimentation, which his father allowed him to pursue in a small room in a building behind their home. Many valuable lessons passed from father to son as the boy watched his father at work in his workshop and learned to help.

At the age of eighteen, having been graduated from the German equivalent of high school, Carl was qualified to enter a university but on the advice of his father chose instead to spend some time as an apprentice in an iron foundry to become more skilled at working with tools and equipment. Accordingly, he affiliated with Marienhutte in the town of Kotzenau, near Liegnitz, and worked there for a year, during which time he absorbed practical knowledge and skills in working with metals and metalworking equipment.

Bosch then continued his education at the Technische Hochschule in Berlin/Charlottenburg, where he studied engineering and attended chemistry lectures and worked in the laboratory. After two years, he moved on to the University of Leipzig, where the physical chemist Friedrich Wilhelm Ostwald (winner of the 1909 Nobel Prize in Chemistry) was a professor of worldwide reputation. Here, in May, 1898, Bosch was awarded the degree of Ph.D. summa cum laude. He continued for two more semesters as assistant to his research director, the organic chemist Johannes Wislicenus.

Industry beckoned, and, in 1899, Bosch became a chemist at BASF in Ludwigshafen am Rhein, where his legendary work on the synthesis of ammonia began in 1908. In 1902, Bosch married Else Schilbach, and they reared a family of two children. As a result of his highly successful research and development work, Bosch prospered at BASF, rising to the post of managing director by 1919. Later, when BASF merged into IG Farben, Bosch became first a principal (1925) and then chairman of the board of directors (1935). This advancement brought him to the very pinnacle of top management in German industry. He was a delegate to the Versailles Peace Conference at the conclusion of World War I. When IG Farben began to be interested in synthetic fuels and rubber, Bosch traveled to the United States in 1926 and later negotiated a joint venture between IG Farben and Standard Oil Company of New Jersey over the production and marketing of synthetic fuels and rubber.

The final years of his life included election to the presidency of the Kaiser Wilhelm Society in 1937, a post of greater prestige than any other in German scientific circles. He used this office to do what he could to protect German science and academic life from the disastrous effects of Nazism and approaching war. He constantly visited all types of scientific installations to offer encouragement and material help. He suffered from fits of depression and other ailments, however, and tried to recover by traveling briefly to Sicily for a vacation. He died upon returning to Germany in 1940.

Scientific Career

Bosch's doctoral thesis was his first and last contribution to purely academically oriented organic chemistry, since his interests turned quickly to physical chemistry and industrial applications. Upon going to work for BASF, Bosch was assigned to a group studying the manufacture of phthalic anhydride (a chemical used in making alkyd resins for paint). He was able to achieve greater economy in the process by developing a new way of heating the reactor. Later, he was assigned to investigate the use of iron wire as a catalyst for the synthesis of ammonia—a suggestion that had come to BASF from Wilhelm Ostwald himself. Through careful experimental work, Bosch was able to show that Ostwald's work was in error, at the same time attracting favorable attention to himself, since Ostwald was a chemist of great standing.

Bosch became involved in research on fixation of nitrogen, bringing the relatively unreactive gas from the air into chemically combined form. Fixation was important, since fixed nitrogen is used in fertilizers, and Germany was dependent on imported nitrates, which were expected to become scarce. Artificial fixation of nitrogen was possible, but uneconomical. Studies were undertaken to find out whether nitrogen would react with metals such as titanium, barium, or aluminum in a useful manner. In this work, Bosch was joined by Alwin Mittasch, and together they made long and systematic studies. None of their chemical processes achieved great commercial success, but they did develop high-pressure apparatus, measuring instruments, and procedures that proved vital later.

In 1908, Fritz Haber came to BASF with the suggestion that the firm should study the commercialization of his high-pressure ammonia synthesis. Haber had successfully prepared ammonia from nitrogen and hydrogen, using either osmium or uranium as catalysts to speed the reaction. A demonstration was planned for Bosch and Mittasch, but it failed on the first try. Later tries were successful, and research began at BASF under Bosch's direction. The course of this work was described by Bosch in his Nobel lecture. The ammonia plant in Oppau was opened for production in 1913, and a larger plant at Leuna began operations in 1917 during World War I. At Leuna, oil hydrogenation and synthesis of methanol were carried out as well as ammonia production. The oil hydrogenation procedures had been worked out by Friedrich Bergius and Mathias Pier and the patents sold to BASF. Vital to the ammonia process was the activated iron catalyst, which replaced the rare and expensive osmium that Haber had used. By the end of the war, German ammonia production had reached 680 metric tons per day.

Soon after war broke out in 1914, it became clear that Germany could not achieve a quick victory. Accordingly, it was of the utmost importance to find a reliable source of nitrates for the manufacture of explosives. The British navy cut off all shipments of nitrates from Chile, the traditional source of this strategic material. The German general staff were unaware of this problem until it was brought to their attention by Walther von Rathenau, head of the German electric power industry. Rathenau was then appointed to head a War Raw Materials Board, and he in turn deputized Fritz Haber to look into the question of nitrates. To summarize the results of these arrangements, it can be said that by May, 1915, Bosch and his coworkers had been able to begin production of nitric acid by oxidation of ammonia. This so-called "Ostwald Process" had existed on a laboratory scale, but was made commercial by an intense crash program. The authorities were so impressed by this achievement that Bosch was able to get tremendous support in money and manpower for the construction of the huge Leuna works. At the same time, BASF enjoyed considerable profits for its shareholders. By the end of the war, Germany was completely self-sufficient in nitrate production.

Germany also lacked a domestic source of petroleum, and with the increasing use of gasoline-powered vehicles in wartime, it was clear that synthetic fuels from coal would be a great advantage. Exploitation of the Bergius process was a long and expensive undertaking, but Bosch pushed ahead. Later, under the auspices of IG Farben, the German synthetic fuel industry grew to twelve production sites and a peak production (in 1944) of 3 million metric tons of synthetic petroleum.

In his career in industrial research, Bosch was granted more than a hundred patents. These covered the preparation of organic and inorganic compounds of potential commercial interest (fertilizers, ammonia, urea, ammonium bisulfite), activation of catalysts, and many novel and useful pieces of apparatus for high-pressure use. As he grew in prestige, Bosch accepted more responsibilities on the management level and in public service, and thus he added a new dimension to his career.

At the end of World War I, Germany was at the mercy of the Allies. The British, and even more so the French, wanted to make sure that Germany could never again threaten Europe militarily. At Versailles, where the peace treaty was negotiated, there were suggestions that the German chemical industry should be prevented from producing war material such as nitrates. Bosch was appointed as a delegate and made arrangements with the French to spare the plants at Oppau and Leuna in return for an exchange of technological personnel and expertise that would enable the French to start their own nitrate industry. This compromise saved the plants for the time being but was not the end of the matter. The Oppau plant was destroyed by an explosion in 1921, together with the town and roughly six hundred people. Bosch appointed Karl Krauch to head a repair effort, which was successful in restoring the plant to operation after a work force of ten thousand men had labored for three months.

The founding of IG Farben in 1925 created a huge conglomerate that could compete more effectively in world markets. Even so, Germany suffered from the severe economic effects of the war—hyperinflation, and shortage of capital made worse by the need to pay reparations. Bosch traveled around Europe and to the United States to negotiate with IG Farben's competitors and to trade knowledge for markets. He earned a reputation as a man who could be trusted. Meanwhile, new products became available. During the postwar period, IG Farben produced ever-greater quantities of synthetic methanol. By 1931, German production was at an annual level of 40,000 tons, and exports to the United States were helping the German economy.

With the rise of Nazism in Germany, unwholesome changes were forced upon many segments of German life, including the chemical industry. At first, the industrialists supported Hitler financially, partly in fear of Communism and in the hope that the country could be saved from a revolution of the Russian variety. As Hitler strengthened his hold on Germany, he started a buildup of military power and pumped money into IG Farben for building synthetic fuel plants and for manufacturing explosives, poison gas, and synthetic rubber. Part of this Faustian bargain was that Nazi agents were installed in the company by order of the Führer: There was a purge of the company's personnel, based on racial, religious, and political factors. In 1933, Bosch had a personal interview with Hitler in which he stated his belief that chemistry and physics would suffer badly under the anti-Semitic policies that had been instituted. Hitler flew into a rage and ended the interview by declaring that the Reich would do without chemistry and physics for the next hundred years rather than reverse its policies. This confrontation left the two men permanently at odds. Bosch lived a life of conflict and pain as he tried to serve Germany, the scientific profession, and his Jewish colleagues without coming to personal ruin in a concentration camp. All the top management people at IG Farben had these conflicts, and some collaborated more than others with the Nazis. At the end of the war, several of Bosch's former close colleagues were tried as war criminals at Nuremburg. Bosch himself died in 1940 in Heidelberg before most of the more horrific activities at IG Farben had begun.

Carl Bosch brought about for the first time the close union of chemistry and engineering, which was necessary for founding the modern chemical industry. He also used his power and prestige to help Germany and to further the scientific professions in difficult times. His many honors in Germany are a tribute to his achievements. He was one of very few industrial chemists to win a Nobel Prize. His enduring monument is the synthetic ammonia industry, which is still based on the technology that Bosch developed, and without which the world's farms could not produce nearly as much grain as they do. His contributions to the synthetic fuel industry may be more appreciated in the coming years, as petroleum becomes scarcer and more expensive.

Bibliography

Primary
CHEMISTRY: "Die Behandlung tuberkuloser Gelenkentzundungen," 1888; "Über die Kondensation von Dinatrium-acetondicarbonsäurediaethylester mit Bromaceto-phenon," 1898; "Karawanenreisen: Erlebnisse sines deutschen Kaufmanns in Ägypten, Mesopotamien, Persien und Abessinien," 1928; "Untersuchung von elektro-nenzählrohren," 1934.
INDUSTRIAL POLICY: *Handelspolitische Notwendigkeiten*, 1932.

Secondary
Borkin, Joseph. *The Crime and Punishment of IG Farben*. New York: Free Press, 1978. Borkin discusses the history of IG Farben from its beginnings in the 1920's until after World War II. Carl Bosch was a director of the company, and he tried unsuccessfully to prevent the conversion of the company into a tool of Nazi aggression. Borkin draws heavily on Karl Holdermann's 1954 biography of Bosch and on the records of the Nuremberg trials.
Farber, Eduard. *Nobel Prize Winners in Chemistry, 1901-1961*. Rev. ed. New York: Abelard-Schuman, 1963. The article on Bosch consists mainly of quotations from

his Nobel lecture, except for a section called "Consequences in Theory and Practice" which explains the industrial significance of Bosch's results and gives production statistics illustrating the growth of the ammonia and methanol industries.

Goran, Morris. *The Story of Fritz Haber.* Norman: University of Oklahoma Press, 1967. Fritz Haber did the basic laboratory research on the synthesis of ammonia from nitrogen and hydrogen. Goran's biography tells of the relationship between Bosch and Haber and of the beginnings of the synthetic ammonia industry.

Hayes, Peter. *Industry and Ideology: IG Farben in the Nazi Era.* Cambridge, England: Cambridge University Press, 1987. Carl Bosch was the first president of the giant corporation known as IG Farben that was formed in 1925 by the merger of several other companies. In Hayes's scholarly study, the attempt is made to understand the role that Bosch and other industrialists played in the rise of Hitler and the conduct of World War II.

Kerstein, Günther. "Carl Bosch." In *Dictionary of Scientific Biography*, edited by Charles Coulston Gillispie. New York: Charles Scribner's Sons, 1976. At the end of this brief biographical note there are several references to Bosch's technical publications in German journals.

Nobelstiftelsen. *Nobel Lectures: Chemistry, 1922-1941.* New York: Elsevier, 1966. A complete English translation is provided for the Nobel lecture presented by Bosch in May, 1932. Includes many photographs of reactors and other technical equipment related to the ammonia synthesis; Bosch discusses the development of the process in detail.

Stranges, Anthony N. "Friedrich Bergius and the Rise of the German Synthetic Fuel Industry." *Isis* 75 (December, 1984): 643-667. After the sale of the Bergius patents to IG Farben, Bosch helped muster the necessary support to create a synthetic fuel industry for Germany in the 1930's. There are many references to the fuel industry here, as well as some discussion of Bosch's role in relation to Bergius.

John R. Phillips

1931

Chemistry
Carl Bosch, Germany
Friedrich Bergius, Germany

Physics
no award

Physiology or Medicine
Otto Warburg, Germany

Literature
Erik Axel Karlfeldt, Sweden

Peace
Jane Addams, United States
Nicholas Murray Butler, United States

FRIEDRICH BERGIUS
1931

Born: Goldschmieden, near Breslau, Germany; October 11, 1884
Died: Buenos Aires, Argentina; March 30, 1949
Nationality: German
Area of concentration: High-pressure chemistry

Bergius developed a method for converting coal into commercially usable liquid fuels through a high-pressure, high-temperature process involving hydrogenation

The Award

Presentation

Professor Wilhelm Palmær, a member of the Nobel Committee for Chemistry of the Royal Swedish Academy of Sciences, presented the 1931 Nobel Prize in Chemistry to Friedrich Bergius and Carl Bosch. Professor Palmær noted that Alfred Nobel had stipulated in his will that the prize for chemistry should go to the chemist whose work most greatly benefited mankind. Prior to 1931, all the recipients of the chemistry prize had been scientists engaged in pure research rather than those chemists pursuing the practical applications of theory to the production of goods and services. The seeming bias toward theoretical research resulted in part from the difficulty of identifying the originator of a practical application technique, since practical applications were more often the result of a team effort than of an individual's achievement.

Professor Palmær then disclosed that the 1931 prize would be shared by two men whose primary contribution to the field of chemistry was in practical application rather than in theory. These two men had, independently of each other, used the theories first proposed by Nobel laureate Fritz Haber (the 1918 prizewinner) concerning high-pressure, high-temperature chemical reactions to produce goods and services of great benefit to all mankind.

After a brief explanation of the theory behind high-pressure, high-temperature chemical processes, professor Palmær traced the technological innovations made by Bosch and Bergius. Professor Palmær first described Bosch's work, then lauded Bergius for introducing high-pressure, high-temperature techniques which made possible the extraction of high-grade oils from coal. Palmær pointed out that modern industrial society depends heavily for its very existence on these oils, which hitherto came mostly from petroleum, a relatively scarce commodity. Bergius' techniques and methods provided an economical and efficient method for the liquefaction of coal, which is much more abundant than petroleum, and produced many useful by-products as well.

Nobel lecture

Friedrich Bergius presented his Nobel lecture, entitled "Chemical Reactions

Under High Pressure," on May 21, 1932. The lecture recapitulated Bergius' experiments and results in high-pressure, high-temperature chemical reactions that took place over a period of almost two decades. The lecture reflected not only the painstaking and often tedious methods that led him to several processes of considerable importance, such as coal liquefaction, but also his intuitive construction of theories that led him to important breakthroughs. The rare combination of theoretical scientist and practical technician that was Friedrich Bergius was reflected throughout his lecture.

He began by relating his introduction to the study of high-pressure chemical reactions in 1908 at the laboratories of Walther Nernst and Fritz Haber, and his subsequent fascination with the possibilities of the processes he observed. His first practical experience in the field came with a series of experiments performed in 1910, which later provided the theoretical and technical framework for his process of the hydrogenation of heavy petroleum and coal. The heavy equipment necessary to exploit commercially the liquefaction process was first conceived and constructed during these early experiments.

By the beginning of World War I, Bergius' lecture continued, his work had progressed to the point that a large industrial plant was built for the hydrogenation of oil, a process he had developed.

Bergius then turned to a description of his work on producing artificial coal, another project he began before the war. He and his coworkers developed a successful process for the creation of coal from other elements, which led him directly to the discovery for which he received the Nobel Prize: a method for liquefying coal (extracting usable oils from coal) through hydrogenation at high pressures. Bergius described his process and its development in some detail, including descriptions of the design of the equipment necessary for its success.

He concluded his lecture with the announcement that he would be turning his attention to other matters and would no longer be involved in high-pressure chemical research.

Critical reception

Newspapers in the United States and in Europe praised the decision to award the 1931 Nobel Prize in Chemistry to Bergius and Bosch. *The New York Times*, which in previous years had paid relatively little attention to Nobel recipients in chemistry who were not United States citizens, devoted two lengthy articles to the German laureates on November 13 and November 15, 1931. The November 13 article pointedly observed that 1931 was the first year in which the prize had gone to individuals involved in the practical industrial application of chemical theory rather than to individuals involved in "pure research." The *Times* writer praised the accomplishments of both men, describing Bosch's work on ammonia synthesis as having "saved German agriculture" during World War I and Bergius' coal liquefaction process as a step toward a virtually inexhaustible source of energy.

In a follow-up article on November 15, another unnamed *Times* writer emphasized the indispensible role of industry in modern chemical research. The article argued that the huge expense involved in building the equipment necessary to conduct high-pressure chemical research virtually ensured that breakthroughs in the field would not come in university laboratories. Instead, they would almost certainly be made in the research facilities of the giants of the chemical industry such as Bosch's employer, Badische Anilin und Soda Fabrik (BASF), and Farbinindustrie, which financed the applications of Bergius' processes. This thesis fit well with a general theme that ran through many articles in *The New York Times* that big business, for all of its shortcomings, still benefits all mankind.

German newspapers reflected much the same (somewhat anti-intellectual) satisfaction that the Nobel Prize in Chemistry had gone to individuals in industry rather than to academic researchers. Articles in the *Berliner Tageblatt* and the *Deutsche Rundschau* on November 13, 1931, hailed the awards as another sign of German economic recovery from the postwar recession and inflation and speculated that the work of Bosch and Bergius heralded the beginning of Germany's emergence from the Great Depression. The Nazis' most widely circulated newspaper, the *Völkischer Beobachter*, was especially ecstatic about the award being given to Aryan scientists engaged in practical research rather than theoretical pursuits, which the paper usually identified with non-Aryan scientists.

The leading professional journals in chemistry voiced no opposition to the selection of industrial chemists as the recipients of the 1931 Nobel Prize. Perhaps the Great Depression convinced virtually everyone that humanity's most pressing need was practical application of science to the immediate problems of society rather than theoretical work that might or might not benefit society at some remote future time.

Biography

Friedrich Bergius was born on October 11, 1884, in his parents' home at Goldschmieden, a village near Breslau. His father owned and managed a nearby chemical plant, to which he frequently took his son. As a result, young Friedrich developed a fascination with practical applications of chemical processes early in his life. Friedrich's mother was the daughter of a professor of classics, and she instilled a love and respect for learning in her son. Thus was forged that rarity among scientists: the pragmatic researcher who not only formulates and tests theories but also searches for ways in which those theories may be utilized to improve human productivity and the quality of life in his society.

Bergius attended several German universities, finally taking his doctorate in 1907 at the University of Leipzig. For the next two years he was assistant to several famous German chemists, including Ernst Bodenstein, all of whom permitted him to participate in their research. In 1909, he qualified as a university lecturer and set up his own laboratory at Hannover, where he began work on high-pressure, high-temperature chemical reactions.

By 1913, he had already begun investigations into the liquefaction of coal, the area that eventually brought him the Nobel Prize. In 1914, he joined the Goldschmidt Company as head of its research laboratory. During World War I he continued his experiments into the extraction of usable oils from coal.

After World War I, Bergius was diverted from his attempts at coal liquefaction by a new challenge. He sold his patents in the old field to another German firm and began to pursue the extraction of usable sugar compounds from wood, the goal being the production of cheap food for cattle. In practice, the processes developed by Bergius during the first four-year plan of the Nazis, which was designed to achieve economic self-sufficiency, furnished a sizable fraction of the foodstuffs consumed in Germany during World War II.

Because of his affiliations with the Nazis, Bergius was denied any sort of meaningful work in Germany after 1945. He emigrated first to Spain, where he founded a company, then to Argentina in 1947. In Argentina he acted as a scientific adviser to the government for two years and transmitted to industrialists in that country much of his knowledge of high-pressure, high-temperature chemical reactions. He died in Buenos Aires on March 30, 1949.

Scientific Career

Friedrich Bergius' achievements represent a general trend in the physical sciences that began in the late nineteenth century—a movement away from strict empiricism (trial-and-error experimentation) and toward the application of scientific principles and theories to guide experimenters in their work. This trend may be traced to the scientific publications of four men in the period before 1900: Svante Arrhenius at the University of Uppsala in Sweden, J. Willard Gibbs at Yale University, Wilhelm Ostwald at the University of Leipzig, and Jacobus Henricus van't Hoff at the University of Amsterdam.

In the early twentieth century, two German chemists in particular continued the trend toward the application of scientific theory to chemical experiments. Walther Nernst and Fritz Haber emerged as recognized leaders in high-pressure chemical reactions, and it was their work that captured the imagination of young Friedrich Bergius during his studies at the universities of Breslau and Leipzig.

Bergius had already acquired considerable practical knowledge of the chemical industry before entering the university. He had made frequent visits to the alumina-producing plant owned and managed by his father and had gone for six months to the Friedrich-Wilhelmshutte, a large metallurgical factory to which his father sent him as an observer. Upon completion of his Ph.D. at Leipzig in 1907, Bergius spent a year studying with Nernst in Berlin and a further six months with Haber in Karlsruhe. Both men allowed him to participate in their experiments into the synthesis of ammonia and its equilibrium at high pressures. This eighteen-month apprenticeship provided much of the inspiration for Bergius' later experiments in high-pressure chemical reactions, as he himself admitted in the foreword to his *Habilitationschrift* (1913).

When Bergius set up his own laboratory for high-pressure experiments in 1909, he expanded his investigations to include the reaction of hydrogen with coal and coal tars. The end he had in mind was to produce liquid fuels from coal, which Germany possessed in abundance, thereby eliminating his country's dependence on imported oil. By 1913, his work had progressed to the point that he and coworker John Billwiller were granted a patent for the manufacture of liquid hydrocarbons from coal. His own laboratory proving inadequate for the further research he envisioned, Bergius accepted a position as head of a new research laboratory at the Goldschmidt Company in Essen in 1914. The owner of the company, Karl Goldschmidt, soon afterward built Bergius a private experimental plant for the processing of petroleum reserves that eventually achieved a daily output of twenty tons.

Because of a multitude of technical problems, Bergius' attempts to liquefy coal did not come to fruition until after World War I. By 1921, Bergius had completed construction of a plant capable of producing 1 metric ton per day of liquid petroleum from coal. The plant, located at Rheinau near Mannheim, included a high-pressure heating apparatus that permitted accurate temperature control to within 5-10 degrees Celsius of the optimal liquefaction temperature, determined by previous experiments to be 450-480 degrees Celsius. In addition, Bergius incorporated a method for producing sufficient quantities of hydrogen by using lower temperatures and higher pressures than previous methods had utilized. His plant accomplished liquefaction in two stages. In the first stage, coal was transformed into petroleum hydrocarbons with the consistency of heavy tar by adding hydrogen atoms at 300-400 degrees Celsius with pressure equal to 1,270 kilograms per square inch. In the second stage, the heavy petroleum hydrocarbons were "cracked" into lighter liquid hydrocarbons at 450 degrees Celsius.

Bergius sold his patents pertaining to the liquefaction of coal in 1925 and pursued other interests thereafter, but it was this work that won for him the Nobel Prize in Chemistry in 1931. The commercial production of usable oil products from coal has unfortunately never fulfilled its promise, despite its auspicious beginnings in the 1930's. In Germany, the government subsidized the construction of a dozen plants using Bergius' processes in the 1930's as part of its plan to establish self-sufficiency. A British firm built a similar plant during this same era. During World War II, the German plants furnished much of the fuel consumed by the armed forces.

After World War II, as part of the "deindustrialization" process decreed for Germany by the victorious Allies, the plants were all either dismantled or converted to other uses. The British plant also closed, unable to compete with cheaper natural petroleum. After the Arabian oil embargo of the early 1970's, there were unsuccessful efforts to revive the synthetic fuel industry in the United States using Bergius' processes. The time may yet come, however, when Bergius' methods will be invaluable to Western society.

After selling his coal liquefaction patents in 1925, Bergius turned his scientific attention to another area of chemical research: the extraction of sugar from the cellulose in wood, a project in which he had become interested much earlier in his career. This new endeavor received much favorable attention from Hermann Göring during the period of the Third Reich in Germany and was ultimately successful. Bergius perfected a process, using highly concentrated hydrochloric acid to produce sugar compounds from wood, which contributed greatly to the German war effort from 1939 to 1945. In a chemical plant near his original coal liquefaction facility, Bergius' processes produced essential food components throughout World War II.

Bergius was, perhaps unjustly, caught up in the "de-nazification" process put into effect in Germany by the victors after World War II. Denied meaningful work, he emigrated to Spain, where he tried to establish a chemical plant to continue his work with cellulose. In 1947, he received an offer from the government of Argentina to aid that country in establishing a chemical industry. He accepted the offer, and he proceeded to help with the economic development of his adoptive country until his death in Buenos Aires in 1949 at the age of sixty-five.

Bibliography

Primary

CHEMISTRY: *Die Anwendung hoher Drucke bei chemischen Vorgängen und eine Nachbildung des Entstehungsprozesses der Steinkohle*, 1913; "Die Verflüssigung der Kohle," *Zeitschrift des Vereins deutscher Ingenieure*, vol. 69, 1926; "Die Herstellung von Zucker aus Holz und ähnlichen Naturstoffen," *Ergebnisse der angewandten physikalischen Chemie*, vol. 1, 1931; "Gewinnung von Alkohol und Glucose aus Holz," *Chemical Age*, vol. 29, 1933; "Chemische Reaktionen unter hohem Druck," *Les Prix Nobel en 1931*, 1933.

Secondary

Dorn, Karl. *Werkstoffe: Miracles of German Chemistry*. New York: German Library of Information, 1941. This work is of limited value because of its obvious propaganda intent. It does contain some information about Bergius' work in coal liquefaction and his later work with cellulose, but virtually nothing about his personal life. Recommended only for those who wish further knowledge about coal liquefaction.

Farber, Eduard. *Nobel Prize Winners in Chemistry, 1901-1961.* Rev. ed. New York: Abelard-Schuman, 1963. Includes a brief biographical sketch of Bergius and an equally brief synopsis of the work for which he was awarded the Nobel Prize. Contains virtually nothing about his career after 1925. Easily understandable.

Stranges, Anthony N. "Friedrich Bergius and the Transformation of Coal Liquefaction from Empiricism to a Science-Based Technology." *Journal of Chemical Education* 65 (September, 1988): 749-751. This article does an excellent job of placing Bergius in the context of twentieth century science and describing his coal liquefaction process. Although some of the language is highly technical, an intelligent nonchemist can follow it easily.

Paul Madden

1932

Chemistry
Irving Langmuir, United States

Physics
Werner Heisenberg, Germany

Physiology or Medicine
Edgar D. Adrian, Great Britain
Sir C. Sherrington, Great Britain

Literature
John Galsworthy, Great Britain

Peace
no award

IRVING LANGMUIR
1932

Born: Brooklyn, New York; January 31, 1881
Died: Falmouth, Massachusetts; August 16, 1957
Nationality: American
Area of concentration: Surface chemistry

Langmuir developed the new field of surface chemistry. He researched the behavior of filaments, principally tungsten, in atmospheres of various gases at low pressures. His theory that such gases are adsorbed on the surface of a solid or liquid in a layer only one atom or molecule thick was revolutionary

The Award

Presentation

Professor Henrik Gustav Söderbaum, Chairman of the Nobel Committee for Chemistry of the Royal Swedish Academy of Sciences, introduced Irving Langmuir and presented the 1932 Nobel Prize in Chemistry. He opened with a short discussion of the phenomenon of adsorption, the area of scientific research for which Langmuir was being honored. Surface chemistry was a special discipline within the broader field of physical chemistry, he said, and was comparatively new as a separate subject. Adsorption falls within that discipline.

Before Langmuir's work, the prevailing opinion had favored a multilayer model for the adsorbed layer on an interface between two phases. The density of the adsorbed layer was believed to decrease continuously outward from the surface in much the same way as the density of the earth's atmosphere decreases upward from the surface of the earth.

Langmuir had put forward a conflicting theory, one which seemed particularly bold. According to Langmuir's theory, the adsorbed layer is extremely thin, consisting of a film only one atom or molecule thick. His work, moreover, was not confined to solid surfaces alone, but extended to include films on liquid surfaces. His work also showed that molecules of an oil film on a water surface behaved like a two-dimensional gas, which opened for theoretical investigation the whole realm of a two-dimensional world. Langmuir's work broke new ground, and large parts of it are of lasting value, Söderbaum concluded.

Nobel lecture

Irving Langmuir gave his Nobel lecture on Wednesday, December 14, 1932, under the title "Surface Chemistry." After being introduced, he opened with a short history of the phenomenon of adsorption, introducing a fundamental equation for adsorption deduced many years earlier by the American mathematician Josiah Willard Gibbs. The Gibbs equation related surface adsorption, surface tension, and concentration of adsorbed substance in the surface layer. Langmuir said that the

Gibbs equation was purely theoretical and had never been tested experimentally.

He related how, when he had first begun work in an industrial research laboratory (General Electric Co., in Schenectady, New York) in 1909, he had found that high-vacuum techniques in the industrial electric lamp factory were far more advanced than those he had known in university laboratories. He saw a wonderful opportunity for the study of chemical reactions on surfaces and of the physical properties of surfaces under well-defined conditions. He began by trying the effect of putting different gases into highly evacuated glass bulbs containing electrically heated tungsten filaments. The filaments could be heated in the vacuum to temperatures of more than 3,000 Kelvins. Working with this method, he studied the effects of adding gases such as hydrogen, oxygen, nitrogen, carbon monoxide, and their mixtures on filaments of tungsten, carbon, molybdenum, and platinum.

When a tungsten filament is heated to temperatures of 1,500 Kelvins in a hydrogen atmosphere at very low pressure, the hydrogen disappears slowly because it is being adsorbed on the surface of the glass bulb, not on the filament, and it is in a chemically very active state. By calculating the number of atoms of hydrogen, their average diameter, and the surface area of the bulb, Langmuir showed that the adsorbed layer of hydrogen was only one atom thick. Similar experiments with other gases—helium, argon, methane, and water vapor—indicated that the adsorbed layers of these gases were also monomolecular in thickness. Adsorbed octane and octyl alcohol behaved in such a way that it could be explained only by assuming special orientation of the octyl alcohol molecules in the adsorbed layer.

One of the most extraordinary parts of Langmuir's address, however, dealt with oil films on water, since such films are familiar to most people. Langmuir showed that these oil films are also monomolecular, and from the area covered by a given weight of oil spread on the surface he was able to measure cross-sectional areas of single molecules of the oily substance. These measurements were carried out with a simple apparatus which has come to be called a Langmuir balance—an apparatus simple enough to be widely used in undergraduate physical chemistry laboratories for making measurements similar to those described by Langmuir in his address. Langmuir went on to show that such monomolecular films behaved as would a two-dimensional gas, for which an equation of state could be deduced. Thus he was showing his lifelong preference for simple experiments, carried out with the simplest possible apparatus, that could be used to demonstrate the most fundamental scientific principles.

He described his adsorption isotherms, subsequently carried in most textbooks of physical chemistry as standard parts of surface chemistry. Based on these principles, he then distinguished several classes of adsorption types, which have also become standards in the field. He concluded with a discussion of the catalytic action of surfaces, which has since led to many advances in catalysis.

Critical reception

The announcement of Langmuir's Nobel award was greeted with enthusiasm at the Chemists' Club in New York City, where a reception was held on November 29, 1932, to mark his sailing to Europe on the *Bremen* to ski in Switzerland and to accept the Nobel Prize from King Gustav of Sweden. *The New York Times* for November 30, 1932, reported that George C. Lewis, president of the Chemists' Club, hailed Langmuir's award and introduced him to a nationwide audience on the network of the National Radio Broadcasting System, and Langmuir attempted to explain to this audience the nature of his work on atoms spread out on a surface.

The New York Times for December 11, 1932, reported that Langmuir was the thirteenth American to receive the prize and listed the earlier winners. The account went on to describe the ceremony of awarding the prizes, at which King Gustav and other dignitaries rose as the procession of prizewinners approached the stage. Dr. Langmuir, *The New York Times* said, praised modern industry for its support of pure science in his address. "Happy is the scientist who works with the cooperation of modern industry, for he knows that society will benefit immediately from his discoveries," Langmuir told the three hundred guests at the ceremonies.

Langmuir had received the Perkin Medal of the American Section of the (British) Society of Chemical Industry a few years earlier, for much of the same work that won for him the Nobel Prize. At that time, W. R. Whitney, the director of the General Electric Company Research Laboratory, commented at length on Langmuir's work, and his remarks were published in *Industrial and Engineering Chemistry*. Whitney stated that in addition to Langmuir's published work, covering such widely differing fields as chemical reactions at low pressures, convection and radiation of heat, vapor pressure of metals, new vacuum pumps and gauges, atomic structure, and theories of surface adsorption, he valued Langmuir's willingness to work with, guide, and direct other workers in the field.

Whitney went on to say that "when Langmuir first told me he thought he could make a better tungsten lamp by putting gases into it, rather than by trying to further exhaust it [create a more effective vacuum], I thought he was dreaming. And so he was. But it was the kind of dream he could make come true."

Katharine B. Blodgett, an associate at the General Electric Research Laboratory in Schenectady, said of Langmuir in the *Journal of Chemical Education* (1933): "A smaller world, composed of two or three hundred workers with whom Dr. Langmuir has been associated in his daily work, has also been appraising his worth for a number of years. . . . His associates, many of whom are themselves inventors of foremost rank, say that 'Langmuir is like none of the rest of us.' . . . From the staff members who bring to Dr. Langmuir's office the problems that nobody else can solve, to the librarian who has just catalogued his 145th published paper, the employees of the Research Laboratory agree that nobody else is like him."

Biography

Irving Langmuir was born in Brooklyn, New York, on January 31, 1881, the third of four boys born to Charles and Sadie (née Comings) Langmuir. The oldest brother, Arthur, often called "A. C.," was nine years older than Irving, and the youngest brother, Dean, was born six years after Irving. Charles Langmuir was in the insurance business. He had to be in Europe for long periods as director of European agencies of the New York Life Insurance Company, and the family moved to Paris in 1893; there Irving attended several elementary schools.

When he returned to the United States, Irving entered Columbia University in 1899 and was graduated with a degree in metallurgical engineering in 1903. Following this, he studied chemistry at Göttingen under Walther Nernst, winner of the Nobel Prize in 1920. Langmuir received his Ph.D. degree there in 1906.

His first job after receiving his doctorate was teaching chemistry at the Stevens Institute of Technology at Hoboken, New Jersey, where he stayed for three difficult years, heavily overloaded with teaching duties and unable to begin a research program. On a summer vacation in 1909, he was invited to spend a month in the laboratory of the General Electric Company in Schenectady, New York. He liked what he saw so much that he stayed for the rest of his life.

He married Marion Mercereau on April 27, 1912, and they had two children, Kenneth and Barbara. He loved the outdoor life and had a summer home at Lake George, in upstate New York; he took every opportunity on his many trips both there and abroad to ski and climb mountains.

He died of a heart attack at Falmouth, Massachusetts, surrounded by his family, on August 16, 1957, at the age of seventy-six.

Scientific Career

One of the best accounts of Irving Langmuir's work before 1928 was given by the man who brought Langmuir to Schenectady and encouraged him in all of his efforts, Dr. Willis Rodney Whitney. Whitney was the founder and director for twenty-eight years of the Research Laboratory of the General Electric Company. Langmuir described how Whitney, on coming into the laboratory in the morning, would ask his staff, "Are you having fun today?" Describing Langmuir's work on the occasion of the presentation to Langmuir of the Perkin Medal, Whitney lauded Langmuir's published scientific work as being "the kind on which he and others will continue to build serviceable structures, and we know that such mental and spiritual advances as it marks are superior to technical ones."

Whitney went on to catalog the work that Langmuir had done during the sixteen years he had known him. In first place he put Langmuir's work on atomic structure, which Bernard Jaffe, in "Crucibles," also called "the crowning achievement of Langmuir's career." Here Langmuir built upon an idea, proposed earlier by Gilbert N. Lewis, for the electronic structure of the atom, the so-called Lewis-Langmuir atom. Lewis, in 1916, had suggested a cubical electron shell for the atom, which explained the octet theory, the theory that eight electrons were required in the outer shell for stability. One electron was placed at each of the eight corners of a cube in Lewis' static model for the atom. Langmuir adopted the Lewis model, because it agreed with his own ideas of atomic structure. The Lewis-Langmuir theory of the atom appeared in undergraduate chemistry textbooks through the 1930's. This model has since been superseded by dynamic models of the atom based mostly on the quantum mechanics developed during the 1920's.

When Langmuir went to work at the General Electric Research Laboratory in 1909, work on improving Thomas Alva Edison's electric lamp had concentrated on ways of improving the vacuum inside the light bulb. Langmuir worked on similar schemes himself at first, cooling the bulb in liquid air, and so forth. Eventually, however, because of his pure research work on gases, he came to recommend a lamp bulb filled with an inert gas such as argon instead of an evacuated bulb, and his idea is now the standard for an industry that produces many millions of light bulbs annually. Not only is Langmuir's bulb a better light source, but also it is a safer one, since the older evacuated bulbs could implode, scattering hazardous sharp glass fragments. Moreover, the tungsten filaments lasted longer in the gas-filled bulb.

Langmuir's work on hydrogen gas led also to his invention of the atomic hydrogen torch. A jet of hydrogen is passed through an electric arc, which causes the hydrogen molecules to break up into atoms. Then the hydrogen atoms, already extremely hot from the electric arc, recombine and liberate still more heat energy, producing temperatures capable of melting the most refractory of metals.

His study of gases on hot filaments also led him to study the emission currents of carbon filaments and to propose pure thermionic emission currents from the filament—ideas which no one accepted at first. He developed the concept of space charge during this period, a concept now used widely in meteorology and physics. This work resulted in the development of a whole family of radio tubes, the kenotron, the pliotron, the magnetron, the thyratron, and many others, which were important items in the early days of radio transmission.

Whitney said that he could put an actual dollar value on Langmuir's work, in the case of the gas-filled light bulb. There were more than 100 million such bulbs manufactured in the United States in 1928, and Langmuir's better bulb saved the American public more than a million dollars every night on its lighting bill.

As an industrial chemist, Whitney probably was more interested in putting a dollar value on research than posterity might be. Today more value is placed on Langmuir's theoretical contributions—his work in surface chemistry for which he was honored in his Nobel award. He pioneered the idea that gases were adsorbed on surfaces of solids and liquids in unbelievably thin layers, layers which he boldly stated were only one atom thick. Other scientists, such as the great Wilhelm Ostwald in Leipzig, were still holding out against the idea that matter was composed of atoms because, as Ostwald put it, no one had yet observed an atom. Now Langmuir was actually observing atoms—layers of atoms, admittedly, but layers that he could demonstrate were only one atom thick. One demonstration could be made with films of oily material on water, in experiments so simple that modern undergraduate students can duplicate them with the aid of the Langmuir balance. Students can actually measure the length and cross-sectional area of molecules.

With such a record of accomplishment behind him, Langmuir might have been expected to fade away quietly as he approached his retirement age. This was not to be the case. He began a new career, in meteorology, at precisely this period of his life: He developed his startling ideas on cloud seeding.

In his address as the retiring president of the American Association for the Advancement of Science, published in *Science* (1943), Langmuir called attention to two classes of phenomena, convergent and divergent phenomena. The first class, convergent phenomena, included those systems whose behavior could be determined from the average behavior of its component parts. The second, or divergent, class of phenomena included those systems in which a single discontinuous event becomes magnified in its effect so that the behavior of the whole aggregate depends upon the small beginning event.

As an example of divergent phenomena, Langmuir cited the "wonderful cloud chamber experiments of Charles T. R. Wilson" (Nobel laureate in physics in 1927) for rendering discernible the course of electrically charged particles. Wilson showed that a single high-speed electron, or an alpha particle from an atom of radium, in passing through a supersaturated water vapor, leaves a visible trail of condensed droplets. Initiation of crystallization in a supersaturated solution is another example of a divergent phenomenon. Langmuir illustrated this with a personal experience: "At a camp at Lake George, in winter, I have often found that a pail of water is unfrozen in the morning in a room far below freezing, but it suddenly turns to slush upon being lifted from the floor."

In one of his last great contributions to science, Langmuir made use of his concept of divergent phenomena to demonstrate how the rainfall pattern over the entire North American continent could be influenced by a single cloud-seeding operation. In a report in *Chemical and Engineering News* (1951), M. L. Kastens stated that Langmuir's data "indicate that a few hundred grams of silver iodide dispersed in [Socorro] New Mexico have changed the weather over most of the United States."

During World War II, Langmuir had helped the Army Chemical Warfare Service develop a new smoke generator that was much more efficient than older models. With his associate, Vincent Schaefer, Langmuir then established a station on Mount Washington, in New Hampshire, at more than 1,800 meters above sea level. For the Air Force, they studied radio interference caused by the impact of snowflakes on the surfaces of airplanes. Later the Air Force, joined by the Signal Corps and the Office of Naval Research, sponsored Project Cirrus, in which the effect of various nucleating agents on supercooled clouds was studied.

Langmuir and his assistants had actually caused ice particles to form in a small cloud created in a cold box in the laboratory. They grated small pieces of dry ice (solid carbon dioxide at a temperature of -80 degrees Celsius) into the artificial cloud and watched as ice crystals settled out onto a piece of black velvet in the box. In November, 1946, Vincent Schaefer scattered granulated dry ice from an airplane into a cumulus cloud near Schenectady, New York, as Langmuir watched from the ground: "The whole supercooled cloud was converted into ice crystals. . . . In five minutes the whole cloud melted away, leaving a thin wraith of snow. . . . It worked!"

Later Langmuir, Schaefer, and Bernard Vonnegut substituted silver iodide for dry ice. It caused the same effect, and it could be dispersed from ground-based generators, such as their World War II smoke generators, instead of having to be scattered from an airplane. In his 1951 report, Kastens gave an "official weather bureau report of daily precipitation" over a large number of stations throughout the midwestern United States in which a seven-day cycle of precipitation was shown, which corresponded to the same cycle of seeding from a silver iodide generator operating in Socorro, New Mexico. Using statistical techniques, Langmuir reported that the odds against such a rainfall pattern occurring by chance were 3.4 to the 12.5 power (more than 4 million to one).

There is little possibility that these effects over the whole continent were caused by silver iodide nuclei actually being physically transported from New Mexico. Rather, it could be another example of Langmuir's divergent phenomena. On the other hand, meteorologists have proposed a theory of oscillations in weather patterns that might account for the effects observed during the April, 1950, experiments. Kastens concluded his report by stating that "no one has as yet presumed to offer a complete explanation of these newly discovered long range effects."

To end this discussion of rainmaking, an old saying might be invoked: "You can't get blood out of a turnip." In other words, there must be clouds containing moisture in order for any cloud-seeding process to have any effect. The cloud patterns on radar shown on evening television reports probably would have delighted Langmuir, because they show an almost continuous movement of clouds from the western to the eastern United States. If cloud seeding in New Mexico were actually an initiating cause, as Langmuir claimed, the divergent effect, causing rainfall over the rest of the country, could very possibly have taken place.

Perhaps Langmuir himself gave the best summation of the situation in *Science* (1950), in a fitting conclusion to this, his last great contribution to science. He discussed his ideas of convergent and divergent phenomena, calling shower formations a good example of divergent phenomena. He stated that a heavy rainshower requires particles, either natural or artificial, "in sufficient numbers to convert a portion of the supercooled cloud into ice crystals, thereby generating heat sufficient to overcome the stability of the atmosphere and set up a chain reaction in the production of new snow crystals." In typical Langmuir fashion, he ended by proposing in the last paragraph that the techniques described here for cloud-seeding should be tested for the prevention or moderation of hurricanes.

Langmuir's address as retiring president of the American Association for Advancement of Science, published in *Science* (1943) as "Science, Common Sense, and Decency," comes as close to being metaphysical as he ever came. Langmuir never displayed any kind of religious faith, but in this address he showed what might be seen as a lack of faith in the ability of science alone to solve humanity's problems:

Our morality is a kind of summation of the wisdom and experience of our race. It comes to us largely by tradition or religion. Some people justify evil things on the basis of morality—but by and large a recognition of right and wrong, even if these concepts are fuzzy, has proved to be of value to mankind.

Bibliography

Primary

CHEMISTRY: "The Dissociation of Water Vapor and Carbon Dioxide at High Temperatures," *Journal of the American Chemical Society*, vol. 28, 1906; "The Dissociation of Hydrogen into Atoms," *Journal of the American Chemical Society*, vol. 36, 1914 (with G. M. J. Mackay); "Arrangement of Electrons in Atoms and Molecules," *Journal of the American Chemical Society*, vol. 41, 1919; "Atomic Hydrogen as an Aid to Industrial Research," *Science*, vol. 20, 1928; "Forces Near the Surface of Molecules," *Chemical Review*, vol. 6, 1929; "Experiments with Oil on Water," *Journal of Chemical Education*, vol. 8, 1931.

METEOROLOGY: "Control of Precipitation from Cumulus Clouds by Various Seeding Techniques," *Science*, vol. 112, 1950; "A Seven-Day Periodicity in Weather in the United States During April, 1950," *Bulletin of the American Meteorological Society*, 1950.

PHILOSOPHY OF SCIENCE: "Science, Common Sense, and Decency," *Science*, vol. 97, 1943.

Secondary

Bacon, Egbert K. "Irving Langmuir, 1881-1957." In *American Chemists and Chemical Engineers*, edited by Wyndham D. Miles. Washington, D.C.: American Chemical Society, 1976. Contains a two-page biography, written with considerable insight into Langmuir's scientific work and personal life.

Blodgett, Katharine B. "Irving Langmuir." *Journal of Chemical Education* 10 (July, 1933): 396. Blodgett was an associate of Langmuir's at General Electric and coauthored several articles with him. She knew him over a period of years and was capable of understanding thoroughly the workings of his mind. She also gives insights (including photographs) into his personal life and his love of the outdoors.

Gray, George W. "A Summer Vacation." *The Atlantic Monthly* 152 (December, 1933): 732-743. A fairly lengthy biography in popular magazine style, which makes for pleasant reading. Gray based his article on interviews with Langmuir, so the material has freshness and originality.

Kastens, M. L. "Weather to Order." *Chemical and Engineering News* 29 (1951): 1090. Written by the associate editor of *Chemical and Engineering News*, this article gives a more quantitative view of Langmuir's meteorological experiments than some other attempts. Includes a table of data on precipitation and the formula that Langmuir used to calculate the probability of his experiments being governed merely by chance.

Langmuir, Irving. *The Collected Works of Irving Langmuir*, edited by Guy C. Suits. Elmsford, N.Y.: Pergamon Press, 1962. These volumes present a thorough view of Langmuir's work in all fields. Volume 12, "Langmuir, the Man and the Scientist," contains a biography.

Rosenfeld, Albert. *The Quintessence of Irving Langmuir*. Elmsford, N.Y.: Pergamon Press, 1966. Rosenfeld presents the most comprehensive biography of Langmuir available. He has sufficient grasp of scientific terms and theories to be able to discuss Langmuir's work intelligently, which is not true of some of his other biographers. Langmuir's philosophy of serendipity and his emphasis on convergent and divergent phenomena are treated with understanding.

"Weather or Not?" *Time* 56 (August 28, 1950): 52-56. The cover shows Langmuir holding an umbrella to fend off the rain he was making. As the first really scientific rainmaker, Langmuir was the victim of considerable raillery. Photographs in the article include a scene of cumulus clouds over Socorro Peak in New Mexico, where early cloud seeding took place.

Whitney, Willis Rodney. "Langmuir's Work." *Science* 20 (1928): 329. Whitney was the founder, and director for twenty-eight years, of the General Electric Research Laboratory; he brought Langmuir to GE and encouraged him in all his work. He gives a good summary of Langmuir's work up to 1928.

Joseph Albert Schufle

1934

Chemistry
Harold Clayton Urey, United States

Physics
no award

Physiology or Medicine
George R. Minot, United States
William P. Murphy, United States
George H. Whipple, United States

Literature
Luigi Pirandello, Italy

Peace
Arthur Henderson, Great Britain

HAROLD CLAYTON UREY
1934

Born: Walkerton, Indiana; April 29, 1893
Died: La Jolla, California; January 5, 1981
Nationality: American
Areas of concentration: Isotopes, cosmochemistry, and geochemistry

Urey applied the modern theories of chemical physics to determine physical properties of heavy hydrogen, an isotope of hydrogen. Using the knowledge of the isotope's calculated properties, he discovered and isolated heavy hydrogen (deuterium)

The Award

Presentation

Professor Wilhelm Palmær, an inorganic chemist and electrochemist and Chairman of the Nobel Committee for Chemistry of the Royal Swedish Academy of Sciences, officially awarded the Nobel Prize in Chemistry to Harold Clayton Urey on December 10, 1934. In his address, Palmær briefly examined the history of isotope chemical studies dating back to 1910. He noted that much of the work in this area grew out of the research of the English scientists Frederick Soddy and Francis Aston, themselves Nobel laureates in chemistry.

Palmær acknowledged the contributions in isotope studies made with Aston's introduction of the mass spectrograph, an instrument that could separate isotopes of an element by means of electrical and magnetic forces, revealing individual isotope atomic weights. These isotope atomic weights always, or very nearly always, occurred as whole numbers, and further, no discernible difference in chemical properties resulted. All the results of isotope studies served to bolster William Prout's hypothesis, advanced in 1815, that the atomic weights of the elements occurred as multiples of that of hydrogen and thus were necessarily whole numbers. The atomic weights of the then-known isotopes differed by only a few percentage points for a given element; further, the chemical properties of the isotopes of an element displayed no measurable difference. Palmær noted the important question facing isotope chemists of the day: What differences in chemical properties may there be between isotopes of an element in which the atomic weights differ by 100 percent? This was exactly the case for hydrogen and its heavy hydrogen isotope. Urey addressed that question and embarked upon his discovery and isolation of the heavy hydrogen isotope.

Nobel lecture

On February 14, 1935, Harold Clayton Urey presented his Nobel lecture, entitled "Some Thermodynamic Properties of Hydrogen and Deuterium." He first acknowledged the work of his predecessors in isotope chemistry, particularly the many contributions of Aston, including his mass spectrograph. Urey recognized the discovery of the oxygen isotopes (17 and 18) by William Giauque and Herrick L. Johnston, nitrogen 15 by Stefan M. Naude, and carbon 13 by Raymond T. Birge and Arthur S. King. He noted that the existence of heavy hydrogen, and, in fact, triple heavy hydrogen (tritium) as well as helium 5, had been implied by the work of William D. Harkins as early as 1928.

The search for deuterium called upon the various theories of atomic structure and thermodynamics of the day. Calculations of the vapor pressures of molecular hydrogen, deuterium hydride, and tritium hydride, the heat capacities of hydrogen and deuterium, and the coefficients of expansion of hydrogen and deuterium were important factors in the search for deuterium. The results of these calculations, when compared to the experimentally determined values, supported the utility of the theories used.

Urey explained the importance he attached to the distillation of liquid hydrogen in order to concentrate the deuterium. He credited his former student and colleague in this work, Ferdinand G. Brickwedde, of the National Bureau of Standards, for the preparation of samples used to detect deuterium's unquestioned presence.

Urey addressed the separation of isotopes at the end of his presentation. He noted that the separation of isotopes of the lighter elements represents a major challenge to chemistry and physics. He lauded the excellent confirmation of theoretical calculations applied to exchange reactions involving hydrogen and deuterium. Those results encouraged similar applications to the isotopes of the other elements. He closed his address with the note that the discovery of deuterium and the resulting efficient means for its separation had set the stage for more interesting research in chemistry, physics, and biology.

Critical reception

Urey was the third American chemist to receive a Nobel Prize, following Theodore William Richards (1914) of Harvard University and Irving Langmuir (1932) of the General Electric Research Laboratories. Announcement of the award to Urey appeared in many sources, including *Science, Science News Letters, Industrial and Engineering Chemistry*, and *Nature*, as well as in the popular press: *Time, Newsweek, The New York Times*, and *The Times* of London. No criticism of Urey or his receiving the award attended its announcement.

As stated in *Industrial and Engineering Chemistry*, the predecessor of today's *Chemical and Engineering News* of the American Chemical Society, "American chemists are proud that this honor should again come to one of their number." Indeed, American society, as judged by press reports, was in general proud and pleased with the award to Urey. *Science News Letters* carried a front-cover photograph of Urey and photographs of his associates Brickwedde and George Murphy in the article. *Nature* offered the prospect that the "discovery of deuterium may be expected to have important consequences for physics as well as chemistry," just as the discovery of the element radium by Marie Curie had. *The New York Times* carried an announcement of the award. When asked how the prize would affect his life, Urey responded that it would "cause little change in my way of life." He went on to say that he is "fortunate in doing exactly what I want to do." In an interview with the National Broadcasting Corporation discussing his discovery of deuterium, Urey pointed out that one gallon of 99.9 percent pure heavy water would cost $75,000.

Time, in an article about Urey's award, noted, "Undoubtedly in considering last week's award the Swedish Academy took cognizance of the fact that no discovery in the physical sciences in recent years has stimulated more widespread research" than the discovery of deuterium. *Newsweek* noted that the eminent British physicist Ernest Rutherford "considers [the discovery] one of the century's six most important finds." In an interview with Urey, *Newsweek* quoted Urey's response that his discovery of deuterium was luck: "Just luck. . . . No, I guess it was more than luck. It was the kind of luck that comes only when you have prepared the way." *The Times* of London announced the award of the Nobel Prize in Chemistry to Urey "for his discovery of heavy water." Of the discovery, they noted that it was of "the greatest physical, chemical, physiological, and medical interest." The announcements concerning Urey's receipt of the Nobel Prize in Chemistry were positive and forthright, and comments on the character or political philosophy of the recipient appeared. The announcements all noted the significance of the discovery, and all noted that deuterium would gather the attention of scientists from diverse fields.

Biography

Harold Clayton Urey was born April 29, 1893, in Walkerton, Indiana, to the Reverend Samuel Clayton Urey and the former Cora Rebecca Reinsehl. His father, who died when Urey was six years old, was a schoolteacher and a minister. Urey's education began in rural Dekalb County, Indiana. He attended high school in Kendallville and Walkerton and was graduated from the latter in 1911. After high school, Urey taught for three years in county schools in both Indiana and Montana.

In 1914, he entered the University of Montana, Missoula, majoring in zoology and minoring in chemistry. He received his B.S. in zoology in 1917. For two years thereafter, Urey worked as a chemist for the Barrett Chemical Company in Philadelphia, which was involved in war chemical production. In 1919, he returned to the University of Montana as an instructor of chemistry. After a few years at Montana, he entered the University of California, Berkeley, in 1921, studying for the Ph.D. in chemistry under Gilbert N. Lewis, earning his doctorate in 1923, with a minor in physics. After graduation, Urey continued his studies under physicist Niels Bohr at the Institute for Theoretical Physics at the University of Copenhagen, Denmark, as an American-Scandinavian Foundation Fellow.

After completing his fellowship, Urey returned to the United States to take a position as an associate in chemistry at The Johns Hopkins University, Baltimore, Maryland, which he held from 1924 to 1929. Urey married Freda Daum in Lawrence, Kansas, on June 12, 1926, she having been a bacteriologist prior to marriage. They were to have four children, three daughters and one son. Urey was appointed associate professor in chemistry in 1929 at Columbia University in New York City and, in 1934, was promoted to professor. While at Columbia, Urey's interests in heavy hydrogen (deuterium) led him to his Nobel Prize-winning studies and discovery. He served as the executive officer of the chemistry department at Columbia from 1939 to 1942. Additionally, he held the post of editor of the *Journal of Chemical Physics* from 1933 to 1940. In 1940, Urey was appointed Director of War Research, Atomic Bomb Project, Columbia University, a post he retained until 1945. Urey had by 1940 earned a reputation as an international authority on isotope chemistry and isotope separations. He was one of the few people who realized that the atomic bomb could indeed be made, and he was a key figure in the successful efforts to separate uranium isotopes for use in the bomb.

Urey became Distinguished Service Professor of Chemistry at the Institute of Nuclear Studies, University of Chicago, in 1945. From 1952 to 1958, he also held the Martin A. Ryerson Professorship there. His westward advance finally took him to California in 1958, where he served as Professor-at-Large at the University of California, San Diego, a position he held until 1970, then becoming Professor Emeritus of Chemistry until his death in 1981.

Urey held political affiliations with the Democratic Party. His pastimes included charcoal sketching, playing the piano, and gardening, in particular raising orchids, further indications of the varied interests of an accomplished and internationally renowned chemist and Nobel laureate. He died at his home in La Jolla, California, on January 5, 1981.

Scientific Career

Urey's scientific career began at the end of World War I, when he rejected an industrial career—a decision born of his experience in wartime chemical production. Urey studied under the tutelage of Gilbert N. Lewis at the University of California, Berkeley, from 1921 to 1923. Lewis was a proponent of thermodynamics in chemistry, as well as having a strong interest in molecular structure. It was in that environment that Urey developed his keen understanding and utility of thermodynamics, a factor that was consistently in the forefront of Urey's approach to chemical studies. This was a period in chemistry when thermodynamics was not universally accepted as an integral component of a chemistry curriculum. After receiving his doctorate in chemistry, Urey went to the Institute of Theoretical Physics at the University of Copenhagen as an American-Scandinavian Foundation Fellow. He studied with Niels Bohr, winner of the Nobel Prize in Physics in 1922, then attacking the mysteries of atomic structure.

In 1929, Urey moved to Columbia University in New York City, where he applied himself to experimental and theoretical studies of spectroscopy and quantum mechanics. He collaborated with Arthur E. Ruark in writing *Atoms, Molecules, and Quanta* (1930), one of the first widely read English books on the emerging field of quantum mechanical chemistry. Subsequent to the publishing of *Atoms, Molecules, and Quanta*, Urey directed his interests in atomic, molecular, and nuclear properties to the ultraviolet absorption spectra of chlorine dioxide with his student, Helen Johnston. He found that isotope effects were useful in the analysis of the observed spectral bands of this compound. While studying chlorine dioxide, he also approached the separation of the chlorine isotopes by applying photochemical methods to the chlorine dioxide in collaboration with Ray H. Crist. During this time Urey designed and constructed a 6.4-meter grating spectrograph with George M. Murphy. They used this device to study the relative abundances of the newly discovered nitrogen and oxygen isotopes.

The discovery of the oxygen isotopes in 1929 by Giauque and Herrick Johnston defined two possible atomic weight scales. The chemists chose one; the physicists chose the other. Hydrogen represented an exception in that its atomic weight was the same in both scales. Birge and Donald Menzel suggested the existence of hydrogen isotopes as an explanation for this atomic weight anomaly. Urey embraced this idea and immediately began the planning of experiments designed to find the hydrogen isotope. Based upon predictions of the ratio of occurrence of the hydrogen isotopes, Urey concluded that isotopic concentration by fractional distillation of liquid hydrogen offered the best means to concentrate the sought isotope. More important, he chose to employ the hydrogen atomic spectrum as the analytical detection method. Urey left the liquefaction and distillation of hydrogen to his former student Brickwedde, then of the National Bureau of Standards in Washington, D.C., who was known for his low-temperature studies.

While waiting for the distilled hydrogen samples, Urey and Murphy began a series of calculations to determine the Balmer spectral lines attributable to the heavy hydrogen isotope of atomic weight 2 by assuming that both double-heavy and triple-heavy hydrogen isotopes existed. The calculations also included the determination of vapor pressures of the isotope. The experiments that they ran on the concentrated liquid hydrogen samples that arrived from Brickwedde justified the calculations. The confirmation of the existence and the discovery of heavy hydrogen (atomic weight 2) occurred on Thanksgiving Day, 1931. They observed no evidence, however, for the triple-heavy isotope of hydrogen.

Urey announced the discovery of heavy hydrogen at the December, 1931, meeting of the American Association for the Advancement of Science in New Orleans. As Murphy notes in his book *Isotopic and Cosmic Chemistry* (1964), Urey's search for deuterium had nothing to do with any applications for heavy water. There had been a blank space in his chart of nuclear species that Urey felt should be filled.

In January, 1934, Urey was awarded the twenty-third Willard Gibbs Medal for his discovery of deuterium. The name deuterium, given to the heavy hydrogen isotope, was proposed by Urey himself. The crowning of his success as a scientist came in November of that same year with the announcement that Urey was being awarded the Nobel Prize in Chemistry for his discovery of heavy hydrogen. He was forty-one years old at the time.

Research interest in deuterium grew so rapidly that the National Research Council formed an oversight committee to serve as a clearing house for the volume of research being applied to this isotope. Urey was named its chairman. He continued his studies of isotopic chemistry through the 1930's, becoming an international authority on isotope chemistry. In 1933 he became the first editor of the *Journal of Chemical Physics*, retaining the post until 1940.

The dawning of the 1940's saw the world in turmoil, hovering at the brink of total global war. Adolf Hitler was dictator in Germany, and Britain was fighting for its life against the march of Nazism. This period also witnessed the psychologically devastating military defeat of the United States Navy at Pearl Harbor by the Japanese Navy. It was this world environment that led to government interest in atomic fission. Urey became a principal in events that forever changed not only science and scientists but also the whole world.

Urey became the Director of War Research, Atomic Bomb Project at Columbia. He devised, in collaboration with John R. Dunning, assistant professor of physics, the gaseous diffusion method for the extraction of the fissionable uranium 235 isotope from the more common uranium 238 and worked on the development of heavy water production. He developed the vacuum techniques applicable to handling uranium hexafluoride on an unprecedented scale. The statistical method employed by Urey paved the way for the successful atomic bomb. The end of World War II saw the transfer of all Urey's work to the newly created Institute for Nuclear Studies at the University of Chicago.

The year 1946 brought Urey's public comment on the future of atomic energy. Urey bluntly expressed his concerns for the future of a nuclear world. He did not think that science and social responsibility could be separate, independent activities. In an address in February to the Independent Citizens Committee of the Arts, Sciences and Professions (Chicago), which was published in the October, 1946, issue of *Science Education*, Urey placed into logical perspective the hope and the horror of atomic energy as he saw it.

In 1948, Urey publicly championed an idea advanced by Clarence Street before World War II. The proposal, that of a world government, appeared in the *Symposium on the Uses of Isotopes in Biology and Medicine* held at the University of Wisconsin, Madison. This proposal arose out of Urey's concern about nuclear proliferation and the inevitable propensity of nations to go to war. The inherent violence of the Soviet state, he believed, needed a constraining influence. The concept of a "federation" composed of the United States, the British Commonwealth, France, Belgium, Holland, the Scandinavian countries, Switzerland, and a few other countries would provide, in Urey's opinion, for the common defense, regulation of money and commerce, a common postal system, and so on. Additionally, the stabilizing influence and prosperity of such a union was viewed as lessening the risks of nuclear war and moderating Soviet foreign designs.

By 1950, Urey's interests expanded from pure isotope chemistry to geochemical and cosmic chemistry. In 1951, he published a paper on the measurement of paleo-temperatures for the determination of ocean temperatures as far back in time as 180 million years before the present. In 1952, he published his book *The Planets:*

Their Origin and Development. In his book, Urey quantitatively described the various chemical and physical processes that decided the evolution of the solar system. It was Urey who theorized that the planets of the solar system may have evolved from a gaseous disk revolving about the Sun. Working under Urey in 1953, Stanley Miller, a graduate student, undertook the first experiments to elucidate the synthesis of prebiological chemical compounds (that is, those leading to living organisms) from a primordial Earth atmosphere consisting of methane, ammonia, and water vapor. These gaseous mixtures had been suggested some twenty-five years earlier by the Russian biochemist Aleksandr I. Oparin and John B. S. Haldane in England. The experiments yielded several amino acid compounds. Urey became fascinated with the origin of the Earth, the planets, and the solar system as revealable by isotope chemistry. By this time, Urey, Harrison Brown, Mark Inghram, Willard Libby, and Hans Suess had studied various problems of nuclear geochemistry and geophysics, establishing Chicago as the international center of geochemistry. In 1955, Urey contributed a chapter to the book *Production of Heavy Water* with coeditors Murphy and Isidor Kirshenbaum.

Urey moved west, to the University of California, San Diego, in 1958. He continued to pursue his interests begun at the University of Chicago, delving into matters of geochemistry, cosmochemistry, and the origin of life. The late 1950's, however, saw the launch of Sputnik, the Soviet satellite, in 1957: The Soviets had taken the first tentative step into the space age, and American science reacted to this technological shock with a shift in priorities. Urey, again, was one of the leaders.

In 1958, Urey was appointed to the Space Science Board of the National Academy of Sciences. In 1960, he wrote two reports for the board. One concerned the Moon, the second, the planets. In those reports he noted that the exploration of space may yield answers concerning the origin of the solar system and life on other planets. When the United States did go into space, Urey was one of the scientists who studied the moon rocks returned to earth during the Apollo missions. He also served as a consultant on the Viking missions sent to Mars. In 1971, Urey contributed a chapter to the book *Physics and Astronomy of the Moon*, edited by Zdenek Kopal. In it, he discusses the history and origin of the Moon, its craters and maria, and the composition and time scale of lunar surface formation.

Urey was outspoken on political matters. During the 1930's, he opposed the Franco rebellion in Spain. He publicly denounced the death sentence imposed upon Julius and Ethel Rosenberg in the famous spy trial concerning the passing of nuclear weapons secrets to the Soviet Union in the early 1950's. He opposed the building of nuclear reactors and favored international bans on nuclear weapons, but he also opposed any unilateral United States disarmament. In the early 1970's, Urey was one of many scientists calling for the immediate withdrawal of all United States forces from Vietnam.

Urey was the recipient of numerous awards and honorary degrees from American and foreign institutions; he was a tireless, dedicated worker. He pursued problems in physics, biology, geology, and astronomy—always viewing them with the chemist's eye. Virtually all of his research made use of isotopic chemical principles, and his discovery of deuterium marked the marriage of theoretical and experimental methods into a unified and systematic approach to solving a problem. His life's work opened new vistas in the fields of chemistry, physics, geology, astronomy, biology, and medicine. The essential concepts that he put forward, though refined and expanded in scope through the years, remain intact.

Urey also attempted to raise the social conscience through his opinions of political events—opinions based upon science and man's historical use of science. He was particularly concerned about the wisdom of using nuclear energy and the proliferation of nuclear weapons. He feared for a world armed with nuclear weaponry yet still accepting the age-old method of resolving disputes—armed combat. Urey himself succumbed to age-old human frailties. Parkinson's disease and a steadily worsening heart condition finally ended the career of a brilliant man. The discoverer of deuterium died at his home in La Jolla, California, on the evening of January 5, 1981.

Bibliography

Primary

CHEMISTRY: *Atoms, Molecules, and Quanta*, 1930 (with Arthur E. Ruark); "A Hydrogen Isotope of Mass 2," *Physical Review*, vol. 39, 1932 (with F. G. Brickwedde and G. M. Murphy); "A Name and Symbol for H_2," *Journal of Chemical Physics*, vol. 1, 1933 (with G. M. Murphy and F. G. Brickwedde); "Some Thermodynamic Properties of the H_1, H_2, H_2H_2 Molecules and Compounds Containing the H_2 Atom," *Journal of Chemical Physics*, vol. 1, 1933 (with D. Rittenberg); "The Separation and Properties of the Isotopes of Hydrogen," *Science*, vol. 78, 1933; *Treatise on Physical Chemistry*, 1936; chapter 6 in *Production of Heavy Water*, 1955 (edited with George M. Murphy and Isidor Kirshenbaum).

COSMOCHEMISTRY: "The Abundance of the Elements," *Physical Review*, vol. 88, 1952; *The Planets: Their Origin and Development*, 1952; "The Composition of the Stone Meteorites and the Origin of the Meteorites," *Geochimica et cosmochimica acta*, vol. 4, 1953 (with Harmon Craig); "Origin and Age of Meteorites," *Nature*, vol. 175, 1955; "Diamonds, Meteorites, and the Origin of the Solar System," *Astrophysical Journal*, vol. 124, 1956; chapter 6 in *Physics and Astronomy of the Moon*, 1971 (edited by Zdenek Kopal).

GEOCHEMISTRY: "Measurement of Paleotemperatures and Temperatures of the Upper Cretaceous of England, Denmark and the Southeastern United States," *Bulletin of the Geological Society of America*, vol. 62, 1951 (with H. A. Lowenstam, S. Epstein, and C. R. McKinney).

SOCIOPOLITICS: "The Social Implications of the Atomic Bomb," *Science Education*, vol. 30, 1946.

Secondary

Duncan, James F., and Gerald B. Cook. *Isotopes in Chemistry*. Oxford, England:

Clarendon Press, 1968. This book describes the properties of isotopes, isotope effects, radioactive recoil, electronic and nuclear excitation, and artificial elements. Notes the developments of its day and gives the reader an understanding of the impact isotope chemistry has had on the physical sciences.

Gamow, George. *Matter, Earth and Sky.* Englewood Cliffs, N.J.: Prentice-Hall, 1958. This book presents a nonmathematical tour of the developments in the physical and chemical sciences as the chemist, physicist, and astronomer have ordered the universe and its workings. Well written, with many illustrations depicting the concepts presented, this book is an excellent beginning source for the junior or senior high school reader.

Gordon, Edgar S., and Perry W. Wilson, eds. *A Symposium on the Uses of Isotopes in Biology and Medicine.* Madison: University of Wisconsin Press, 1948. This work provides, in scientific writings of the day, a historical view of how scientists viewed the rapid developments in isotope chemistry applicable to studies in biology and medicine. In the light of modern practices, this work reveals the insights and directions taken by the physical and biological sciences in the minds of the researchers of the 1940's. Urey's presentation, "Separation of Stable Isotopes," takes the reader through several different methods employed for the separation of isotopes. A compilation by nineteen contributors, this work is moderately technical.

Guest, Gordon H. *Radioisotopes: Industrial Applications.* New York: Pitman Publishing, 1951. This publication provides a nontechnical explanation of the uses of isotopes in industrial applications such as metallurgy and chemical processing; it also reviews isotope use in friction and lubrication studies, the petroleum and rubber industries, and industrial hygiene and public health. Beginning with a general discussion of atoms and atomic energy, it goes on to reveal the isotope as a tool in industry. Includes many figures, photographs, graphs, and tables.

Sacks, Jacob. *The Atom at Work.* New York: Ronald Press, 1951. Intended for the general reader, *The Atom at Work* presents a nontechnical presentation of the basics of atomic structure, isotopes, and radioactivity. With many illustrations, the book guides the lay reader through the physicist's and physical chemist's world of atomic structure and introduces the reader to the use made of radioactivity and isotopes in business, biology, and medicine.

Urey, Harold C. *The Planets: Their Origin and Development.* New Haven, Conn.: Yale University Press, 1952. Urey's book discusses the evolution of the solar system, the origin of the Moon, and the chemical origin and chemical development of the planets. Chapter 5 discusses the heat balance of the Earth, including the convection theory of mountain building. The final chapter discusses the abundances of the elements in stars, meteorites, origin and age of meteorites as well as the origin of comets. The book, written as a scientific presentation, shows Urey's ability to marshal different disciplines to address a complex topic.

Eric R. Taylor

1935

Chemistry
Frédéric Joliot, France
Irène Joliot-Curie, France

Physics
Sir James Chadwick, Great Britain

Physiology or Medicine
Hans Spemann, Germany

Literature
no award

Peace
no award

FRÉDÉRIC JOLIOT

IRÈNE JOLIOT-CURIE

FRÉDÉRIC JOLIOT and IRÈNE JOLIOT-CURIE
1935

Frédéric Joliot

Born: Paris, France; March 19, 1900
Died: Paris, France; August 14, 1958
Nationality: French
Areas of concentration: Radioactivity, radioisotopes, and nuclear fission

Irène Joliot-Curie

Born: Paris, France; September 12, 1897
Died: Paris, France; March 17, 1956
Nationality: French
Areas of concentration: Radioactivity, radioisotopes, and nuclear fission

Continuing the radiation research of Marie and Pierre Curie, the Joliot-Curies developed the technique of producing artificially radioactive isotopes, followed by investigations into their medicinal and research uses and the production of nuclear fission

The Award

Presentation

Irène and Frédéric Joliot-Curie were presented for their Nobel award by Wilhelm Palmær, the Chairman of the Nobel Committee for Chemistry. Palmær began by recalling the 1911 presentation to Marie Curie, mother of Irène Curie. It was her second award—she had also shared the 1903 physics prize with her husband Pierre and Antoine-Henri Becquerel. Both awards were for research related to studies in radioactivity. Professor Palmær then emphasized the importance of the Curies' work by noting that two other Nobel awards had been made for work in radiation, the 1908 prize to Ernest Rutherford and the 1922 prize to Frederick Soddy.

In discussing the nature of the radioactive process, Palmær explained that this natural transmutation does not accomplish the alchemist's goal of transforming base metals into precious ones, since it is a spontaneous process that can neither be initiated nor halted. This led directly to a statement of the contribution of Irène and Frédéric Joliot-Curie: the induced transmutation of the elements.

Palmær recounted the view of atomic structure consisting of a positively charged nucleus, containing protons and neutrons, surrounded by negative electrons arranged somewhat like a "planetary system." In presenting the work of the Joliot-Curies, he explained that they bombarded aluminum with high-speed alpha particles (helium atoms stripped of their electrons) from a polonium source, an element discovered by Madame Joliot-Curie's mother. They discovered that the aluminum then began to emit rays of positrons, positively charged electrons, indicating that a new radioisotope had been created. The emission continued for some time after the source was removed, indicating that the new isotope was unstable and was itself decaying. Their isotope was a new form of phosphorus, which they called radio-phosphorus.

In reference to other work on radioactivity, Palmær recalled that because of the small quantities available, most radioisotopes are identified by their characteristic radiation. In the case of the work being honored, the Joliot-Curies had established a chemical identification as well. They also produced radio-nitrogen from boron and radio-silicon and radio-aluminum from the isotopes of magnesium. Palmær pointed out that Rutherford had earlier used alpha rays to cause transmutations but had produced only known isotopes. The Joliot-Curies had synthesized new elements.

In recalling the reservations stated by Robert Boyle in his definition of an element as consisting of an "indivisible atom," in which he stated that it might be possible to find a "subtle and powerful means" to decompose these atoms, Palmær stated the true significance of the work of the Joliot-Curies. They gave the world "that vision of the future."

In concluding his presentation, Palmær indicated the practical application of artificial radioactivity as tracers in studying biological mechanisms and in medicine. Palmær ended by again recalling the memory of Madame Joliot-Curie's parents and by stating that the work of the younger researchers was "of capital importance" in making the dream of the alchemists at last reality.

Nobel lectures

Each of the recipients delivered a lecture on December 12, 1935, with Irène Joliot-Curie indicating that they had divided the subject matter as "a matter of convenience." It is ironic, however, that Madame Joliot-Curie, a chemist by training, recounted the discovery of positron decay in a lecture entitled "Artificial Production of Radioactive Elements." Frédéric Joliot, considered to be a physicist, used his lecture, "Chemical Evidence of the Transmutation of Elements," to address their work on the chemical identification of the artificial radioisotopes.

Madame Joliot-Curie spoke first and began by stating their pleasure at receiving the award which had earlier been given to her parents jointly (in physics) and her mother singly (in chemistry). Joliot-Curie then recounted the recognition of the process of natural radioactive decay, a property exhibited by about thirty elements, and the characteristics of the particles and energies emitted, showing that the process cannot be altered by man. She pointed out that the radioelements have recognizable chemical properties, along with a characteristic half-life, the time needed for half the atoms to decay. Rutherford's induced transmutations were fundamental in the understanding of these nuclear processes, which were then used for artificial transmutations and in James Chadwick's discovery of the neutron, being honored that same year by the Nobel Prize in Physics.

Madame Joliot-Curie then explained their experimental work using transmutations to produce artificially radioactive substances. Alpha-ray bombardment of some elements was accompanied by neutron emission; in those cases, new isotopes were produced. They also observed that positive electrons were emitted. It was the positron emission that continued after alpha bombardment was stopped that indicated the existence of newly created radioactive elements. The lecture concluded with an explanation of their hypothesis that the transmutations occur in two stages: the capture of an alpha particle by the nucleus, with expulsion of a neutron, followed by spontaneous decay of the isotope produced.

Frédéric Joliot then began his lecture by explaining their applications of the methods of radiochemistry to identify the unstable isotopes, whose existence they postulated in their transmutation schemes. These methods allowed the identification of materials present in amounts too small to be weighed by studying their radiations. Previously these methods had been applied to the identification of the known elements produced in natural transmutations. He explained that in their work they had used chemical reactions to form compounds containing the new radioelement. They could then identify these compounds by their chemical properties. Joliot explained in detail their formation of zirconium phosphate containing the "radiophosphate" produced from their alpha-ray bombardment of aluminum.

Joliot then turned his attentions to further applications of their work by other experimenters using bombardments with other particles, such as protons and deuterons, a heavier isotope of hydrogen. He listed several of the artificial isotopes produced in this work and indicated that production of large amounts of the isotopes would allow their use as tracers in studying the processes of living organisms.

In concluding, Joliot stated that their work had changed the view of existing matter, showing that only the most stable elements survive in the physical world. Others, such as the ones they synthesized, had surely existed at earlier times. He ended by hinting at the future potential of developing transmutations that would involve the release of enormous amounts of energy, such as is seen in exploding stars. He stated their hope that work to realize that possibility would be performed with "the necessary precautions."

Critical reception

The awarding of the Nobel Prize to Irène and Frédéric Joliot-Curie was announced in Stockholm on November 14, 1935. Word of the award reached them that same day in a telegram delivered to their home in Paris. The response of the world press was immediate and enthusiastic. *The New York Times* of November 15, 1935, called the work that won that year's awards in chemistry and physics "two of the most revolutionary achievements in modern science." In their assessment of the award-winning work in both fields, they cited the Joliot-Curies' award in chemistry for the discovery of artificial radioactivity as being "the more spectacular of the two." (The other award was the physics prize to Chadwick for the discovery of the neutron, an accomplishment that the Joliot-Curies narrowly missed.) *The New York Times* was also representative of most commentators in recalling the award-winning work of Madame Joliot-Curie's mother.

In an editorial the following day, November 16, 1935, *The New York Times* continued its commentary by referring to a "Curie dynasty" in the study of the chemistry and physics of radioactivity. In comparing the work of the younger researchers to that of Madame Joliot-Curie's parents, it stated that the new laureates were not only continuing a family tradition for brilliant scientific research but also carrying on "the human and social tradition of husband and wife as professional collaborators." In a statement as true now as then, they described the Curies as being "in the front rank of Nobel families of all time."

Along with recognizing the Joliot-Curies' work as honoring the memory of Marie and Pierre Curie, *Time* magazine of November 24, 1935, was typical of many publications in pointing out its regret that Madame Curie had not lived to see the award, having died on July 4, 1934. They did note that when the award-winning work was being performed, Marie Curie "was proud that her shy young daughter and her brilliant son-in-law were showing themselves to be able and devoted scientists." In a final reference to the family connection, *Time* commented that even more than the monetary award of more than $40,000 accompanying the prize, the Joliot-Curies would value "the scroll which they can now put beside" the 1903 and 1911 "awards to her father and mother."

The prizewinning research itself had also elicited a tremendous response in both the scientific and lay press when it was announced in January of 1934. In reporting the discovery, *Time* magazine stated that their work provided a confirmation of the existence of the neutron and was "hailed in every physical journal in the United States and Europe." The medicinal applications of the artifically produced radioisotopes were immediately recognized. Dr. Henry Aksew Barton, of the American Institute of Physics, commented in the same issue of *Time* that these substances would serve as substitutes for the effective, but very expensive, radium in the treatment of malignancies.

Ernest Rutherford also commented on the initial publication of their work. He wrote the Joliot-Curies to "congratulate you both on a fine piece of work which I am sure will ultimately prove of much importance." Rutherford himself was recognized in the scientific community as a master experimentalist, so his concluding statement to the Joliot-Curies that his own experiments in the area "were without any success" had great meaning.

In remarks made following Frédéric Joliot's death, Louis de Broglie, who was the Permanent Secretary of the Academy of Sciences, noted that at the time the Nobel Prize was awarded, the Joliot-Curies had earned an international reputation as scientists but "had yet to make a great discovery which they could call their own. This great discovery . . . was that of artificially radioactive elements." In commenting on their Nobel award-winning work at the time of Irène Joliot-Curie's death, *The New York Times* stated that the neutron had opened "a new region in nuclear physics" for study and that the "exploration began with the Joliot-Curies."

Biographies

Irène Curie was born in Paris on September 12, 1897. She was the older of the two daughters of Marie and Pierre Curie. Madame Curie helped to organize an education cooperative with members of the Sorbonne's intellectual elite, and it was there that Irène received her early education. Physics was taught by her mother, while Paul Langevin instructed in mathematics, Jean Perrin in chemistry, and Henri Mouton in natural history. While her parents spent long hours in the lab, Irène and her sister, Ève, developed a deep relationship with their grandfather, Eugène Curie, a physician. He imparted to them his own liberal and socialist tendencies, which were to influence every aspect of Irène's life. Her parents reared her with a strong sense of responsibility to both science and social service.

She prepared for her baccalaureate at Collège Sévigné, starting in 1912, and became her mother's assistant at the Radium Institute of the University of Paris in 1918. Receiving her license in physics and mathematics at the Sorbonne in 1920, she began her own research. This culminated with the defense of her doctoral thesis in 1925. She continued her researches and was appointed director of the institute in 1946; in 1947, she became a professor at the Sorbonne. In both cases she rose to positions previously occupied by her mother.

Frédéric Joliot was born in Paris on March 19, 1900, to Henri and Émilie Roederer Joliot and was the youngest of six children. His father was a successful tradesman, and Frédéric received his early education at the prestigious Lycée Lakanal, where he was noted more for his accomplishments in athletics than academics. After his father's death, he was forced to enter a municipal school to prepare for his entrance to the École de Physique et de Chimie Industrielle, from which he received his engineering degree in 1923, ranked first in his class. When he completed his military service, Paul Langevin—who had been director of studies at the École—recommended him to Marie Curie, who hired him as a special assistant in October of 1925. While learning research techniques at the Radium Institute, Joliot studied for his *licence en sciences*, which he received in 1927. He then began his own investigations, which won for him his doctoral degree in 1930. In 1937, he was appointed professor at the College of France, a position he held during his entire career, later adding the professoriate at the Sorbonne that had been his wife's.

Upon his arrival at the Radium Institute, Joliot met the daughter of the director. They were married a year later, on October 9, 1926, at which time he added the Curie surname to his own, prompted by the fact that the Curies had had no sons. Soon afterward, the two combined their research interests and began publishing their work jointly, in a collaboration that was to last throughout their careers.

In response to their sense of social responsibility, they joined the Socialist Party in 1934, later also joining the Vigilance Committee of Anti-Fascist Intellectuals. During World War II they remained in France until 1944, when Irène and the children were smuggled to Switzerland for safety. Both Frédéric and Irène were active in the Resistance and were members of the French Legion of Honor. Irène served in the cabinet of the socialist Léon Blum during 1936, and Frédéric joined the French Communist Party in 1942. After the war, Joliot served as head of the French atomic energy commission until he was removed in 1950 for his political leanings. In 1951, he was awarded the Stalin Peace Prize, in recognition of his active participation in antibomb peace activities.

The Joliot-Curies were the parents of two children. Their daughter, Hélène, born in 1927, also became a nuclear physicist, marrying the grandson of Paul Langevin, with whom she collaborated during her scientific career. Pierre, their son, born in 1932, chose a career in biophysics, and in marrying a biophysicist, Anne, completed the third generation of extremely successful husband-wife teams.

The Joliot-Curies died within a few years of each other. Irène, like her mother, succumbed to leukemia on March 17, 1956. The illness was no doubt caused by her exposure to radiation in the laboratory as well as during her time as a nurse radiologist operating a battlefield ambulance X-ray unit during World War I. Frédéric died following surgery for an intestinal illness on August 14, 1958. Both funerals were held in the courtyard of the Sorbonne.

Scientific Careers

Irène Joliot-Curie's first scientific investigations were begun when she joined her mother at the Radium Institute. After learning the necessary techniques of radiochemistry, she began work on the fluctuations of the rays emitted by polonium, the radioactive element discovered by Madame Curie. These results became her doctoral thesis in 1925. The studies on polonium remained a prime focus of work at the institute, and Frédéric Joliot's first independent work there was also concerned with it. He studied the electrochemical properties of the element and presented the results in his doctoral defense in 1927. The newly married couple continued their independent researches. Irène continued working under her mother's direction on the properties of radioactive elements, while Frédéric accepted a scholarship at the Physical Chemistry Laboratory at the College of France, because there was at that time no position for him at the institute. While there he assembled his own equipment for the observation of radioactive emissions. He designed an improved cloud chamber, which allowed visualization of the tracks the particulate rays formed as they passed through vapor contained in the chamber. He coupled this to an extremely sensitive Geiger counter to detect the number of particles emitted.

They then combined their efforts on the problem of developing new chemical techniques for separating polonium. They used these methods to produce a sample whose emission of radiation was ten times stronger than any previously known. In 1931, they used this polonium source to begin to study what had come to be known as "the mystery of beryllium."

Earlier, in 1930, Walther Bothe and Herbert Becker had reported that both beryllium and boron emit radiation when subjected to alpha-ray bombardment. Their studies did not, however, reveal the nature or origin of the radiation. In investigating this, the Joliot-Curies subjected a plate of elemental beryllium to the alpha rays emitted from their intense polonium source. They detected the radiation noted by Bothe and Becker in an extremely sensitive ionization chamber. In December of 1931, they reported that the beryllium radiation produced in their apparatus was more intense than that reported by earlier workers and that the radiation emitted had three times the energy of the alpha particles used in the bombardment.

To ensure that the radiations they were observing were not secondary radiations being produced by bombardment of the walls of the ionization chamber itself, they used sheets of other elements between the beryllium and the chamber. When they used metals such as aluminum, silver, or copper, there was no effect on the amount of radiation. When they used materials such as paraffin wax or cellophane, however, there was a large increase in the observed radiation. In January of 1932, they reported to the Academy of Sciences their conclusion that the radiations were knocking protons out of any materials which contained hydrogen, whose nuclei contain only a single proton. In subsequent work they used Joliot's cloud chamber to track the emitted protons.

They continued their studies on the Bothe and Becker radiation from 1932 to 1934, determining that it was a complex phenomenon and that the radiation emitted included highly energetic gamma rays. They theorized that these gamma rays, when passing through materials, resulted in the emission of positive electrons. The existence of these positrons had been predicted from theory by Paul Adrien Maurice Dirac (Nobel Prize in Physics, 1933) and had earlier been observed in cosmic rays by Carl David Anderson (Nobel Prize in Physics, 1936). Again using Joliot's cloud chamber, they demonstrated the existence of these positrons. It was in repeating the work of the Joliot-Curies on the alpha-ray bombardment of beryllium that James Chadwick realized that the long-sought-for neutron, whose existence had also been predicted from theory, was contained in the complex radiation mixture the Joliot-Curies were observing.

Substituting boron for beryllium led them to their greatest discovery. At the Solvay Physics Conference of 1933, they reported that alpha-ray bombardment of boron produced protons, neutrons, and positrons. They then concentrated their efforts on more intensive study of the positron emission. When they returned to their studies of the total emission from the boron bombardment, they observed that the emission of radiation continued for a short time after the alpha ray source, their concentrated polonium sample, was removed. To investigate this, they used Joliot's Geiger counter and measured the half-life of the radiation. The Joliot-Curies reported the creation of new artificially radioactive isotopes in January of 1934, again to the Academy of Sciences. Within a matter of weeks they had developed radiochemical techniques to provide conclusive chemical identification of the new isotopes.

This work was repeated in many laboratories, and other workers began to use neutron bombardment in place of alpha rays. When Otto Hahn (Nobel Prize in Chemistry, 1944) suggested that neutrons were also a product of the bombardment, the Joliot-Curies turned their experimental efforts to a verification of the earlier experiments and detected the high-speed neutrons necessary for the process in an experiment involving the bombardment of a sample of uranium with high-speed neutrons.

In the years preceding World War II, the Joliot-Curies began an investigation into the phenomena associated with this neutron bombardment of uranium, building on the work of Enrico Fermi (Nobel Prize in Physics, 1938), Hahn, and Lise Meitner, who had postulated that several transuranic elements and new artificial radioisotopes were produced in the process. It was Meitner who published the first report of nuclear fission. Joliot-Curie, working with P. P. Savic, a Yugoslavian, performed a brilliant radiochemical analysis to separate a new isotope of barium, a suspected product of nuclear fission, thus confirming the splitting of an atom of uranium into two smaller nuclei of nearly equal mass. As a result of further work on fission with Hans von Halban and Lew Kowarski, Joliot demonstrated that the neutron released in the process would enable a chain reaction to take place. Realizing that to control the reaction these emitted neutrons would need to be slowed, he purchased the largest known supply of heavy, or deuterated, water from Norway to use to control, or moderate, the neutrons. In 1939, when the war caused them to suspend this research so that it did not become accessible to the Germans, the Joliot-Curies wrote out the theory of the process to initiate an enormously energetic fission chain reaction. This was sealed and kept in the Academy of Sciences until after the war.

During the war, the Joliot-Curies remained in their laboratories to ensure that none of their results or equipment became of use to the Germans. They turned their research efforts to production of radioisotopes for medical applications, such as radio-iodine for the study of thyroid disease, and conducted research in their use. They formed a commercial company to deal with the production and use of these isotopes. This allowed them to provide work certificates for their fellow scientists during the German occupation of France, which kept them from being sent to Germany. Their resistance activities extended to using Joliot's laboratory at the College of France to produce explosives during the battle for the liberation of Paris. The war also catalyzed their social activism: It was during that time that they actively engaged in socialist activities and Joliot joined the French Communist Party.

In the years after the war, Joliot convinced the French government to establish an Atomic Energy Commission to ensure that France received some benefit from the earlier discoveries made in their laboratories. Acting as High Commissioner, Joliot, with Madame Joliot-Curie developing necessary improvements in methods and materials, directed the construction of the first French nuclear reactor in 1948. This was the first reactor in the world not under the control of the English-American wartime collaborators. This success was followed, however, by Joliot's removal as director in 1950, followed a year later by Joliot-Curie's removal as a member of the commission. These actions were taken by the French government in response to the anti-Communist movement that characterizes this period of both scientific and political history. With their access to the classified information needed for research in nuclear physics restricted as a result of their political activities, the husband-wife team concentrated on research in their own isotope laboratories and their teaching—she at the Sorbonne, he at the College of France. They became increasingly involved in Communist-inspired peace movements. In 1953, the American Chemical Society, in an unprecedented move, denied Madame Joliot-Curie's application for membership, citing her avowed Communist sympathies. Although Joliot-Curie never held membership in the French Communist Party, she was a member of the Committee of the France-Soviet Union Association, had presided in 1948 at a scientific conference held in Warsaw, and was a member of the Union of French Women, a group thought to be financed by the Communist Party. Joliot attracted additional attention during the years of the Korean conflict, when he supported claims made by the Chinese that the United States was employing tactics of germ warfare.

These activities did not prevent Madame Joliot-Curie, in 1955, from drawing up the plans for the large laboratory to be constructed at the University of Orsay, outside Paris, for advanced research in nuclear physics with state-of-the-art equipment and facilities. The supervision of the construction of these laboratories and their inauguration was finished by Joliot after his wife's death.

In the postwar years, their political activities and the notoriety they gained from them overshadowed their scientific accomplishments. Perhaps the most startling feature of the Joliot-Curies' career is not in their accomplishments, but rather in the monumental discoveries they narrowly missed. Their experiments produced the neutron, but they failed to recognize it. They were beaten by a matter of months in the discovery of the positron. They also narrowly missed the discovery of fission. Yet the similarity of Irène's career to her mother's is unmistakable. Her life was focused on her scientific researches; she, too, collaborated in that work with her husband. Their work was also recognized with a Nobel Prize. Their tremendous success, particularly in giving science the means to produce needed and useful radioisotopes, rested on their care in experimentation. Frédéric Joliot expressed their view, when he said that every experiment should be designed and conducted not only with attention to detail but also "to open as many windows as possible on the unforeseen."

Bibliography

Primary
Joint publications
CHEMISTRY: "Sur le nombre d'ions produits par les rayons alpha du RaC' dans l'air," *Comptes rendus hebdomadaires des séances de l'Académie des sciences*, vol. 186, 1928; "Sur la nature du rayonnement absorbable qui accompagne les rayons alpha du polonium," *Comptes rendus hebdomadaires des séances de l'Académie des sciences*, vol. 189, 1929; "Préparation des sources de polonium de grande densité d'activité," *Journal de chimie physique*, vol. 28, 1931; "Émission de protons de grande vitesse par les substances hydrogénées sous l'influence des rayons gamma très pénétrants," *Comptes rendus hebdomadaires des séances de l'Académie des sciences*, vol. 194, 1932; "New Evidence for the Neutron," *Nature*, vol. 130, 1932; "Contributions à l'étude des électrons positifs," *Comptes rendus*

hebdomadaires des séances de l'Académie des sciences, vol. 196, 1933; "Production artificielle d'éléments radioactifs" and "Preuve chimique de la transmutation des éléments," *Journal de physique*, vol. 5, 1934.

Frédéric Joliot

CHEMISTRY: "Sur l'excitation des rayons gamma nucléaires du bore par les particules alpha. Énergie quantique du rayonnement gamma du polonium," *Comptes rendus hebdomadaires des séances de l'Académie des sciences*, vol. 193, 1931; "Preuve expérimentale de la rupture explosive des noyaux d'uranium et de thorium sous l'action des neutrons," *Comptes rendus hebdomadaires des séances de l'Académie des sciences*, vol. 208, 1939; "Liberation of Neutrons in the Nuclear Explosion of Uranium," *Nature*, vol. 143, 1939 (with H. von Halban and L. Kowarski); "Mise en évidence d'une réaction nucléaire en chaîne au sein d'une masse uranifère," *Journal de physique*, vol. 10, 1939 (with L. Kowarski and F. Perrin); "Sur la possibilité de produire dans un milieu uranifère des réactions nucléaires en chaîne illimitée. 30 octobre 1939," *Comptes rendus hebdomadaires des séances de l'Académie des sciences*, vol. 299, 1949 (with H. von Halban and L. Kowarski).

Irène Joliot-Curie

CHEMISTRY: *"Sur la vitesse d'émission des rayons alpha du polonium,"* Comptes rendus hebdomadaires des séances de l'Académie des sciences, vol. 175, 1922; "Sur les particules de long parcours émises par le polonium," *Journal de physique et le radium*, vol. 6, 1925 (with N. Yamada); "Extraction et purification du dépôt actif à l'évolution lente du radium," *Journal de physique et le radium*, vol. 22, 1925; "Sur la quantité de polonium accumulée dans d'anciennes ampoules de radion et sur la période du radium D," *Journal de physique et le radium*, vol. 10, 1929; "Sur la création artificielle d'éléments appartenant à une famille radioactive inconnue, lors de l'irradiation du thorium par les neutrons," *Journal de physique et le radium*, vol. 6, 1935 (with H. von Halban and P. Preiswerk); *Les Radioelements Naturels: Propriétés chimiques, préparation, dosage*, 1946; "Autoradiographie par neutrons. Dosage séparé de l'uranium et du thorium," *Comptes rendus hebdomadaires des séances de l'Académie des sciences*, vol. 232, 1951.

MISCELLANEOUS: *Œuvres scientifiques complètes*, 1961.

Secondary

Biquard, Pierre, *Frédéric Joliot-Curie: The Man and His Theories*. New York: Paul S. Erikson, 1966. A somewhat flowery account of the life, both scientific and personal, of Joliot. The author was involved in the peace movement with Joliot and has produced an extremely sympathetic biography that includes excerpts from speeches and letters.

Bundy, McGeorge, *Danger and Survival: Choices About the Bomb in the First Fifty*

Years. New York: Random House, 1988. This is a scientific and political history of the period beginning with the work leading to the development of the atomic bomb. In considering "How American Went First" (chapter 1), Bundy considers in more detail than other works the political activity of Joliot regarding the French efforts to achieve a nuclear device.

Cotton, Eugenie. *Les Curies.* Paris: Seghers, 1963. The accomplishments of Irène and Frédéric Joliot-Curie are included in this work, which deals with the achievements of the entire Curie family. Madame Cotton was an associate of Joliot in the peace movements of the 1950's.

Goldsmith, Maurice. *Frédéric Joliot-Curie: A Biography.* London: Laurence and Wishart, 1976. Recognized as the most comprehensive biography of Joliot, this work includes a detailed assessment of his scientific accomplishments as well as an analysis of his political activities.

McKown, Robin. *She Lived for Science: Irène Joliot-Curie.* New York: Messner, 1961. This work presents a complete summary of Madame Joliot-Curie's life. It includes the details of her scientific career as well as insights into her personal and political activities.

Pais, Abraham. *Inward Bound.* New York: Oxford University Press, 1986. The work of the Joliot-Curies is put into its historical and scientific context in this history of the physics of matter. Beginning with the earliest studies on the structure of the atom and ending with concepts of modern particle physics, this work clearly explains the importance of the production of artificial radioactivity accomplished by the Joliot-Curies. The chapter notes contain references to the original scientific literature.

Reid, Robert. *Marie Curie.* New York: New American Library, 1974. In writing this modern biography, Reid made use of the Curies' letters contained in the French National Library. Although the work focuses on Marie Curie, it contains excellent portraits of Irène and Frédéric Joliot-Curie, especially the details on Joliot's introduction to the Radium Institute, their early married life, and a readable account of their research activities.

Trudy A. Dickneider

1936

Chemistry
Peter Debye, The Netherlands and United States

Physics
Victor Franz Hess, Austria
Carl David Anderson, United States

Physiology or Medicine
Sir H. H. Dale, Great Britain
Otto Loewi, Germany

Literature
Eugene O'Neill, United States

Peace
Carlos Saavedra Lamas, Argentina

PETER DEBYE
1936

Born: Maastricht, The Netherlands; March 24, 1884
Died: Ithaca, New York; November 2, 1966
Nationality: Dutch; after 1946, American
Areas of concentration: Molecular structure and X-ray diffraction

Debye was a pioneer in the study of molecular structure, especially as it applies to gases and to dissolved particles in solutions. Utilizing molecular dipole moments, X-ray and electron diffraction, and other techniques, he was able to ascertain the arrangement and bonding of atoms in molecules

The Award

Presentation

Peter Debye was presented at the 1936 Nobel ceremonies by Professor Arne Westgren, Secretary of the Nobel Committee for Chemistry of the Royal Swedish Academy of Sciences. The award was being given to Dr. Debye, Westgren stated, for his extensive and pioneering work on the determination of molecular structures. Utilizing the latest experimental innovations of the period, he was able to apply these techniques to gaseous molecules and later to selected dilute solutions of molecules.

Debye not only expanded upon experimental procedures, notably X-ray diffraction and electron diffraction, but also developed his own experimental approaches in the area of "dipole moment" measurement, a measurement relating to the distance between the positive and negative centers within a molecule. The experimental procedures used by Dr. Debye and the results they produced were supported by detailed theoretical considerations based upon the latest current theories proposed to explain atomic and molecular structure. In turn, Debye's conclusions regarding molecular properties derived from experimental data served to support the theoretical concepts used to reach the same conclusions.

The value of Dr. Debye's work, Westgren continued, was in its elucidation of chemical structures. The arrangement of atoms within a molecule determines, to a large extent, the behavior of that molecule—its physical and chemical properties. Debye was able to discern bond lengths, the distances between atoms joined together in a molecule, bond strengths and rotations, the force (tensity) with which one atom is joined to another and its ability to move relative to its joined neighbor without bond breaking, and molecular geometry, the spatial arrangement of the atoms within a molecule. Chemists eagerly sought the results of his structural measurements on a variety of chemical species. This information was used to aid in explaining observed chemical reactions and to predict the outcome of proposed, but untried reactions.

Nobel lecture

Dr. Debye delivered his Nobel address, entitled "Methods to Determine the Electrical and Geometrical Structure of Molecules," on December 12, 1936. He traced the experimental and theoretical procedures used by him and his research associates over the years to arrive at the structures of chemical compounds. He concentrated his efforts mainly on gaseous molecules and on dilute solutions of polar molecules in nonpolar solvents. Three broad areas of experimentation were used in his studies. These were dipole moment measurements, X-ray measurements, and experiments using electron beams rather than X rays. Dr. Debye's studies also enhanced the understanding and usefulness of each of these techniques. His talk described his work in these areas from 1912, when he first reported on dipole measurements, through the period of the presentation.

Molecules with symmetrical structures about an imaginary point at their centers have an equal distribution of electrical charges about that point; they are termed nonpolar. Unsymmetrical molecules, in contrast, have an unbalance of charge about their center points and are termed polar. When placed inside an external electrical field, molecules affect the electrical field strength between the charged sources. The extent of this effect is called the dielectric constant of the interposed substance. Polar molecules possess a permanent dipole moment even in the absence of an external field. Nonpolar molecules do not, but they can exhibit an induced dipole because of their interaction with the external field. Dr. Debye described his studies on the variation of temperature and the application of a varying external electric field and on the effects these had on dipole moments. From these effects, and from theoretical considerations used to explain how individual atoms are perturbed by external probes, he was able to postulate how the atoms within molecules were attached to one another. If the proposed structures based upon the dipole measurements lead to the same structures as those from the theoretical considerations, then the proposed structures of the molecules must be the correct assignments. Debye was able to correlate successfully experimental and theoretical findings.

X-ray diffraction, soon after its development by Max von Laue and William H. and William L. Bragg (father and son), was adopted by Debye as an alternate tool to determine molecular structures. X rays, a form of electromagnetic radiation, have wavelengths roughly equivalent to the spacing of atoms within molecules and crystals. When X rays strike a molecule or crystal, they bounce off the atoms within the structure. Some of the deflected (the scientific term is "scattered") rays combine to produce bright spots on a photographic plate. Other rays interfere with one another, canceling themselves. This results in dark spots—absence of radiation—on the photographic plate. From the locations of the bright and dark spots, the diffraction pattern, one can calculate the atomic spacings, thus gaining information on bond distances of atoms within a molecule or crystal. Debye used these patterns and the changes in these patterns caused by varying sample temperatures to calculate structures of gaseous molecules and of molecules in nonpolar solvents.

Because of the dual nature of electromagnetic radiation and subatomic particles, electron beams can be substituted for X rays in the study of molecular and crystalline structure. Dr. Debye used these, too, in his reporting of molecular structures. Numerous chemical compounds were characterized by Debye and his research group using the techniques described, and they were illustrated in his Nobel presentation.

Critical reception

Dr. Debye's work was well known to his fellow scientists, and his structural characterizations had been well received by the chemists who used them in predicting and describing their chemical reactions. Yet to the general public, even in Europe, he remained largely unknown, preferring his scientific studies to achieving a popular image. *The New York Times* of November 13, 1936, carried as one of its front-page stories the announcement of the Nobel Prize winners in literature, physics, and chemistry for that year, but the article dealt almost exclusively with Eugene O'Neill, the American author, for his achievements in literature. Brief mention was made of Dr. Carl D. Anderson, the California physicist, who, as discoverer of the subatomic particle, the positron, shared the physics prize for 1936. Dr. Debye's recognition was relegated to one sentence midway through the article. In a follow-up article, *The New York Times* of November 15, 1936, did devote five paragraphs to Debye and his work. The article's lead sentence stated that "Peter Joseph Wilhelm Debye, winner of The Nobel Prize in Chemistry, is a research scientist who has succeeded completely in escaping the notice of the general public of the city where he lived for years." Although at the time of being awarded the Nobel Prize Debye was director of the Kaiser Wilhelm Institute and professor at the University of Berlin, he was a native of The Netherlands in a German university. The article went on to say that, aside from a weekly Friday lecture to advanced chemistry students, he was seldom seen away from his research activities. The article stated that Dr. Debye expressed a desire to use the money received, approximately equivalent to $40,000, to construct and equip new laboratory facilities necessary to further his research interests. It also alluded to the possible unrest building in Germany in the mid-1930's and to the unique status of Debye, a citizen of The Netherlands, holding so prominent a position in Berlin.

Time magazine of November 23, 1936, took a different approach to reporting the awarding of the Nobel Prizes in Physics and Chemistry. Devoting a single paragraph to each of the three recipients, it focused upon Debye's contributions in X-ray structure determinations. Specifically, it selected a brief comment made by Debye prior to his Nobel award relating to the ordering of molecular geometry in crystals: "Chemist Debye pointed out to The American Chemical Society that water has a quasi-crystalline structure, therefore resembles a diamond more closely in arrangement than it resembles its own gaseous form, steam." One may note from this misleading statement that the structure of liquids, midway between the discrete molecules of gases and the ordered array of crystalline solids, was then (and still is) a poorly understood area of structural characterization.

Biography

Born on March 24, 1884, Peter Joseph William Debye received his early schooling in Maastricht, The Netherlands, where he received his degree in electrical engineering in 1905. While at Aachem, he became assistant to the physicist Arnold Sommerfeld. When Sommerfeld accepted a position in Munich, Germany, Debye accompanied him. Continuing both his work and his studies, he received his doctoral degree from the Ludwig-Maximilian University in Munich in 1908. Following a year as *Privatdozent* (lecturer) at Munich, he accepted the professorship at the University of Zurich, Switzerland, recently vacated by Albert Einstein. Debye changed positions frequently for the next few years, returning to his homeland as professor of physics at the University of Utrecht, The Netherlands, in 1912. With the anticipation of more extensive laboratory facilities, he moved to the University of Göttingen, Germany (1914), where he resided until 1920. These early years in Debye's career were scientifically productive, providing insight into studies that would be pursued in future years. They were fruitful, too, in his marriage to Mathilde Alberer on April 10, 1913, in Munich, Germany. The Debyes had two children, Peter Paul, born in 1916, and Mathilda Maria, born in 1921. Dr. Debye returned to Zurich, Switzerland, in 1920 as professor at the Eidgenössische Technische Hochschule. There he stayed until 1927, when an opening occurred at the University of Leipzig, Germany. From there he traveled to the University of Berlin (1934) as professor and supervisor of the Kaiser Wilhelm Institute. Political pressures in Germany in the late 1930's, coupled with his refusal to accept German citizenship, forced Debye to seek alternate employment. He left Germany in 1939 and, after passing through Italy, arrived in the United States on February 1, 1940. He had been invited to give a series of lectures at Cornell University; upon completing the lectures he accepted a position as professor of chemistry at Cornell. He served as chairman of the chemistry department until his retirement in 1952. After retirement, he actively continued his research, traveled, and lectured extensively.

Dr. Debye was an astute scientist and leader. An excellent lecturer, he was able to present difficult topics to his students in a clear and understandable manner. Physically robust, he led an active life; he enjoyed fishing and a good cigar. His contributions to science were many, and Debye received numerous scientific awards and honorary degrees from around the world. He was a member of various national and international scientific organizations, and he served as editor of the scientific journal *Physikalische Zeitschrift* (physical journal) from 1915 to 1940. He was active nearly until his death at eighty-two on November 2, 1966.

Scientific Career

Master of the Molecule was the nickname by which Dr. Debye was known in his later years. Although his research interests ranged far beyond those studies for which he received the Nobel Prize, there was a common theme in all of his investigations: the search for molecular identity and interactions within molecules both simple and complex. One method of determining molecular structure was through measurement of "dipole moment" for a molecule.

Molecules are composed of individual atoms joined (bonded) together. Every atom has both a positive center and a negative electron cloud. When bonded together as a molecule, if it is symmetrical, the composite positive point representative of all atomic nuclei in the molecule coincides with the composite negative point representative of all the electrons within the molecule. The molecule is nonpolar. Nonsymmetrical molecules, in contrast, possess a separation of positive and negative centers because of the uneven pull upon the molecular cloud by the unbalanced position of the atomic nuclei. These molecules are polar, and they possess a permanent dipole moment. Dipole moment is an experimental quantity measurable in the laboratory. It increases in magnitude with an increased distance of separation of the positive and negative centers of charge.

It was Debye who first recognized the existence of permanent dipole moments in unsymmetrical molecules. If molecules are placed within an electrical field, between positively and negatively charged plates separated in space, the molecules tend to align themselves in the direction of the applied field (recall that unlike electrical charges attract and like electrical charges repel). The extent to which the electric field between the plates is affected is measured by the dielectric constant of the medium between the plates. It is different for media of different polarity—that is, possessing different dipole moments. Dipole moments can thus be measured experimentally, their value being expressed in electrostatic units (esu) of measure. In terms of esu values, the magnitude of molecular dipole moments is very small, on the order of ten to the negative eighteenth power (10^{-18} esu). To comprehend more easily the significance of dipole moment variation, a new unit of measure was coined, the debye, to represent the magnitude of a molecular dipole moment. One debye is equivalent to one times ten to the negative eighteenth esu unit. Dipole values for molecules in debye units are thus expressed as simple numbers, often varying between one and ten.

Dr. Debye applied several experimental techniques to the study of dipole moments and dielectric constants. Primarily these studies focused upon gaseous molecules, pure polar liquids, and dilute solutions of polar solutes dissolved in nonpolar solvents. As a result of this work, he was able to deduce structural characteristics of these substances—that is, to deduce which atoms within the molecule are bonded to which other atoms and to determine their structural arrangement in space. It became possible to deduce whether molecules are linear, planar, or three-dimensional, whether they perhaps form the corners of a tetrahedron or exist in some other spatial arrangement. The force that holds the atoms together within the molecule could be investigated. This force is known as the bond strength; the greater the bond strength, the more difficult it is to break a molecule apart. Conversely, molecules with weak bonds are highly reactive. All these bits of information about a molecule proved invaluable to chemists who, in order to understand the physical and chemical properties of substances, required a knowledge of their structural characteristics and bond strengths.

One of the techniques used by Debye in his study of molecular structure through dipole moment measurements was to vary the strength of the applied electric field in which a particular chemical species was placed. This caused a variation in the degree of molecular orientation: The stronger the external field, the greater the alignment of molecules. When the field was then suddenly decreased in strength, the time needed for the molecules to move back to their less ordered condition (the relaxation time) could be used to calculate various molecular structural information. An alternate approach to the study of relaxation time was to subject the sample to electromagnetic radiation of a specific frequency. In certain instances the refractive index of the substance was altered (the refractive index measures the ability of a material to change the direction of an electromagnetic ray passing through it). As with changing electric fields, the resulting relaxation time could be used to calculate molecular structural information.

Debye used techniques other than dipole studies to discern molecular geometry. X rays, a form of electromagnetic radiation of very short wavelength, were known to interact with solid crystals, producing diffraction patterns consisting of dark and bright spots on a photographic film or plate. Each crystalline substance produced its own unique diffraction pattern, and from the spacings between spots one could calculate the spacing of nuclei within a crystal. Debye applied X-ray diffraction to gaseous molecules and used the resulting patterns in his calculations of atomic spacings in these molecules. Prior to his work, diffraction patterns had been observed only with single crystals of a solid material. Debye, with the aid of a colleague, Paul Scherrer, demonstrated that the procedure worked equally well for powdered solid samples in which a multitude of minute crystals, rather than one single large crystal, served as the sample. Although they were also independently discovered by others, powder diffraction measurements are still referred to as the Debye-Scherrer method of X-ray diffraction. Variations of X-ray diffraction patterns with temperature allowed even more detailed calculations of molecular structure parameters.

To be able to use these experimental measurements upon dipole values and X-ray data to arrive at molecular geometry, bond lengths, and bond strengths required a thorough knowledge of the theoretical concepts developed for understanding atomic and molecular structure. During the time that Dr. Debye and his research associates were most active with their molecular structural studies, the accepted theoretical concepts for the understanding of matter were undergoing marked changes. The classical, mechanical, ideals of atomic and molecular structure were being replaced by the more abstract, more mathematical quantum molecular theory. Debye was able, using these new mathematical approaches, to mesh brilliantly his experimental observations with theory, thus solidifying the correctness of his results in the light of modern accepted theoretical predictions. It was this work for which he received the Nobel Prize in 1936.

During the time that Debye was developing the concepts and measurements relative to his structural studies, other studies also occupied his attention. These were significant studies, studies for which he would have assured himself an ever-lasting place in science irrespective of his dipole and X-ray work. One such study involved the theory necessary to calculate variations in molar heat capacity of a substance at very low temperatures. Heat capacity is the quantity of heat energy (measured in calories or joules) taken in by one mole of a substance to raise its temperature by one degree Celsius. Previous interpretations of how the individual particles within a substance responded to this influx of energy were sufficient to account for observed data at ambient temperatures, but they failed to explain experimental values if measurements were made at low temperatures, such as the temperature of liquid hydrogen. The problem had been studied by Albert Einstein, who proposed a more complex interaction effect between the heat energy taken into a substance and the resulting oscillations of its particles. It was Debye, however, in 1912, who correctly extended Einstein's work to explain and calculate heat capacity values theoretically in a way that matched experimental results over a broad temperature range.

Equally well known as his studies on the structures of gases were the contributions that Dr. Debye made to the study of charged atoms (ions) in solution. He and his student Erich Hückel formulated a theory in 1923 to explain the actions of dissolved ionic solids in solution that is still widely used, the Debye-Hückel theory of electrolytes. Weak acids and bases (weak electrolytes) dissociate in solution, producing, for acids, hydrogen ions and, for bases, hydroxide ions. The theory explaining these phenomena was well understood, and it properly explained experimental findings. What was not understood was the behavior of strong electrolytes that, when dissolved in solution, ionized completely, forming (in the case of a one-one electrolyte) two charged particles for every formula unit of substance present. There are various solution properties that depend not upon the particular substance dissolved but only upon the number of dissolved particles in solution irrespective of whether the particles are charged (electrolytes) or uncharged (nonelectrolytes). The Debye-Hückel theory correctly interpreted events occurring within dilute solutions of strong electrolytes. Using their calculations and correction terms, known as activity coefficients, Debye and Hückel properly accounted for the behavior of dilute strong electrolyte solutions.

During the course of Debye's investigations, other interesting avenues of exploration presented themselves. In general, these were related to his main research interest, molecular structure determinations, and were pursued to varying degrees as time and interest allowed. Notable among these investigations was the suggestion, in 1926, that if certain magnetic substances were placed in a strong external magnetic field (thus aligning the unpaired electrons within the substance) and then kept in a condition in which no further heat energy could enter the substance from outside its container, then, when the field was removed, the energy required to randomize the electrons' orientations would come from the substance's own internal energy. The consequence of this is that the temperature of the substance decreases. Debye thought this procedure might be used to approach temperatures near absolute zero, the theoretical limit of lowest temperature. This idea was also proposed by William Giauque, an American chemist who pursued it further and eventually won the Nobel Prize in Chemistry in 1949 for his low-temperature studies.

Arriving in the United States at the outbreak of World War II, Debye concentrated his efforts on research related to the war effort: the study of synthetic rubber and other polymers. So engrossed did he become that he directed the remainder of his research activities to polymer research. It was, in fact, a logical extension of his earlier work on the molecular structure of gases and smaller molecules. The techniques that Debye had applied to gaseous molecules using X rays he now adapted to study polymer molecules using visible light rays. Light scattering measurements, as the technique is known, allow one to calculate both the molecular weight and molecular size of large molecules. Although the principles of these measurements were well known, having been developed by others, they were perfected by Debye with great success in the study of various polymeric materials—plastics, elastomers, proteins, and the like. Other techniques were also employed by Debye in his study of polymers; they included viscosity measurements, sedimentation rate studies, and osmotic pressure measurements. In later years he applied his interest in polymers to colloidal suspensions and micelle studies. Dr. Debye actively continued his research and lecturing activities until near the time of his death in November, 1966.

Bibliography

Primary

CHEMISTRY: "Zur Theorie der spezifischen Wärmen," *Annalen der Physik*, vol. 39, 1912; "Einige Resultate einer kinetischen Theorie der Isolatoren," *Physikalische Zeitschrift*, vol. 13, 1912; "Interferenz von Röntgenstrahlen und Wärmebewegung," *Annalen der Physik*, vol. 43, 1914; "Zur Theorie der Elektrolyte," *Physikalische Zeitschrift*, vol. 24, 1923 (with Erich Hückel); "Note on the Scattering of X-Rays," *Journal of Mathematics and Physics*, vol. 4, 1925; "Einige Bemerkungen zur Magnetisierung bei tiefer Temperatur," *Annalen der Physik*, vol. 81, 1926; *Quantentheorie und Chemie*, 1928; *Polare Molekeln*, 1929; *The Dipole Moment and Chemical Structure*, 1931; *The Interference of Electrons*, 1931; *The Structure of Molecules*, 1932; *Magnetismus*, 1933; *The Structure of Matter*, 1934; *Kernphysik*, 1935; "Light Scattering in Solutions," *Journal of Applied Physics*, vol. 15, 1944; "The Structure of Polymers in Solution," *Record of Chemical Progress*, vol. 8, 1947; "Light Scattering in Soap Solutions," *Annals of the New York Academy of Science*, vol. 51, 1949; "Structure Determination by Radiation Scattering," *Chemical and Engineering News*, vol. 41, 1963; "Light Scattering as a Tool," *Pure and Applied Chemistry*, vol. 12, 1966.

Secondary

Brown, J. G. *X-Rays and Their Applications*. New York: Plenum, 1966. This small paperback book introduces its reader to the study of X rays. A significant portion of the book deals with X-ray powder diffraction, a technique developed by Debye and others.

Chu, B. *Laser Light Scattering*. New York: Academic Press, 1974. Written by a former student of Debye, this work outlines in modern terms the technique of light scattering. It was using this approach that Debye studied the polymer solutions that were the focus of his research during his tenure at Cornell.

Davies, M. "Peter J. W. Debye (1884-1966)." *Journal of Chemical Education* 45 (1968): 467-473. Written by a chemist shortly after Debye's death, this is a general, but scientifically sound, account of his work. The reader is assumed to possess some chemical knowledge.

Debye, Peter J. W. *The Collected Papers of Peter J. W. Debye*. New York: Interscience, 1954. With the help of Dr. Debye himself, fifty-one of his papers written up to 1954 were presented in a single volume. All had been translated into English, thus allowing the English-speaking reader easy access to Debye's early writings.

"Debye Named Gibbs Medal Winner." *Chemical and Engineering News* 27 (April 25, 1949). Written on the occasion of Debye's receipt of the Willard Gibbs Medal awarded by the American Chemical Society for outstanding contributions in the area of physical chemistry, this one-page announcement cites numerous personal details of Debye's life.

Kittle, C. *Introduction to Solid State Physics*. New York: John Wiley & Sons, 1956. This advanced textbook presents in detail the mathematical formula developed by Debye in support of his treatment on dipole moments and specific heat.

Mahan, B. M., and R. J. Myers. *University Chemistry*. Menlo Park, Calif.: Benjamin/Cummings, 1987. This general chemistry textbook presents a brief introduction to the study of dipole moments, one of the areas developed by Debye and his coworkers.

Meites, L. *An Introduction to Chemical Equilibrium and Kinetics*. Oxford: Pergamon Press, 1981. This modern textbook details the development and implementation of Debye's work on solution equilibria.

Moritz, Charles, ed. *Current Biography Yearbook: 1963*. New York: H. W. Wilson, 1963. The biography on Debye, written while he still lived in Ithaca, New York, chronicles in detail his life to 1963. Emphasis is on factual information, the extent of his scientific contribution being mentioned only briefly.

Pratton, C. F., and S. H. Maron. *Fundamental Principles of Physical Chemistry*. New York: Macmillan, 1951. This textbook introduces the topics of specific heat, dipole moments, and solution equilibria, areas in which Debye excelled.

Smyth, Charles P. "Peter Joseph William Debye." In *Dictionary of Scientific Biography*, edited by Charles Coulston Gillispie. New York: Charles Scribner's Sons, 1971. This relatively long account of Dr. Debye's life intersperses the scientific investigations undertaken by him with the chronological sequence of his life, showing where and when his significant studies were made.

Williams, J. W. "Peter Debye." In *Biographical Memoirs*, vol. 46. Washington,

D.C.: National Academy of Sciences, 1975. This long memoir traces the scientific achievements of Debye from his early days in Germany through his studies at Cornell. Written by a knowledgeable scientist, it assumes some scientific competence upon the part of the reader. An extensive bibliography lists his major publications year by year.

Gordon A. Parker

1937

Chemistry
Sir Walter Norman Haworth, Great Britain
Paul Karrer, Switzerland

Physics
Clinton Joseph Davisson, United States
Sir George Paget Thomson, Great Britain

Physiology or Medicine
Albert Szent-Györgyi, Hungary

Literature
Roger Martin du Gard, France

Peace
Viscount Cecil of Chelwood, Great Britain

SIR WALTER NORMAN HAWORTH
1937

Born: Chorley, Lancashire, England; March 19, 1883
Died: Birmingham, England; March 19, 1950
Nationality: British
Areas of concentration: Carbohydrate chemistry and vitamin synthesis

Haworth proved the chemical structure of vitamin C, opening the way to its artificial production—the first artificial production of a vitamin

The Award

Presentation

Professor Wilhelm Palmær, Chairman of the Nobel Committee for Chemistry of the Royal Swedish Academy of Sciences, presented the 1937 Nobel Prize in Chemistry to Walter Norman Haworth and Paul Karrer. In his address, Palmær cited the earlier investigations concerning sugars that were conducted by Emil Fischer, recipient of the second Nobel Prize in Chemistry (awarded in 1902). He emphasized that Haworth's research regarding the different forms and the different arrangements of the atoms in the molecules of various sugars deserved special recognition. Palmær further explained, however, that it was also Haworth's research in vitamin C that had been the basis for awarding him the 1937 prize.

Palmær reviewed the brief history of vitamin research. He pointed out that, in 1929, one-half of the Nobel Prize in Physiology or Medicine had been awarded in recognition of the discovery of the cause of beriberi, a deficiency of the antineuritic vitamin (vitamin B_1), and the other half for the discovery of the vitamin of growth, vitamin A. Palmær reminded his audience that the 1937 prize in medicine was being awarded for discoveries in vitamin C. The prize awarded to Haworth was motivated, he said, by his having proved the vitamin's chemical structure, thereby making possible its artificial production for use in the treatment and prevention of disease, notably scurvy.

Nobel lecture

On December 11, 1937, Haworth delivered his Nobel lecture, entitled "The Structure of Carbohydrates and of Vitamin C." He began with a brief review of the problem and its history, pointing out that, while for a time it had been recognized that complex carbohydrates were built of simple ones, it had not been understood how nature combined molecules in order to produce materials such as cellulose (the building material of plants), glycogen, and starch from simple sugars, particularly glucose. He went on to explain how he had extended the work of Emil Fischer, who proposed that linear formulas should be used to express the open chain structure of sugars. Haworth explained how he had succeeded, however, in showing that the carbon atoms in sugars are instead linked by oxygen into rings, not chains—that either there are five carbon atoms and one oxygen atom, giving a pyranose ring, or there are four carbon atoms and one oxygen atom, giving a furanose ring. When the appropriate oxygen and hydrogen atoms are added to these rings, the result is sugar. After reviewing at some length the results of his inquiries into the manner in which sugars unite, giving numerous examples of the differences in linking, which provide different identities for sugar, he then described his end-group method. The supposition that in nature polysaccharides are built up according to common patterns had led him to develop this method as a means for studying the finer details of the molecular structure of complex carbohydrates.

Haworth mentioned and paid tribute to the work of Albert Szent-Györgyi, among others, who contributed to the research that led to the synthesis of vitamin C. He described the methods used to establish the main features of ascorbic acid's constitution. He closed his lecture with descriptions of the synthesis of ascorbic acid.

Critical reception

The "discovery" of vitamin C received worldwide attention. Not only was it the first vitamin to be synthesized, but its production would have great practical importance in medicine for the prevention and cure of disease. Large-scale artificial production made the vitamin's price much lower than that of the natural product; thus availability to the public was enhanced.

When it became known that the vitamin had been discovered, there was controversy as to which of the several scientists whose research provided a contribution and to which of their countries credit should be given. A Swiss group had reported the synthesis of ascorbic acid in the same year as had the Birmingham group, headed by Haworth. Haworth's documentation acknowledged the fact that other scientists had also contributed. (While Haworth received the Nobel Prize for the achievement, as did Albert Szent-Györgyi in the same year, the leader of the Swiss group obtained a series of monetarily lucrative patents for the commercial production of the vitamin.) Haworth's work constituted a valuable addition to the knowledge of organic chemistry and made possible the inexpensive production of vitamin C for medical purposes, and it also serves as an important example of the great advances made in twenty-five years as compared with the previous two hundred. *The New York Times* of November 12, 1937, reporting the announcement of the prize recipients, stated in part, "The complete renaissance that carbohydrate chemistry has undergone in the last decade is credited to a great extent to Professor Haworth's work."

It was Albert Szent-Györgyi, when many years later he recalled his own reactions to his and others' vitamin research, who expressed the view that because a vitamin was something to be ingested, its study belonged more suitably in the realm of the cook than of the scientist. Such an observation probably did not express the opinion of the majority of contemporary scientists.

Biography

Walter Norman Haworth was born on March 19, 1883, in the northwest of England at White Coppice near the town of Chorley, Lancashire. He was the fourth child of

Thomas and Hannah Haworth. Haworth's family, well known and highly respected over the course of its several generations in the area, had produced lawyers, clergymen, and businessmen. His father was manager of a local factory where Walter Norman, leaving the local public schools at age fourteen, became employed in the trade of linoleum design and manufacture. Haworth's introduction to the practical application of chemistry in industry came as he acquired knowledge in the use of dyes in the incorporation of color and pattern in the linoleum product. Meanwhile, he learned good business practices. This early employment experience was to influence Haworth's choice of chemistry as a course of study as well as to provide him with skills useful in the administrative positions in which he later found himself.

Haworth's desire for education was very strong. After a period of private tutoring, he was able to pass the entrance examination of the University of Manchester. He began his education there in 1903, his intention being to obtain a position in the chemical industry. The quality of his work as a student of William H. Perkin, Jr., head of the university's chemistry department, resulted in Haworth's being awarded a scholarship which he used, after being graduated with first-class honors in 1906, for further study at the University of Göttingen in the laboratory of Otto Wallach. After obtaining his Ph.D. in only one year, Haworth returned to the University of Manchester, where he completed a second Ph.D. in 1911 and was subsequently appointed senior demonstrator in chemistry at the Imperial College of Science and Technology in London. While in London, he spent much of his spare time in the city's numerous museums, where he rounded his education and developed an interest in the arts and in period and antique carpets and furnishings.

From 1912 until after the end of World War I, Haworth served as lecturer and reader in chemistry at the United College of the University of St. Andrews in Scotland. In 1920, he accepted a position as professor of organic chemistry at Armstrong College (subsequently King's College) at the University of Durham, Newcastle upon Tyne. He became head of the department the following year, and in 1922 he married Violet Chilton Dobbie.

In 1925, Haworth became Mason Professor of Chemistry at the University of Birmingham, where he remained until his retirement some twenty-three years later. He was active during World War II in chemical research required in the atomic energy project. In 1947, he was knighted. His retirement years were busy with membership on various professional boards and committees and wherever his advice was requested. During his career and in retirement, he traveled to Europe, the United States, and Canada, as well as to New Zealand and Australia, attending conferences and lecturing. At the time of his sudden death in 1950, he was at his home at Barnt Green, Birmingham. His wife and two sons survived him.

Scientific Career

From 1908 to 1914, principally while at Manchester, Göttingen, and the Imperial College at London, Haworth concentrated in his work on the chemical substances found in members of the terpene group, specifically fir needle oil and pine root oil.

His teachers had been W. H. Perkin at Manchester and Otto Wallach at Göttingen. Both had been prominent in research on essential oils, therefore it was to be expected that this was the area first explored by Haworth. His first publication, with Perkin, was entitled "Experiments on the Synthesis of the Terpenes." This was followed by numerous papers in which Haworth documented his own independent researches in the subject.

Once he had accepted appointment, in 1912, at St. Andrews, Haworth continued work on the terpenes, but he soon became influenced by work being done there by Thomas Purdie and James C. Irvine in the field of carbohydrate chemistry. (The group of substances named carbohydrates is very important among the chemical compounds. The name carbohydrate came about because in their composition these substances may be said to be built up by a combination of carbon and water. The word hydrates is used to describe chemical compounds that contain water.)

The two fields of research, terpenes and carbohydrates, were not unrelated, wood being the common starting material from which both essential oils and a complex sugar can be extracted. The various types of sugar are known as saccharides. Among the least complicated forms of carbohydrates is the sugar present in the juice of grapes. Simple sugars such as grape sugar are monosaccharides. By a combination of particles or molecules from a simple sugar and a separation of part of the water, more complex sugars are derived: first disaccharides such as cane sugar, milk sugar, and maltose, then polysaccharides, which include the various starches in the human diet as well as cellulose, the building material of the plants. The more complex the saccharide, the less like sugar in taste and the less soluble in water it becomes. The number of atoms in a molecule of a monosaccharide is very small, while the number in a polysaccharide is very large.

Little had been known in the area of the structure of the more complex sugars until the work of Purdie and Irvine began to bring some order into the unexplored field of sugar chemistry. Haworth undertook the study of the structure of sugars, but many years of patient work were required, work that was needed for the comprehension of the central role of the sugars in metabolism as well as in their technical applications. It was at St. Andrews that Haworth's scientific career began to take shape. Here he began work toward what became his lifelong aim— understanding the correlation of chemical structure with biological function.

The first account of Haworth's work in the carbohydrates appeared early in 1915. He had devised a new method, that of the preparation of methylated derivatives, which were, in turn, used to characterize the constitution of sugars. This method proved very valuable and became a standard procedure applicable to most sugars.

During the war years, beginning in 1914, the St. Andrews laboratory, like most engaged in academic research, was called upon to perform work crucial to the defense effort, work on the production of fine chemicals and drugs. Haworth demonstrated considerable ability in organizing teams of workers and in inspiring them to solve problems and to yield that which the laboratory had been designated to produce.

With the cease-fire on November 11, 1918, laboratories began returning to their prewar function, and large groups of students began resumption of their interrupted studies. At St. Andrews, structural work in the carbohydrate group was renewed, Haworth's areas of interest being the disaccharides, sucrose, lactose, maltose, cellobiose, and the trisaccharide, raffinose.

By 1922, Haworth's administrative duties as head of the chemistry department at the University of Durham demanded much of his time. The research school was growing, and there was an increased demand for facilities because of the enlarged student population. By the end of that year, the carbohydrate school had become well established, and numbers of postgraduates were engaged in work on the somewhat more complex sugars built from a small number of simple sugars, the oligosaccharides. Haworth was largely responsible for the design and equipment of the science laboratories built at the University of Durham in the early 1920's.

Haworth's move to the University of Birmingham in 1925 as Mason Professor of Chemistry caused little disruption in the research effort, as many postgraduates moved with him from Durham, and Birmingham's carbohydrate school grew rapidly in numbers and influence. In Haworth's early days at Birmingham, the group became preoccupied with the study of the nature of the ring structures. Until fundamental problems were solved in the structural determination of complex sugars, it would be impossible for the study of the chemistry of sugars to develop. Haworth was later to report that the experimental work at Birmingham in the mid-to-late 1920's had resulted in confirmation of the structures of many sugars, among which were maltose, cellobiose, lactose, gentiobiose, melibiose, gentianose, raffinose, and the glucoside ring structure of normal sugars. The ring structure, which became known as the "Haworth formula," more accurately presented the molecular structure and was more useful in describing chemical reactions in which sugar was involved.

In 1928, Haworth participated in an academic exchange during which he lectured to the Swiss Chemical Society at Neuchâtel and at Mulhouse to the Chemical Society of France. In 1930, Haworth attended the tenth conference of the International Union of Chemistry at Liège, where he gave an account of ring structures in the various levels of saccharides. In 1932, he lectured before the German Chemical Society on structural features in the carbohydrate group. In the same year, the problems of the structure and synthesis of vitamin C were undertaken by the Birmingham group.

Vitamin C had been shown by F. Micheel to be related to carbohydrates as a special product of oxidation. It can be derived from a sugar, sorbitose, which is similar to fructose. Albert Szent-Györgyi, in 1928, had isolated from the adrenal cortex and from orange juice and cabbage juice a substance having many of the properties of a carbohydrate. This substance became known as hexuronic acid—*hex* referring to the six carbons present in its molecular composition. Among scientists it was unclear from the data available whether hexuronic acid was antiscorbutic. (Scorbutus is the medical name for scurvy, a disease appearing among those who lack a ready supply of fresh fruits and vegetables. It was Haworth who eventually gave vitamin C the name ascorbic acid, once he had determined that it was, indeed, the anti-scurvy vitamin.) While on a visit to the United States, Szent-Györgyi prepared a large quantity of his crystals, half of which he sent to Haworth at the Birmingham laboratory. Here, early in 1933, Haworth announced that the main features of the constitution of ascorbic acid were now established. The following year, Haworth and his colleagues derived a procedure for synthesizing the substance.

Studies in the polysaccharides occupied Haworth during the final years of his research. Their significance was of great importance to him in his quest to coordinate the chemical, physical, and biological. He early recognized the importance of X-ray studies. In 1932 he had introduced his end-group method of studying the fine details of polysaccharide structure.

In 1941, after recovering from an extended illness, Haworth was appointed chairman of the British Chemical Panel for Atomic Energy, where he was in charge of the preparation of highly refined metallic uranium and of organic fluorine compounds. During a period of some thirty years, ending with his retirement in 1948, Haworth's laboratories generated more than three hundred publications on the chemistry of the carbohydrates. Haworth himself wrote many scientific papers, and he was a contributor to *Advances in Carbohydrate Chemistry*, for which he was the British member of the committee producing the first volume in 1945. His book, *The Constitution of Sugars*, was published in 1929.

Among the numerous positions and offices that Haworth held were Fellow of the Royal Society in 1928, president of the Chemical Society during the years 1944 to 1946, and vice president of the Royal Society in 1947. He represented the Royal Society at the Seventh Pacific Science Congress in New Zealand in February, 1949. Haworth received honorary science degrees from the universities of Belfast, Zurich, and Oslo, as well as Cambridge; an honorary doctor of law degree from the University of Manchester; and honorary memberships in numerous foreign scientific academies. In 1933, he was named by the Chemical Society (London) as recipient of the Longstaff Medal. In 1934, he was the Davy Medallist of the Royal Society, and was its Royal Medallist in 1942. He was knighted in 1947.

By training a classical organic chemist of the older school, Haworth was among the first to recognize that the problems that he wished to solve required not only the discipline of chemistry but those of physics and biology as well. His contribution in the academic field cannot be overlooked; he helped to build institutions and to establish reputations for excellence in teaching as well as in research. He worked diligently to make those resources available to the defense effort in both world wars, ready and capable of assisting in whatever ways were possible. His work in the synthesis of vitamin C was a landmark among investigations in the field of carbohydrate chemistry, as evidenced by his having received the Nobel Prize.

Bibliography

Primary

CHEMISTRY: *The Constitution of Sugars*, 1929; "The Constitution of Some Carbohydrates," *Chemische Berichte*, vol. 65A, 1932; "Synthesis of Ascorbic Acid," *Chemistry and Industry*, 1933 (with E. L. Hirst); "The Structure, Function, and Synthesis of Polysaccharides," *Proceedings of the Royal Society*, vol. 186A, 1946; "Starch," *Journal of the Chemical Society*, 1946; "Carbohydrate Components of Biologically Active Materials," *Journal of the Chemical Society*, 1947.

Secondary

Carpenter, Kenneth J. *The History of Scurvy and Vitamin C*. Cambridge, England: Cambridge University Press, 1986. This book is primarily for the scientist but can be enjoyed by the layperson as a history of the disease that probably has caused the most suffering due to specific nutritional deficiency. Mentions the work of Haworth and the Birmingham group as well as that of their contemporaries in other laboratories. Cites articles by Haworth.

Farber, Eduard. *Nobel Prize Winners in Chemistry, 1901-1961*. Rev. ed. New York: Abelard-Schuman, 1963. Has an article for each of the prize recipients for the years covered. Of the five-page article entitled "Walter Norman Haworth," two pages are devoted to biographical information, two pages contain quotations from his Nobel lecture, and the final page is an evaluation of the work for which the prize was awarded.

Frejka, J. "The Recipients of the Nobel Prize in Chemistry." *Chem. Listy* 32 (1938): 175-181. The author summarizes the contributions of Haworth to carbohydrate chemistry. Not readily available, the article provides information that can be obtained from other sources.

Hirst, E. L. "Walter Norman Haworth." *Journal of the Chemical Society*, October, 1951: 2790-2806. This obituary presents comprehensive biographical information and appears to be the source of information for other researchers. Not only does it detail every event in Haworth's life, but also it provides extensive esoteric information for the scientist in regard to the researches of the Birmingham group.

Pigman, William Ward, and Rudolph Maximilian Goepp, Jr. *Chemistry of the Carbohydrates*. New York: Academic Press, 1948. Revised, as *The Carbohydrates*, 1957. This volume was meant for use by students and researchers. It provides an introduction to the study of carbohydrates, covering all aspects of the subject from organic to industrial. It contains dozens of index references to Haworth.

Wise, Louis E. "Walter Norman Haworth and Paul Karrer." *Paper Industries* 19 (1938): 1178-1180. This brief article provides a review of Haworth's and of Karrer's work on cellulose chemistry, for which they shared the Nobel Prize in 1937. Because of its age, however, this publication is not available in all libraries.

P. R. Lannert

1937

Chemistry
Sir Walter Norman Haworth, Great Britain
Paul Karrer, Switzerland

Physics
Clinton Joseph Davisson, United States
Sir George Paget Thomson, Great Britain

Physiology or Medicine
Albert Szent-Györgyi, Hungary

Literature
Roger Martin du Gard, France

Peace
Viscount Cecil of Chelwood, Great Britain

PAUL KARRER
1937

Born: Moscow, Russia; April 21, 1889
Died: Zurich, Switzerland; June 18, 1971
Nationality: Swiss
Areas of concentration: Structural analysis and natural product synthesis

Karrer was a pioneer in the determination of the structures of certain natural products, plant pigments, carotenoids, and flavins. His research led to the first elucidation of the chemical structure of a vitamin, vitamin A, and to the commercial manufacture of vitamin B_2, the structure of which he also determined

The Award

Presentation

The 1937 Nobel Prize in Chemistry was presented to Paul Karrer, jointly with Walter Haworth, by Sweden's King Gustav V. The presentation speech was given by Professor Wilhelm Palmær, Chairman of the Nobel Committee for Chemistry of the Royal Swedish Academy of Sciences. Palmær first explained the importance of carbohydrates (sugars) in relation to the work of Haworth, noting that Karrer had made significant contributions in the field. He then discussed those "mysterious substances" called vitamins, which seemed to play such an important role in metabolism. He reminded the group that, only eight years ago, Nobel Prizes had been awarded for the discovery of vitamin B_2 and of growth vitamins but added that, in order to understand the biochemistry of these compounds and the way they behave in the body, their chemical structures must be known. Both Haworth and Karrer succeeded in determining the three-dimensional structures of vitamins, which has led to their manufacture and will lead to the synthesis of new medicines.

Karrer came to his determination of the structure of vitamin A through the study of the carotenoids, the yellow-red pigments present in carrots, tomatoes, and many other vegetables, in the shells of crayfish and lobsters, and in saffron and paprika. He isolated vitamin A and determined its form and composition—the first such determination of a vitamin. Karrer also clarified the structure of vitamin B_2, lactoflavin, and other flavins, natural compounds that often glisten with a yellow glow. Palmær noted that Karrer was an independent thinker who invented unique methods for carrying out his research in an area of chemistry that borders on physiology and is certainly of "the greatest benefit to mankind."

Nobel lecture

Paul Karrer presented his lecture, "Carotenoids, Flavins and Vitamin A and B_2" on December 11, 1937. He first observed that chemists, in the first half of the twentieth century, had been doing research primarily in two areas: the structure of atoms and the study of the living cell, biochemistry. Biochemistry, however, is based upon classical chemistry and has proved capable of study because of recently invented laboratory methods: ultracentrifugation; chromatography, the separation of chemical compounds through their different adsorptions on certain materials; and other selective adsorption processes. In the past, the red and blue pigments in plants were thought to be one compound, but use of these new techniques showed that they were, instead, mixtures. New compounds are constantly being discovered. In 1922 there were six known carotenoids; in 1937 there were forty.

The yellow pigments, the carotenoids, have a unique structure and are related to vitamins. In 1930, the structure of beta-carotene was elucidated and, in 1931, that of vitamin A, a closely related compound. Karrer observed that until this structure was determined, many scientists considered vitamins to be merely different physical forms of matter, not distinct chemical entities. The composition of the carotenoids had been determined by breaking them apart chemically and through the synthesis of similar compounds. It was found that the carotenoids and vitamin A were related to camphor and natural rubbers. Karrer discussed the spatial orientation of these molecules and the effect of this orientation on their stability. He showed how vitamin A, which Hans von Euler-Chelpin had demonstrated could be replaced by carotene in nutrition experiments, contains one-half the skeleton of the beta-carotene. With von Euler-Chelpin, Karrer discovered that some of the carotenes could be used by the body to form vitamin A.

Karrer noted that vitamins have very specific activities and that many vitamins are part of enzymes, the all-important biological catalysts which make possible reactions in the body. He discussed the relationship between vitamin B_2, lactoflavin, and the "yellow oxidation enzyme," which is actually vitamin B_2 combined with phosphoric acid. Karrer described the synthesis of many flavins, compounds similar to vitamin B_2, and showed that effective biological action, in bacteria as well as in higher organisms, depends upon only a few closely related chemical structures.

Karrer closed the scientific portion of his lecture with a description of the current research into the nature of the vitamins. He explored the possibility of the existence of two vitamins A with similar action but slightly different structures. He also noted that there is still little understanding of the way vitamin A works in the cell, although the roles of B and B_2 have been explained. He discussed the effect of vitamin A on epithelial tissue and on the eyes, and its newly discovered role in the chemistry of vision. Karrer observed that investigations into biologically important compounds, such as the vitamins, are often the result of research on other related compounds. Not only did the carotenoid study lead to vitamin A, but also recent studies on nicotinic acid amide, which explain how the compound changes chemically, have led to its use to cure black tongue disease in dogs, thereby showing it to be a new vitamin.

Karrer declared that the chemical side of the vitamin problem has been essentially solved and that the physiologist must now explain how vitamins and cells interact. He noted, however, that because this is also a chemical process, the chemist surely will become involved again.

Critical reception

There was little comment in either the public or scientific press about the 1937 Nobel Prize in Chemistry. *The Times* of London and *The New York Times* printed concise announcements, as did *Science* and *Industrial and Engineering News*. *The New York Times* referred to the "complete renaissance" that had occurred in carbohydrate chemistry within ten years, a statement perhaps more relevant to cowinner Haworth's work than to Karrer's. *Nature's* short article contained more detail about the work, citing Karrer's many papers on vitamins A and B and related compounds. It noted that he confirmed the constitution of ascorbic acid proposed by Albert Szent-Györgyi. The research on the carotenoids is described, emphasizing that beta-carotene is the chief precursor of vitamin A in the animal body. Karrer's investigations on vitamin B_2 and the flavins, it said, led to the discovery that lactoflavin is a part of that vitamin complex and the yellow oxidizing enzyme. The recent work of Karrer and Solomon in isolating chromatographically a compound from the unsaponifiable matter of wheat-germ oil that may be vitamin E is mentioned.

Biography

Paul Karrer was born in Moscow on April 21, 1889, the son of Paul Karrer and Julie Lerch, Swiss nationals. His father, a dentist, brought the family back to Switzerland in 1892, and Karrer attended schools in the rural communities of Wildegg and Lenzburg, and in Aarau. It was in these institutions that he developed an interest in science, and in 1908 he enrolled in the University of Zurich. He received his Ph.D. three years later and remained at the university as an assistant in the laboratory of Alfred Werner, the famous inorganic chemist, for an additional year.

Karrer was invited by Paul Ehrlich to come to Frankfurt am Main to do research in the chemistry section of the Georg Speyer Haus. In 1914, Karrer married Helen Froelich, daughter of the director of the royal psychiatric clinic. They had three sons, one of whom died early in life. Karrer served in the Swiss army as an artillery officer during World War I. Upon the death of Ehrlich in 1915, Karrer was made director of the laboratory; the situation in Germany became so unfriendly toward foreigners, however, that he had to return to Zurich in 1918 and was appointed reader in chemistry at the university.

In 1919, Karrer became director of the Chemical Institute and professor of chemistry at the University of Zurich, where he remained, also serving as Rector, until his retirement in 1959. He was instrumental in continuing the outstanding research for which the university was famous. He published more than one thousand papers and a textbook of organic chemistry that had thirteen editions and was translated into English, Italian, Spanish, French, Polish, and Japanese. Karrer received many honors, including twenty honorary degrees. In addition to the Nobel Prize, he was awarded the Marcel Benoist Prize (1922) and the Cannizzaro Prize of the Italian Chemical Society (1935). From 1924 to 1926 he served as president of the Swiss

Chemical Society and, in 1955, presided over the fourteenth International Congress in Pure and Applied Chemistry. He was a former vice president and chair of the section on organic chemistry of the International Union of Pure and Applied Chemistry and a foreign member of many societies, including the (United States) National Academy of Sciences. Karrer died, in Zurich, on June 18, 1971.

Scientific Career

When Paul Karrer entered the University of Zurich, he found there two excellent chemists who would inspire him and stimulate his interest in research: Paul Pfeiffer, an organic chemist (a chemist who studies carbon compounds), and Alfred Werner, the most renowned Swiss chemist of the early twentieth century. Werner had received the Nobel Prize in 1913 for his investigations of "the linkage of atoms in molecules, by which he . . . opened up new fields of research, particularly in inorganic chemistry." Werner was studying the complex metallic compounds which seemed at the time to be the only mysterious chemicals left for research by non-organic chemists. These compounds usually contained ions (charged particles) and metals such as copper or cobalt, but also incorporated chlorides, ammonia, cyanides, or organic fragments. It eventually became known that some of the most important biological molecules, such as hemoglobin, are examples of these "coordination compounds." Werner postulated that there were two kinds of bonding within these molecules: ionic bonding, such as that which holds the positive sodium ion to the negative chloride ion in ordinary table salt, and secondary bonding, which holds some molecules or ions to the central metallic particle.

Use of this theory explained how these compounds could conduct electricity when dissolved in water and led to the understanding of how they existed in space, their stereochemistry. Werner showed that these inorganic compounds could exist in two forms, each with the same number of atoms of each element but with a different spatial configuration, which, as in sugars and other organic compounds, created mirror images. A good analogy to this phenomenon is the relationship between a person's two hands. When placed palm to palm, they are mirror images of each other, but, when one is put on top of the other, they cannot be superimposed. Chemical compounds that are mirror images are distinguishable by having different properties. Karrer's scientific career was to combine the interests of Pfeiffer and Werner, organic chemistry and the study of stereochemistry, but in the field of natural products.

Karrer entered Werner's laboratory at a time when the research on coordination compounds was most fruitful. His doctoral thesis (1911) examined the properties of a cobalt compound that contained organic molecules, an organometallic salt, and, during his year as assistant at Zurich (1912), he began a study of organoarsenic compounds. This work caught the attention of Paul Ehrlich, who had received the Nobel Prize in Physiology or Medicine in 1908 for the discovery of the first drug effective against syphilis, Salvarsan, the "magic bullet," which was an arsenic compound. During the next five-and-one-half years in Ehrlich's laboratory in Germany, Karrer studied organic compounds of arsenic and other metals such as bismuth and antimony and examined the reaction of Salvarsan with silver and gold.

On Karrer's return to Zurich in 1918, he turned from research on organometallic compounds to a study of simple sugars, which contain one sugar unit, and polysaccharides, which contain many sugar units. He combined the simple sugar glucose with many reagents, producing compounds similar to natural substances, thereby elucidating the constitution of these natural products. He devised important ways to carry out these reactions and improved the method of using enzymes to split polysaccharides such as starch in order to determine their structure. He began a study of the surface properties of cellulose, a polysaccharide, which led to an improvement in the dyeing of cotton. He also studied chitin, a polysaccharide present in lobster shells, and lichenin (reserve cellulose), found in certain lichens. His highly praised monograph "Polymeric Carbohydrates" was published in 1925.

During this early period of his career, Karrer also studied the structures of amino acids, peptides, and proteins, particularly albumin, demonstrating that all these related compounds had the same configuration in space (stereochemistry). As a by-product of this research, he discovered a new local anesthetic, Panthesin. He investigated the structure of tannins, used in the curing of leather, and lecithin, a natural product present in large quantities in egg yolks and in the brain, showing that this phosphate-containing compound existed in two forms.

In 1926, Karrer began the study of plant pigments—anthocyanins, flavins, and carotenoids. The anthocyanins are the red and blue compounds found in blossoms and berries: roses, delphiniums, blue grapes, violet pansies, and so on. Karrer developed an efficient method for isolating these compounds from naturally occurring mixtures and recognized their chemical similarity to flavonols, yellow plant pigments.

While investigating crocetin, the pigment found in saffron, he found that chemicals of the group it represented, the carotenoids, were highly unsaturated—that is, they contained many double bonds within their molecules. The study of the tomato pigment, lycopin, showed that these molecules included in their structures a group similar to one present in rubber, which consists of eight isoprene units. By 1930, Karrer had determined the structure of both lycopin and carotene, the yellow-red pigment in carrots. Although carotene had been isolated one hundred years before, this was the first determination of its structure. Karrer, with B. and Hans von Euler-Chelpin, discovered that carotene had the same biological activity as did vitamin A. With the addition of two molecules of water, carotene could produce two molecules of the vitamin. In 1931, Karrer was able to determine the chemical structure of vitamin A before it had actually been isolated. This showed that vitamins were chemical compounds of knowable structure rather than special physical forms of matter, as some scientists believed. Later, it was in Karrer's laboratory that George Wald (Nobel Prize in Physiology or Medicine, 1967) showed that vitamin A played an important part in the chemistry of vision.

Karrer and his students investigated carotenoids for some forty years, isolating and/or determining the structure of many compounds, including zeaxantin from corn; mutatoxanthin, antheraxanthin, auroxanthin, and chrysanthemaxanthin from flowers; and xanthophyll, the yellow pigment in autumn leaves. He introduced a method for converting one carotenoid to another and developed a general method of synthesis. In addition, he determined the spatial configuration of many of these compounds, noting the surprisingly small number of possible forms, or isomers, that were actually found in nature. Karrer, with Ernst Juncker, published a standard work, *Monographie über Carotenoide*, in 1948; the English translation, *Carotenoids*, appeared in 1950.

The total synthesis of a natural product, starting with simple organic compounds, is a rigorous challenge for chemists. Such a synthesis can give clues to how the substance is made naturally and perhaps provide insight into its function. The total synthesis of lycopene was achieved by Karrer in 1950. Although the synthesis of squalene, in 1931, cannot be classified as total, it was also an important achievement. This natural product, which is found in large quantities in fish liver, is important in the biosynthesis of cholesterol, sex hormones, and adrenal hormones, and Karrer's synthesis confirmed that it contains isoprene units.

Karrer and his students also studied the nature of other vitamins. Biochemistry in the 1920's and 1930's was primarily concerned with nutrition and the deficiency diseases. The need for vitamins was recognized in 1912 by Casimir Funk as a result of studying beriberi. Physiological experiments showed the importance of these trace nutrients, and chemists flocked to study the composition and structure of these compounds. The Nobel Prizes of this era reflect the value placed upon vitamin studies. In 1929, Christiaan Eijkman was honored for the discovery of the need for nutrients found in rice hulls (vitamin B_1), along with Frederick G. Hopkins, who discovered the action of vitamin A. Both Sir Walter Haworth, who shared the prize with Karrer, and Albert Szent-Györgyi, who received the 1937 Prize in Physiology or Medicine, had worked on vitamin C. Richard Kuhn, who was a rival of Karrer in many areas of research, was awarded the chemistry prize the following year, and Henrik Dam and Edward Doisy were later honored for their work on vitamin K. By 1935, Karrer had accomplished the synthesis of riboflavin (vitamin B_2), which is also called lactoflavin. His preparatory method led to a process for the industrial manufacture of this yellow pigment, found in the "yellow oxidation ferment" of yeast. B_2 is present in milk, animal tissues, and eggs, and is a necessary growth factor for many mammals. It acts as part of a coenzyme, a substance which makes possible the action of an enzyme. The synthesis of vitamin E was carried out in 1938. This fat-soluble vitamin is necessary for reproductive activity, and Karrer's synthesis verified the structure postulated by several chemists. The isolation of vitamin K_1 (phyllochinon) from alfalfa was achieved the following year, and the correct formula of K_2 was determined in 1940. The K vitamins are found in green plants and are manufactured by the intestinal bacteria, and they are essential to the function of the clotting action of the blood. Karrer reported the synthesis of vitamin K_3 (menadione); vitamins C and B were also investigated by the Zurich group.

While studying riboflavin, Karrer became interested in nicotinic acid amide, which had been recognized by Otto Warburg as a constituent of an important coenzyme. In 1936, Karrer found that a derivative of this compound was present in a form of Warburg's coenzyme, nicotinic amide adenine dinucleotide (NAD), the substance responsible for bringing about the transfer of electrons during metabolism. Later Karrer synthesized portions of two other important coenzymes.

Late in his career, Karrer returned to the study of alkaloids, particularly those in curare, the poison used by South American Indians to kill their prey. This muscle relaxant has been used in medicine during surgery. Karrer elucidated the composition and structure of more than fifty new alkaloids and succeeded in the partial synthesis of some of these complicated compounds.

The achievements of Karrer and his laboratory group were truly amazing. In order for an analysis of an unknown natural product to be done, a pure sample must be obtained. Experiments were therefore often carried out on extremely tiny amounts of these chemicals. These small portions had to be extracted, however, from hundreds of pounds, often tons, of the plant or animal source. Karrer was one of the first to introduce the use of modern instruments to measure the physical properties of the compounds with which he worked in order to follow the progress of the isolation or reaction. He brought to the University of Zurich physical chemists with knowledge of the latest instruments and the best ways in which they could be used. Karrer employed chromatography to separate small amounts of substances and spectral analysis to follow the course of a reaction and to identify unknown compounds. He used the ultracentrifuge and was a master at adapting current methods of synthesis to his needs. At the presentation of the Nobel Prize, Karrer was described as a scientist who was able to visualize the important problems as well as their smaller parts. Without his genius and the papers he published, knowledge of plants and animals and an understanding of the ways the human body functions would have been long delayed. The large number of students he inspired and instructed continued his investigations, and at least one, George Wald, was awarded the Nobel Prize for studies begun in Karrer's laboratory.

Bibliography

Primary

CHEMISTRY: "The Coloring Materials of Plants. XVI Carotene I," *Helvetica Chimica Acta*, vol. 12, 1929 (with A. Helfenstein); "The Configuration of 1-Phenylalanine, 1-Tyrosine and 1-Dihydroxyphenylalanine," *Helvetica Chimica Acta*, vol. 13, 1930 (with W. Kehl); "Syntheses of Squalene," *Helvetica Chimica Acta*, vol. 13, 1931 (with A. Helfenstein); "Synthesis of Lactoflavin (Vitamin B_2) and other Flavins," *Helvetica Chimica Acta*, vol. 18, 1935 (with Hans von Euler, M. Malmberg, K. Schoop, F. Benz, B. Baker, and H. Frier); "Vitamin E," *Helvetica Chimica Acta*, vol. 21, 1938 (with H. Salomon and H. Fritzsche); "Synthesis of α Tocopherol," *Helvetica Chimica Acta*, vol. 21, 1938 (with H. Fritzsche, B. H. Ringer, and H. Salomon); "Vitamin K from Alfalfa," *Helvetica Chimica Acta*, vol. 22, 1939 (with A. Geiger); "Crystalline Methyl-o-dihydronicotinamide," *Helvetica Chimica Acta*, vol. 30, 1947; *Monographie über Carotenoide*, 1948 (with Ernst Juncker; *Carotenoids*, 1950).

Secondary

Farber, Eduard. *The Evolution of Chemistry*. 2d ed. New York: Ronald Press, 1969. Has a good discussion of Karrer's work in biochemistry and discusses the importance of his synthesis of squalene.

_____. *Nobel Prize Winners in Chemistry, 1910-1961*. Rev. ed. New York: Abelard-Schuman, 1963. An older volume on the prizewinners, this includes a short biography and excerpts from Karrer's Nobel speech. Contains some technical information.

Ihde, Aaron. *The Development of Modern Chemistry*. Mineola, N.Y.: Dover, 1984. This book is a comprehensive study of chemistry and chemists from the eighteenth century. Karrer's work is discussed in chapters on biochemistry.

Leicester, Henry M. "Paul Karrer." In *Dictionary of Scientific Biography*, edited by Charles Coulston Gillispie. New York: Charles Scribner's Sons, 1978. A good short biography in English.

Nobelstiftelsen. *Nobel Lectures: Chemistry, 1922-1941*. New York: Elsevier, 1966. A record of the Nobel Prize presentations and lectures, it presents a translation of Karrer's entire Nobel address.

Sebrell, W. H., Jr., and Robert S. Harris. *The Vitamins*. 2d ed. New York: Academic Press, 1968. A comprehensive study of the vitamins in several volumes that gives references to the important work on these compounds. It is written primarily for scientists.

Wettstein, A. "Paul Karrer." *Helvetica Chimica Acta* 55 (1972). In German, this is the best and most complete biography of Karrer.

Williams, Trevor I., ed. *A Biographical Dictionary of Scientists*. New York: John Wiley & Sons, 1987. Includes a short biography of Karrer.

Jane Miller